OF THE PYRENEES

P.H.

THE
STORY OF ROLAND

The Story of Roland

BY JAMES BALDWIN

Illustrated by Peter Hurd

CHARLES SCRIBNER'S SONS
NEW YORK · LONDON

Printed in the United States of America

FOREWORD

THE fairyland of romance is not far removed from the more sober domains of history. Indeed, the territory of the one sometimes overlaps that of the other; and the boundary line between them is often dim and ill-defined. This truth is illustrated in the legends which have come down to us from the middle ages. In those rude, uncultured times, men did not care greatly to sift fact from fiction, nor to pry into the likelihood of things. No matter how improbable a story might be, if it were pleasing to them, they never thought of questioning its truth. Most of the earlier legends began in song: they were sung or recited by wandering bards or minstrels long before they were written down. They have in them usually some slender thread of real history, so covered over with traditions, and mixed up with mysteries and marvels, that it is impossible to know how much is fact, and how much is fable. We read them chiefly to learn how the men of those far-off cloudy days thought and felt, what they believed, and with what kind of literature they were entertained. Yet if we remove the dress and impurities which obscure the fairer and nobler parts of these legends, and adapt them to our own modes of thinking and expression, we shall not fail to find some things that will instruct, and many that will please.

Jean Bodel, a minstrel of the thirteenth century, wrote, "There are but three subjects which interest men,—the tales of France, of Britain, and of Rome the great; and to these subjects there is nothing like. The tales of Britain* are so light and pleasant; those of Rome† are wise and of teachful sense; those of France‡ truly every day of greater appearance."

In this story of Roland as I propose telling it, I shall introduce you to some of the most pleasing of those "tales of France." The poems and legends which embody them were written in various languages, and at widely different times; but in them two names, Charlemagne and Roland, are of very frequent occurrence. Charlemagne, as you know, was a real historical personage, the greatest monarch of mediæval times. His empire included France, the greater part of Germany, and Italy; and his power and influence were felt all over the Christian world. The fame of his achievements in war was heralded and sung in every country of Europe; his name was in the mouth of every story-teller and wandering bard; and it finally became customary to ascribe all the heroic deeds and wonderful events of three centuries to the time of Charlemagne. The songs and stories in which these events were related were dressed up with every kind of embellishment to suit the circumstances of their recital. Wild myths of the Pagan ages, legends and traditions of the Christian Church, superstitious notions of magic and witchcraft, fantastic stories derived from the Arabs of Spain and the East,—all these were blended in one strange mass, and grafted upon a slender core of historical truth. The result was a curious mixture of fact and fiction, of the real and the marvellous, of the beautiful and the impure, of Christian devotion and heathen superstition. And it was thus that "the tales of France," which we may term the legendary history of Charlemagne, came into being.

*The romances of King Arthur. †The Gesta Romanorum.
‡The legends of Charlemagne.

FOREWORD

The Charlemagne of romance is a very different personage from the Charlemagne of history; and the tales which cluster around the name of that monarch must not be regarded as true pictures of life and manners during his reign, but rather as illustrations of the state of society at the various times of their composition. In the romances, Charlemagne is represented as the patron of chivalry, and his warriors as possessing all the knightly virtues. But we know, that, in his time, the institution of chivalry did not exist, and that there were no knights. In the tenth century, however, when men first began to write down the tales of France, chivalry was in its prime; and it was but natural that the poet who wrote and sang for feudal chiefs and lords should invest his heroes with knighthood, and represent Charlemagne as the founder of the order.

Roland, the nephew of the Charlemagne of romance, and his companion in all great enterprises, is unknown to history. Yet he is the typical knight, the greatest hero of the middle ages. His story, as I shall tell it you, is not a mere transcript of the old romances. The main incidents have been derived from a great variety of sources, while the arrangement and the connecting parts are of my own invention. I have culled the story from the song-writers and poets of five centuries and of as many languages. Sometimes I have adhered closely to the matter and spirit, and even the words, of the originals; sometimes I have given free rein to my own imagination; and throughout I have endeavored so to arrange and retouch the individual parts of the story as to lend interest to its recital, and adapt it to our own ways of thinking, and our modern notions of propriety. The oldest story of Roland was doubtless that which was sung by the minstrel of William the Conqueror, in 1066. Wace, in his account of the battle of Hastings, says, "Taillefer, who sang very well, rode before the duke, singing of Charlemagne and of Roland and of Oliver, and of the vassals who died at Roncevaux." The song which Taillefer sang must have been the "Chanson de Roland," written by one Turold, perhaps as early as the tenth century. It is by far the finest of all the "tales of France." More than twenty years after the battle of Hastings, there appeared a Latin work, entitled "The Life of Charles the Great and of Roland," which, it was claimed, had been written by Archbishop Turpin, the father-confessor of Charlemagne. The falsity of this claim is too apparent to need any proof; and yet the work, having been sanctioned by Pope Calixtus, and placed by him upon the roll of canonical books, exerted no small influence over the poetical literature which followed it, and supplied materials and suggestions to many later romancists. In England, in the thirteenth and fourteenth centuries, there appeared several rhyming romances relating to our hero. Among these were "Sir Ferumbras," an adaptation of a French poem, entitled "Fierabras," "Otuel," and "Roland and Ferragus." One of the first books printed in our language was a legendary history of Charlemagne, entitled "The Lyf of Charles the Great, fynysshed in the reducing of it into Englysshe the xviii day of Juin MCCCCLXXXV. Explicit per William Caxton." In our own time Mr. John Malcolm Ludlow, in his "Popular Epics of the Middle Ages," has given us a valuable critical analysis of some of the most noticeable legends of Roland and Charlemagne. In Germany we find an adaptation of the "Chanson de Roland" in an old poem, entitled "Ruolandes Liet," which appeared, probably, as early as 1177, and has recently been edited by William Grimm. Karl Simrock's "Kerlingisches Heldenbuch" contains some of the most delightful traditions of Roland and Charlemagne; and the "Kaiser-chronik," published in 1849, gives a complete legendary history of Charlemagne and his peers from a German point of view. In Italy the story of Roland was long a most fertile and attractive theme, and gave rise to more than one great poem. The legends relating to his parentage and boyhood are contained in the "Innamoramento di Milone d'Anglante," printed in the sixteenth century, and in several other poems much older; the "Orlando Innamorato" of Boiardo tells us of the marvellous adventures of our hero in Fairyland and in the Far East; the "Orlando Furioso" of Ariosto tells of his prowess as a knight, his disappointment in love, his madness and ultimate recovery; the "Morgante Maggiore" of Pulci relates the story of his later adventures and his death. In the mediæval romances of Spain the name of Roland is of frequent occurrence; and the story, modified to suit the prejudices of Spanish readers, is found in numerous old songs and poems, some of them as early as the twelfth century. There is, in short, no country in Europe, and no language, in which the exploits of Charlemagne and of Roland have not at some time been recounted and sung.

In relating the story of Roland it would, of course, be impossible to avoid some mention of Oliver and Reinold, and Ogier the Dane,—heroes who were his companions in arms, and who rivalled him in the number and greatness of their exploits. I have therefore been at some pains to give, from the same ancient sources, the most popular and pleasing legends concerning these valorous knights, one of whom, at least, can lay claim to an historical existence.

The old bards and story-tellers who invented, embellished,

and sang these famous "tales of France," were accustomed to modify, recast, and remodel their stories so as to adapt them to the tastes and demands of their audiences. In presenting the story of Roland for the first time in a connected form and to a popular audience, I shall certainly be pardoned if I endeavor to follow their example.

CONTENTS

CONTENTS

ILLUSTRATIONS

ILLUSTRATIONS

ROLAND

ROLAND

ADVENTURE I

ROLAND AND OLIVER

ONE summer afternoon rather more than eleven hundred years ago, the boy Roland was sitting in the cleft of a broken rock that forms the crest of one of the hills in the neighborhood of Sutri. Above him was the deep blue sky of Italy, unflecked by any cloud: on either side of him stretched a dull, uneven plain, broken here and there by wet marshes, and long lines of low hills. A mile or more to the south, and partly hidden behind the brow of the hill, could be seen the old town, with its strong castle, and its half-ruined amphitheatre, and its white-walled monastery. Directly beneath him was the dusty high-road, which, after winding among the straggling vineyards and the little farms that dotted the plain, was lost to sight in a strip of dusky woodland a league and more to the northward. Along that road King Charlemagne, with the flower of his great army, was hourly expected to pass, marching on his way to the castle of Sutri, where he was to be entertained for a time as a guest; and it was for this reason that the lad sat so still, and watched so long, in his half-hidden perch on the hilltop.

Every thing, as if awed by the near coming of the hero king, seemed strangely still that afternoon. Scarcely a sign of life was to be seen; and the places which at other times had been noisy with busy workers were now silent and deserted. The reapers, who yesterday had made the wheat-fields ring with their gay jests and their rude songs, had left their sickles in the fields, and stolen silently away. The young girls who had been gleaning the fallen grain, and whose laughter had awakened the echoes among the hills, were nowhere to be seen to-day, although the eagle eyes of Roland sought them on every hand. Along the highroad, which at other times seemed alive with the busy folk coming and going between Sutri and Viterbo, neither man, woman, nor beast was stirring. But off toward Sutri the boy could see that things were quite different. The town seemed to be decked in holiday attire: the governor's castle was draped with gay bunting, and flags and banners floated from the turret-tops. Companies of knights dressed in rich livery rode hither and thither, impatiently waiting the word from the watchman above the gates to go out and meet the kingly guest. The streets were crowded with hurrying, eager folk, who knew not whether to hail the coming of Charlemagne and his host as a blessing, or to look upon it as a calamity.

Now and then the sound of voices from the town or the cries of the soldiers in the garrison, came to Roland's ears; and anon he heard the monks in the monastery drowsily chanting their prayers. And there he sat, waiting and wondering, and anxiously watching for any sign of the coming host. The fair face of the lad, and the long flaxen hair which fell in glistening waves upon his bare shoulders, showed his kinship to the hardy races of the North. And there was something in the piercing look of his eye, in the proud curl of his lip, in the haughty turn of his head, which made him seem like a young king among men, and which often had caused those who met him to doff the hat in humble courtesy. He was very poorly clad: his head and limbs were bare; and the thin, scant clothing which covered his body was nought but rags and shreds. Yet he bore himself proudly, as one who knew his own worth, and who, having a blameless heart, had nothing of which to feel ashamed.

And now the sun began to slope toward the west; and, with each moment that passed, the lad's eagerness seemed to grow greater. By and by another boy came over the crest of the hill, and stood in the cleft of the rock by the side of Roland, and with him gazed down the deserted road. He seemed to be of about the same age as Roland, and, like him, was tall and sparely built. His dark hair and overhanging brows, his ruddy face and flashing eyes, betokened an equal kinship with the danger-daring North-folk and the leisure-loving people of the South. He wore the rich dress of a court page, and carried himself with a lofty grace such as only those who bear brave hearts can ever show.

"I feared you were not coming, Oliver," said Roland offering his hand, but not once turning his head, or taking his eyes from the distant woodland.

"It was indeed hard for me to get leave," answered the other. "But the ladies at the castle are very kind, and here I am; and I mean to be, with you, the first to see the great king and his valiant knights. Yet he is late."

"I think I see them coming now," said Roland. "There is a glimmering of light among the trees, which I think must be the flashing of the sun upon their armor. And it grows brighter, and seems to come nearer."

He had scarcely finished speaking, when the clear notes of a bugle were heard, borne faintly to them on the breeze. And soon they heard a sound like the distant dashing of waves against the seashore, the rustling of myriads of dry leaves in the autumn woods, the faint rumbling of a far-away storm cloud. They knew that it was nought but the noise made by the trampling of many feet, the heavy tread of war-horses, the rattling of arms and armor. Then a great cloud of dust was seen rising like a mist above the treetops; and the rainbow-hued banners of the coming host hove in sight.

Presently the edge of the wood seemed ablaze with flashing shields and glittering war coats. The boy Roland leaped to his feet. He stood on tiptoe, and strained himself eagerly forward; his face beamed with delight; and his eyes sparkled with that strange wild fire which in after-days, in the midst of the battle's din, was wont to strike his foes with terror. Oliver climbed to the highest point of the rock, and gazed with an eagerness half mixed with fear, at the wonderful array of steel-clad warriors, who now could be plainly seen issuing from the woodland. Like a torrent of rolling, flashing waters, the host of Charlemagne came moving along the line of the highway, and spreading across the plain. They came not, however, in all the array of battle, nor with their terrible engines of war, nor, indeed, as enemies bent on pillage, or seeking revenge; but they came, rather, as an army of peace, with music sounding, and banners flying, and words of good-will and friendship to all. For Charlemagne, having left off fighting with the Lombards, was on his way to Rome, with the best and bravest of his warriors, to receive the homage and the blessing of the Pope.

The vanguard of the procession drew rapidly nearer. In front rode four and twenty knights, the heralds of the king, bearing aloft the silken banner of France and the golden eagle of Rome. They were clad in rich armor, which glittered like gold in the sunlight; their shields were inlaid with many priceless gems, and polished as bright as mirrors; and the sharp points of their long lances flashed around them like the restless gleams of lightning in the van of a summer storm-cloud. They were mounted on milk-white horses trapped with white cloth-of-gold, with gold-red saddles, and housings of bluest silk.

The boy Roland had never seen any thing so beautiful or so grand, and he thought that one of these knights must surely be Charlemagne. And as they drew very near to the foot of the hill, and he could look down almost upon the heads of the brilliant company, he called to Oliver, and asked,—

"Which of these knights is the great Charles? Is it not he who rides nearest the standard-bearer? He, surely, is the noblest warrior of them all; and he rides with a grace which well becomes a king."

But this scene, which filled the mind of Roland with such astonishment, was not altogether new to Oliver. Not many months before, his father, the governor of Sutri, had taken him on a visit to the court of Charlemagne; and there he had witnessed the splendor of the king's surroundings, and had heard of the fearful might of his warriors.

"No," he answered. "The great king is not one of these. They are but heralds and messengers, who ride before to my father's castle to see that every thing is in readiness for their master. They are right courtly fellows, I ween, fair of speech, and comely of form; but I doubt if any of them would be ranked among his bravest knights."

Following the heralds came a body of guards,—a thousand men of giant stature, and muscles of iron,—incased from head to foot in strongest armor, and riding heavy war-steeds trapped with steel. After these came a long line of bishops and abbots and monks and priests, most of them dressed in the garb of their office or profession, and riding on the backs of palfreys or of mules.

"See you the tall bishop, dressed partly in armor, and carrying a crucifix in one hand, while with the other he toys with his sword-hilt?" asked Oliver. "That is the brave Turpin, one of the peers of Charlemagne. He is at home in the battlefield as well as before the altar, and many an unbelieving Pagan has felt the thrust of his lance. But see! here comes the king himself!"

The whole highway and the fields before them now seemed filled with steel-coated men, and horses clothed in steel trappings; and the long lances in the hands of the knights seemed as thick-set as the blades of grass in an autumn meadow. Everywhere were seen the gleam of polished steel and the waving of gay plumes and many-colored pennons; and here and there were banners, of varied shapes and every hue, on which were emblazoned mottoes, and the strange devices of the warriors who bore them. First and foremost in this company was Charlemagne himself, clad in steel from head to foot, and riding a horse of the color of steel and the strength of steel. Roland, as soon as he saw him, knew that this must be the king; for there was no other man who seemed so kingly, or who bore himself with so lordly a grace. The noblest knight among his followers seemed but a weak stripling when seen by the side of the matchless Charlemagne. In his left hand he carried a lance of steel of wondrous length, while his right hand held the reins of his fiery steed. His head was bare, for he had laid aside his helmet; and his long hair fell in waves upon his steel-covered shoulders. His broad shield, which was carried by an attendant knight, was of plated steel of three thicknesses bound together with iron bolts. His thighs were encircled with plates of steel, and his hands were garnished with steel gauntlets. On his kingly face a smile lingered; and from his gleaming gray eyes sparks of fire seemed to shoot; and under a weight of armor which would have borne down a common man he carried himself erect and proud, like one who was every inch a king.

With wonder, rather than with awe, Roland kept his eyes fixed upon the noble figure of Charlemagne; and he did not withdraw his gaze until a sudden turn of the road around the hill toward Sutri hid the steel-clad company from his sight. He did not care to see that part of the host which followed. He had no thought for the throng of squires and pages, and the crowd of common soldiers and grooms, who brought up the rear with the baggage and the camp equipage and the led horses of the knights. He had seen the great Charles, and that was all he wished. He beckoned to Oliver; and the two boys climbed down from their well-hidden lookout, and started homeward.

To keep out of the way of the soldiery, and to shun other hinderances, they followed a narrow pathway which led them over the hill, and down the slope on the other side from that where the highway ran. Not a word did either speak until they reached the level fields; but here they paused, for here they must needs part. The path which Oliver was to take led southward to the lordly castle of Sutri, where, that night and the following day, Charlemagne and his warriors were to rest and be entertained. But Roland's way lay across the lonely fields to a far different dwelling among the barren hills. Before they parted, each took the other's hand; and both stood for some time in silence, their hearts full of thoughts too big to find utterance in speech. Roland spoke first.

"Some day, Oliver," said he, "we, too, shall be knights, and we shall ride with Charlemagne and his peers as proud as the proudest warriors we have seen to-day."

"Yes," answered Oliver, his face beaming with delight. "And boldly will we fare over land and sea, fighting the Pagan folk, and doing worthy deeds for the honor of God, the king, and the ladies."

"My mother has often told me," said Roland, "that the day when I should first see Charlemagne would be to me the beginning of a new life. I know not why she said it; but I have seen the great king, and I feel that a wonderful change has come to me, and that I shall no longer be a mere beggar boy. I must soon be up and away, doing my part in this busy world. Let us now, like real knights, pledge ourselves as brothers-in-arms. Next to my mother, you are my dearest friend. Let me call you my brother."

"You are indeed my brother, Roland," answered Oliver earnestly. "You are my brother. Don't you remember, that, since the day when you gave me such a well-deserved drubbing for laughing at your ragged clothing, we have been sworn brothers-in-arms? Did any one ever apologize for a fault more heartily than I did then? And did any one ever forgive with freer grace than you forgave me? And have any two persons ever loved with a truer love than that which binds us together?"

"But we are only boys," said Roland. "You are a page and a prince. I am a beggar and a prince: at least so I have been told in my dreams. The next time we meet, we may both be knights. Let us pledge ourselves, that, let that meeting be when it may, it shall be a meeting between brothers-in-arms."

Without more words, the two boys, still holding each other's hands, knelt together by the roadside. And they vowed to be true to each other so long as life should last; to share together whatever fortune might betide, whether it should be good or ill; to meet all dangers together, and to undertake all great enterprises in company; to rejoice together in success, and grieve together when sorrow should come; to devote their lives to the succor of the helpless and to the defence of the right; and, if need be, to die for each other.

"And now," said Oliver, as they rose to their feet, "let us, like true knights, seal our vow of brotherhood by exchanging tokens."

And with the word he took from his girdle a little dagger with long gleaming blade and a handle of ivory richly carved, and inlaid with gold. It was a gift from his grandfather, Gerard of Viana, and had once belonged to the Pagan king of Morocco. It was the dearest of Oliver's possessions, and hence the fittest token to present to his brother-in-arms. As Roland took it from his hand, and gazed with pleased eyes upon its razor edges, gleaming like lines of silver light, tears stood in his eyes, for he knew how highly its owner prized it. Then from the folds of his ragged garment he drew the short, broken fragment of an old sword-blade, dimmed with age and much rust, and dull with many notches.

"My token," said he, "is but a poor return for the beautiful keepsake you have given me. But it is very dear to me, and I know that it will also be dear to you. It is all that was left of my father's sword, when, hemmed in by Pagan foes, he sold his life dearly in fight, and died for the honor of the king and the church."

Oliver took the proffered token reverently, for he already

knew its story. He gazed a moment at the curious letters carved on its sides, and at its hacked and battered edge; and then he placed it carefully in his girdle. And the two boys, after many earnest words and many kind good-bys, turned away, and each hastened toward his own home.

By this time the sun had gone down, and the short twilight was fast giving place to darkness. With hasty steps Roland made his way across the fields toward the low line of yellow hills, which now could be scarcely seen, lying more than a league away, dimly outlined against the western horizon. It was quite dark long before he reached them. But he knew the way well, and a light shining in the door of his mother's dwelling helped to guide his steps across the uneven ground. And what kind of a dwelling was it that Roland called his home? It was nothing more than a little cave hollowed out of the rocky hillside, where, long before, a holy hermit had made himself a quiet cell in which to live, and worship God. The narrow entrance to the cave was in great part hidden by flowering vines, which Roland's mother had with daily care coaxed to grow in the barren soil, and had trained to cling to the rough rocks and twine among the crevices overhead. Inside every thing betokened poverty. A single stool, a broken table, a few earthen dishes, the simple articles which the hermit had left,—these were the only pieces of furniture. In one corner of the room hung an old set of armor, dinted with many a lance-thrust, and hacked in many a battle, but still kept bright against the day when Roland should become a knight. Near it leaned a long, broken lance which had done duty in more than one tourney; and beneath it was a battered shield, on which were emblazoned the arms of Charlemagne. The stone floor was bare, and the rough stone walls were grimed with smoke, and the low ceilings were damp with moisture. Few were the comforts of home in that humble dwelling; and but for the kind welcome of his queen-like mother, the Lady Bertha, small would have been the cheer that Roland would have found there.

"I have seen him, mother!" he cried, rushing into her arms. "I have seen the great Charles and his glorious army and his gallant peers. Would that I were a man, that I, too, might ride forth with the king, the bravest of the brave!"

Then the gentle Bertha took the lad's hand in her own, and the two sat down together in their lowly dwelling, and Roland told her of all that he had seen that memorable afternoon; but he talked most of the noble Charlemagne, and of his kingly grace and bearing. Then he spoke again of his own hopes and of his high ambition, and of the time when he should be a knight, and, mayhap, one of the peers of the king.

"And now, dear mother," said he, "the time has come for me to learn the great secret of my life. To-day I am twelve years old,—old enough to be a page; to-day I have seen Charlemagne; and to-day you have promised to tell me all about my kinsfolk and myself, and the great destiny which lies before me."

Then the Lady Bertha drew the lad close to her, and told him the story of her own life and his,—a story so full of strange surprises to Roland, that, when he heard it, he wept for joy and for the big thoughts that came welling up from his heart. She told him that the great king whom he had seen that day, and whose fame was known in every land, was his uncle and her own brother. She told him how she, the spoiled and petted daughter of Pepin, had been brought up at the French court; and how, after her father's death, she had lived in her brother's kingly palace at Aix, loved and honored next to Charlemagne himself. Then she told, how, on a time, there came to Charlemagne's court a worthy knight named Milon,—a warrior poor and needy, but brave, and without reproach. "Milon boasted that his kin had been the noblest heroes of all time. Through his father he traced his descent from the Greeks; and he wore the arms of Trojan Hector engraved upon his shield; and he numbered among his ancestors the godlike hero Hercules. On his mother's side he claimed kinship with the fair-haired heroes of the North, with the fearless Vikings, with Siegfried the dragon-slayer, with the mighty Thor, and the matchless Odin.

"And when your mother, then the Princess Bertha, saw the gallant Count Milon, and heard of his nobleness and learned his true worth, she loved him. And your uncle Charlemagne hated him, and banished him from France, and sought even to take his life; for he wished to wed his sister to Duke Ganelon of Mayence, one of his peers. But, when Milon fled from the king's court at Aix, he went not alone; he took me, the Princess Bertha, with him as his wife: for the good Archbishop Turpin had secretly married us, and given us his blessing, and promised to help us on our way to Italy. When Charlemagne heard how he had been outwitted, he was very angry, and he swore that he would do his uttermost to ruin Count Milon, and to bring me back to France, and make me the wife of the hated Ganelon. And so, to escape his anger, we dressed ourselves in the guise of beggars, and wandered on foot from town to town and through many countries, begging our bread. And wherever we went we met the spies of Charlemagne seeking for Milon, and offering a price for his head. At last we came to Sutri, tired and footsore, and unable to go any farther. And, when none would take us into their houses, we found shelter in this wretched cave, which we fitted up the best that we could, to serve as a home until we could soften the anger of Charlemagne, and obtain his forgiveness. But soon after you were born, Roland, the Pagan folk crossed the sea, and came into Italy, and threatened Rome itself. Then your father, the gallant Milon, remembering his knightly vows, once more donned his armor; and, taking his lance and his shield, he went out to do battle for the king and for the holy church. You know the rest. You know how bravely he fought, and how he died, as heroes die, with his face toward the foe. All this I have told you often. And you know how we have lived these long, weary years in this wretched hermit cell, dependent on our kind neighbors for food, and hoping always for brighter and better days.

"And now you have learned the story of your birth and your kinship, and you know the destiny that is yours if you but do your part. The blood that flows in your veins is the blood of heroes, and it will not belie itself. You have seen Charlemagne, and to-day is the turning point in your life. Before the king leaves Sutri, he must acknowledge you as his nephew, and take you as a page into his court."

Then mother and son sat long together in the quiet cell, talking of the past, so fraught with distress and poverty and wretchedness, and of the unknown future with its vague promises and uncertain hopes. But so great was the lad's trust in his own strength, and so firm was the mother's faith in her son, that not once did clouds of doubt darken the bright pictures which their fancy painted of the good fortune yet in store for them. And the little candle which lighted the humble room burned down, and left them in darkness; and the moon rose over the hills, and peeped in through the doorway, and sloped downwards toward the west; and the stars, one by one, looked in between the vines, and then went onward in their endless journey around the world; and at length the eastern sky began to brighten, and then to blush at the coming of the sun; and still the Lady Bertha and the boy Roland sat, unmindful of the passing hours, and talked of the new life which they felt must soon be theirs. But when the morning had fairly come, and the first rays of the sun shot in upon them, Roland, as if suddenly awakened, sprang to his feet, and cried,—

"Mother, the night is past, and the day has dawned!—the first day in the great new life which is mine. I will go at once to my uncle, the king, and demand my rights and yours."

And with his mother's blessing and many a word of advice well fixed in his memory, the lad hurried away, walking rapidly across the fields toward Sutri.

ADVENTURE II

THE KING'S GUEST

It was a great day in Sutri. Never since the old Roman days had so brilliant a company of warriors and noble men been seen in that quiet town. In the governor's castle the king and the peers of the realm were being entertained and feasted. The chambers and halls and courts were full of knights and squires; and every one talked of the noble order of chivalry, and of war, and of arms and armor, and of the king's progress on the morrow to Rome. In the broad feast hall, Charlemagne and his peers were dining. On the dais, by the side of the king, sat Count Rainier, the governor of Sutri. Around them stood many of the noblest knights, attentive to their slightest wishes. Next below the king sat Turpin, the warrior bishop, clad to-day, not in his war coat of steel, but in his rich official robes, and looking much more the priest than the knight. Next to him sat Duke Namon of Bavaria, the king's counsellor, gray-bearded and sage, strong in fight, and wise in statesmanship,—the oldest and the most trusted of all the peers. On the other side was Malagis, the cunning dwarf, who, it was said, had power over the unseen creatures of the air, and by means of witchery could sometimes foretell the things that were about to befall. Next to him was old Ganelon of Mayence, at heart a vile traitor, the smile of a hypocrite resting on his thin lips, and his serpent-eyes twinkling with an evil light. On either side of the long table below sat many worthy knights, the most trusted warriors of Charlemagne, and the doughtiest heroes in

Christendom. I doubt if ever more valor was seen in castle hall.

Mirth and revelry ruled the hour; and the long, low hall rang with the sound of the harp and the flute and the glad voices of the singers. The great oaken table groaned beneath its weight of good cheer. The lordly Count Rainier had provided for this feast every thing that was pleasant to the taste, or that could add zest to the appetite. The richest meats and the rarest fruits, sparkling wine and foaming ale, the whitest bread and the most tempting sweetmeats—all were offered in generous profusion as if on purpose to make the knights forgetful of their vows of temperance. In the courtyard, around the open door, stood numbers of the poor people of the town, listening to the music, and waiting for the morsels that would be left after the feast. Suddenly a young boy, ragged and barefooted, appeared among them. All stood aside for him, as, with proud step and flashing eyes, he entered the great hall. With the air of a lord he pushed his way through the crowd of attendant knights and squires, and walked boldly up to the table. Then, without saying a word, he seized upon a basket of rare fruit and a loaf of bread that had been placed before the king.

"Indeed," said Charlemagne, "that is a bold boy. He will make a brave knight."

But those who stood around were so awed by the lad's proud bearing and by the strange flash of his eyes, that they dared not touch him; nor did they think of placing any hinderance in his way until he had seized the golden wine-cup which Charlemagne was on the point of lifting to his lips.

"Stop!" cried the king. "How dare you be so rude?"

But Roland held fast to his prize; and, fearless as a young eagle, he gazed into the face of the king. Charlemagne tried hard to appear angry; but, in spite of himself, a pleasant smile played upon his face, and his eyes twinkled merrily.

"My boy," said he, "the forest is a fitter place than this banquet hall for such as you. You would do better picking nuts from the trees than snatching dishes from the king's table; and the wine which you have taken from my hand is not nearly so good for you as the water in the flowing brook."

"The peasant drinks from the brook," answered Roland proudly; "the slave gathers nuts in the forest. But to my mother belong the best things that your table affords. The choicest game, the rarest fish, the reddest wine, are hers."

"Ha!" cried the king. "Your mother must indeed be a noble lady! And I suppose you will tell me that she lives in a lordly castle, with scores of brave knights and gentle dames about her, and that she sits daily in her great feast hall at a table loaded with every delicacy. How many servants has she? Who is her carver? and who is her cup-bearer? Come, tell us all about it."

"My right hand is her carver," answered Roland; "and my left hand is her cup-bearer."

"And has she soldiers and watchmen and minstrels, this wonderful mother of yours?"

"Indeed she has. These two arms are her soldiers; these eyes are her watchmen; these lips are her minstrels."

"That is a numerous household and a worthy one," answered the king, now very much amused. "But your good mother has strange taste in the matter of livery for her servants. I see they are all bareheaded and barefooted; and their clothing, what there is of it, is made of all the colors of the rainbow. How came she to furnish you with a robe so rich and rare?"

"My robe is of my own furnishing," answered Roland. "Eight boys in the town do me homage; and they pay me tribute in cloth, each a different color. And now, my lord, since you have learned all about my mother and her household, will you not visit her in her castle?"

Before the king could answer, the boy had turned on his heel, and, with the basket of food and the cup of wine in his hands, he fearlessly walked out of the hall. Charlemagne was surprised at the boldness of the lad, and delighted with his witty answers.

"Let him go," said he. "A braver lad I have never seen; and he well deserves his prize. He will yet become the noblest knight in Christendom."

Then, turning to Duke Namon, he whispered, "Saw you that strange flash in his eye? Was there ever a fairer countenance, or a more king-like form? Tell me truly, did he not remind you of some one you have seen elsewhere?"

"He did, my lord," answered Namon. "He reminded me of your worthy father, the great Pepin. He has the same noble features, the same broad brow, the same clear gray eyes flashing with a strange light. He reminded me, too, of yourself. Had he been clothed in a garb befitting a prince, I should have imagined that I saw you again as you appeared when a boy. But he reminded me most of your lost sister, the fair Princess Bertha. The same gentleness of manner, the same proud carriage of the head, the same curl of the lip,—qualities that we once admired so much in the Lady Bertha,—may all be seen in this wonderful boy."

The boyhood of Roland.

"I dreamed last night," said the king, "that my darling sister came to me, leading just such a boy as this. And I thought that he grew tall and strong, and that the whole world looked up to him as a pattern of knightly valor and courtesy, and that he carried my whole kingdom upon his shoulders. Now this boy is no common lad; and the mother of whom he speaks can be no common beggar. My heart tells me that she is the long-lost, long-forgiven Bertha."

"Your heart speaks rightly," answered Namon. "The son of no other lady could bear so perfect a likeness to the Pepins. I am sure that we have found her at last."

Then Charlemagne turned to the dwarf Malagis. "What say you, sir wizard?" he asked. "You have the gift of foresight, and you can read that which lies hidden to the eyes of others. What think you of a boy who comes thus boldly to our table, and levies mail from us as if it were his right?"

The dwarf twisted and writhed about in his seat: he smiled, as only wizards can smile, and then he humbly but wisely answered,—

"My lord, the lad is no beggar. The blood of heroes flows in his veins. Kings are his kinsmen. Great deeds await his coming into manhood. Harm him not, but have him sought out, and brought again before you. I have read in the stars that somehow the woof of your life is strangely interwoven with that of a lad like this."

Charlemagne at once ordered a dozen squires to follow the boy secretly to find where he dwelt, and then, without harming him, to bring both him and his mother to the castle. And then the feasting, which had been so strangely broken off, was begun again. And the wassail bowl went round, and many a weak-souled knight forgot his solemn vows of temperance; and the old hall again resounded with music and with uproarious mirth; and the boy Roland was for a time forgotten.

Very anxiously did the fair Bertha in the lonely hermit cell await the return of her son that day. He had left her in the morning, determined to make himself known to Charlemagne, and to demand the forgiveness of his mother, and her re-instatement in the king's palace. He had promised to be back very soon, with a palfrey for his mother to ride upon, and a company of knights and squires to escort her to the castle. But hour after hour had passed by; and it was now high noon, and still the boy did not come. Could it be possible that he had been too rash, and had been imprisoned, or otherwise severely punished, for his boldness? Another hour went by; and Bertha was about to despair of his return, when Roland suddenly appeared around the foot of the hill, carrying on his left arm a basket of food and in his right hand a golden goblet of wine.

"Mother," he cried, as he set his burden down in the doorway of the grotto,—"mother, I have brought you some share of the feast. You shall not starve while your brother, who is no better than you, eats and drinks and has such plenty of other luxuries that he knows not what to do with them."

Then he placed before her the bread and the wine, and a delicately baked fowl, and the rare fruits; and, while she ate, he told her all that had happened to him since he had left her in the morning. He had waited a long time about the palace doors, trying in vain to be allowed to see the king. The guards said that he was sleeping, and would not be disturbed. If he could only have found his friend Oliver, all would have been well. But the page was nowhere to be seen; and a squire whom he asked said that he had gone that morning, with a company of knights and dames, to Rome, and that it would be long ere he returned again to Sutri. At length, by the merest chance, he had peeped in through the open door of the banquet hall, and had seen the king himself seated at the table.

"I could not bear," he said, "to see so great plenty of all that was good, and to hear the mirth of the greedy revellers, and know that you were here in this wretched cave without a morsel of food. I walked right in and took the best, nor did I regard that I was robbing the king. He talked to me, and seemed not a bit angry; and I feel sure that he will send for me to come again before him, and then I will tell him all."

"Ah, Roland," said the Lady Bertha doubtfully, "you do not know your kingly uncle. He is hot-tempered and violent; and he may yet punish you for your rashness, and listen to no word of explanation or excuse. Many an innocent man has suffered from his unreasoning anger."

"I am not afraid," answered the boy. "He was altogether too jolly to be angry. And I expect, ere this time to-morrow, to be installed as a page to the king or to one of his peers."

He had scarcely spoken these words, when the squires who had been sent in search of him came around the foot of the hill, and halted only a few yards from the entrance to the grotto. Some were on foot, some on horseback; and all were armed with sticks, and more or less under the influence of the strong ale which they had drunk at the banquet. As soon as they saw Roland, they called out loudly to him, ordering him to surrender himself as their prisoner.

"Come along at once, my little one," cried the leader. "The king wants you for robbing his table."

Had the squires approached Roland in a respectful manner, he would have gone with them gladly. But their insolence maddened him.

"Tell the king," he answered, "that I am holding high court at home to-day, and that, if he wants me, he must come after me himself."

"But you must come with us," cried the squires. "You, and your mother the beggar woman, must come with us to Sutri, and lose no time."

"Beggar woman, indeed!" cried Roland, overflowing with rage. "How dare you speak thus of the sister of Charlemagne? Go back to the king, and tell him that his nephew is not wont to do the bidding of squires and churls. Tell him that only by the worthiest of his peers will my mother and I be taken into his presence."

At this boastful speech of one whom they looked upon as only a beggar, the squires laughed heartily; and one or two of them shook their sticks in a threatening manner, and made as if they would seize upon the boy. Roland ran quickly into the grotto, and soon came out again, bearing the long, broken lance in his hands. But it was a heavy weapon, and, as he found it, an unwieldy one. The squires closed in upon him from every side; and, as the great length of the lance prevented him from turning it quickly enough to guard himself at all points, he was obliged to drop it to the ground. In its stead, he seized a stout light club that lay in his way, and then, taking his stand in the doorway, he dared his assailants to come within his reach.

"You shall see," said he, "whether I cannot defend my mother's castle."

The squires, astonished at the quickness and the pluck of

the boy, fell back, and began trying to persuade him to go with them peaceably. But Roland stood warily in the doorway of his castle, and answered them only by swinging his club in the faces of the nearest, and by withering glances of defiance. It is uncertain how long this strange scene would have lasted, or how it would have ended, had it not been unexpectedly interrupted. A knight, unarmed, and mounted on a coal-black steed, rode suddenly around the hill, and reined up in the midst of the excited crowd. His long hair and flowing beard were white with age, and his pleasant face beamed with kindliness, and was lighted up with lines of far-seeing wisdom.

"Ha, my brave men!" he cried in tones of merriment. "What have we here? Twelve gallant squires in combat with a single boy! And the boy holds his castle against them all. Surely this is chivalry! What does it all mean?"

"It means," answered Roland, "that these fellows want to take me by force to the king at Sutri, and they have insulted me and my mother. Were they knights, or even gentlemen, I would go with them; but they are neither. They are mere churls and hangers-on about the governor's court, and they know nought of honor and knightly courtesy. It will be long ere they are worthy to wear the golden spurs."

The knight was amused at the boy's earnestness; and he said, "I cannot blame you for refusing to be taken by them. Yet I know that the king wishes very much to see you and your good mother, and he has sent me to hasten your coming. I am Namon, Duke of Bavaria, and I am sometimes known as one of Charlemagne's peers. Perhaps you will be willing to go with me if I send these squires away."

Roland, without a word of dissent, dropped his club to the

ground, and promised to go with the good knight at once if he would only find some means by which his mother might be helped to reach Sutri castle without the fatigue of walking so far. Duke Namon dismounted from his steed, and, having sent the squires away, went with Roland into the little cavern. There he was welcomed heartily by the Lady Bertha, who remembered him as a firm, kind friend in former days, when both were inmates of Charlemagne's palace at Aix. And the fair lady and the noble knight talked long together of things that had happened since then in France,—of the gallant deeds of her brother the king, and of his many triumphs at home and abroad; of the death of the gallant Milon, and of the long years of wretchedness and want that had since dragged by. And the knight told her how Charlemagne had sought in every land for her, and had sent messengers beyond the sea to inquire for her, in order that he might grant her his forgiveness, and make some amends for his former harshness. But all in vain. The messengers had brought back word that Milon was dead, but they could find no traces of his noble wife; and Charlemagne mourned her as lost. And then Namon told her of Roland's strange, daring deed in the feast hall at Sutri castle that day, and of the thoughts that he and the king had had about the boy; and lastly he spoke of the king's desire that she should appear at once before him, and, if she were indeed the lost Princess Bertha, she should be restored to her old place in his court and in his affections.

And toward evening the noble duke, with the Lady Bertha mounted behind him on a pillion, rode gayly over the fields to Sutri; while Roland, proud and happy, and carrying his father's broken lance on his shoulder, followed them on foot.

Glad, indeed, was the greeting with which the king welcomed his sister; but not a word could the fair Bertha speak, so overwhelmed was she with gratitude. Roland, still wearing his livery of many-colored rags, but holding himself erect and haughty as a prince, raised his wondrous gray eyes until they met Charlemagne's gaze.

"Sister," said the king, "for this boy's sake, if for nought else, all shall be forgiven. Let the past be forgotten in the joy of the present hour."

"Dear brother," said fair Bertha, "your kindness shall not go unrewarded. Roland will not disappoint you. He will grow up to be, next to you, the pattern of all heroes and the type of all manly virtues."

And the next day a great feast was held in the banquet hall of Count Rainier's castle, in honor of the fair princess and her gallant little son. And not only the bravest warriors in Charlemagne's service, but also many noble ladies and many knights from Rome and the country round about, sat down with the king at the festal board. And this time Roland was not an uninvited guest; but he sat in the place of honor at the king's right hand, while squires and servitors waited his call, and hastened to do his bidding. And Charlemagne rested two days longer at Sutri before proceeding on his march; and then he sent his sister, the princess, with a guard of trustworthy knights, back to France and to the pleasant palace and halls of Aix. But Roland was made a page in the service of good Duke Namon; and, when the grand army moved on again towards Rome, he bade good-by to his humble friends in Sutri, and made ready to go too. No happier, prouder heart beat in Italy that day than Roland's. Dressed in a rich gown of green velvet bordered with crimson and gold, and mounted on a white palfrey most handsomely harnessed, he seemed not like the barefooted beggar to whom the boys of Sutri had been wont to do homage. But it needed not that one should look closely to recognize that same noble form, those wonderful gray eyes, that proud but kind-like face. And he rode not with the rout of squires and soldiers and hangers-on who brought up the rear of the army, but by the side of Duke Namon, and in company with the bravest knights and the peers of the realm.

All along the road the people of the towns, the castles, and the countryside, crowded to see the conquering hero; and they welcomed him with shouts and glad songs as the guardian of Italy and the champion of all Christendom. Three miles this side of Rome all the noblest men of the city came out, with music playing and banners waving, to escort the grand army through the gates. At a mile from the walls the children of the schools met them, bearing palm leaves and olive branches in their hands, and strewing flowers in the way, and singing hymns in honor of the hero king. Charlemagne had laid aside his arms and his armor; and, dressed in his kingly robes, he rode by the side of the good Archbishop Turpin. His mantle was wrought of the finest purple, bordered with gold and ermine; upon his feet were sandals sparkling with priceless gems; upon his head was a coronet of pearls and flashing jewels. His horse was harnessed in the most goodly fashion, with trappings of purple damask bordered with ermine and white cloth-of-gold.

At the gate of the city the procession was met by a company of priests and monks bearing the standard of the cross, which was never taken out save on the most solemn and magnificent occasions. When Charlemagne saw the cross, he and his peers alighted from their horses, and went humbly on foot to the steps of St. Peter's Church. There he was met by the Pope, the bishops, and a great retinue of priests and monks, dressed in their richest vestments, who welcomed him to Rome, and blessed him. And on every side, in the streets and in the church, loud shouts rent the air, and the people joined in singing the chant, "Blessed is he that cometh in the name of the Lord."

The boy Roland, having never seen such grandeur, was filled with wonder and astonishment. "Surely," said he, "this is the happy vale of paradise, of which my mother has so often told me, where every Christian knight hopes one day to find a home."

"It is not that vale," answered good Duke Namon; "but it is the beginning of the road which leads thither."

Not many days did Charlemagne remain at Rome. Messengers came to him from France, who said that the Saxons and other Pagan folk had crossed the Rhine, and were carrying fire and sword into the fairest portions of the land; and they begged him to hasten his return to his own country, that he might protect his people from the ravages of their barbarous foes. So, having received the homage and the blessing of the Pope, and having been crowned with the iron crown of the Lombards, he marshalled all his forces, and set out on his journey back to France. And late that same autumn, Roland saw for the first time the noble city of Aix, and was formally installed as page in Duke Namon's household.

ADVENTURE III

THE WAR WITH THE SAXONS

A STORMY winter had set in. It was unlike any thing that Roland had ever seen in his sunny southern home; and he was scarcely more astonished by the grandeur of Charlemagne's court than by this wonderful war of the elements. The bleak north winds, like so many giants let loose, came roaring through the forests, and shrieking among the house-tops and the castle towers, carrying blinding tempests of sleet and snow in their arms, and hurling them angrily to the ground. The rivers were frozen over; the roads were blockaded; there was little communication between Aix and other parts of Charlemagne's dominions. The main part of the army was still in Southern France, and there it was ordered to stay until the opening of spring should make it possible to advance against the Saxons.

Very pleasant to Roland was his first winter at Charlemagne's court. Within the palace halls there were comfort and good cheer; the fires blazed high and warm in the great chimney places; there was much music and merry-making; and for Roland there were many agreeable duties. Much of his time was spent in the service of the ladies at court, and especially of the Duchess Blanchefleur, the wife of good Duke Namon. And he was instructed in the first duties of the true knight,—to reverence God, and honor the king; to speak the truth at all times; to deal justly with both friend and foe; to be courteous and obliging to his equals; to be large-hearted and kind to those beneath him in rank; and, above all, to help the needy, to protect the weak, and to respect and venerate the ladies. Some time, too, he spent in the company of his lord, Duke Namon. He waited on him at table, he poured out his wine, he carried his messages; and much wisdom did he learn, listening to the words that fell from the lips of the sage counsellor. He became acquainted, too, with the officers of the court, and with the squires and grooms about the palace. And he learned how to manage horses, and how to mount and ride a high-mettled steed. He was taught how to hold a lance with ease, how to handle the broadsword dexterously, and how to draw the long-bow, and shoot with sharp-sighted skill. When the weather was fine, and the snow not too deep on the ground, he often rode out with his master and other knights to hunt the deer and wild boars in the forest. And he learned all about the training and care of falcons and merlins and hunting-hounds, and how to follow the game in the wildwood, and how to meet the charge of a wounded buck or a maddened boar. Sometimes, during the long winter evenings, he sat in the school of the palace with Charlemagne and the members of the family, and listened to the wise instructions of Alcuin, the English schoolmaster. And he learned to read in the few Latin books that were treasured with great care in the *scriptorium,* or writing-room, of the palace; and sometimes, under the direction of the schoolmaster, he tried to copy the beautiful letters of some old-time manuscript. At other times he sat with the knights and the squires in the low-raftered feast-hall, and listened to the music and the song-stories of some wandering harper.

And thus the winter months sped swiftly by; and as the days began to grow longer and warmer, and the snow melted from the ground, and the ice thawed in the rivers, Charlemagne thought it time to make ready for the long-deferred campaign against the Saxons. Messengers were sent out in every direction to summon every true knight and every loyal fighting man to join the king's standard at Aix; and it was expected, that, by the time of the Easter festival, a hundred thousand warriors would be there, ready to march against the Pagan folk of the North. About the king's castle many busy preparations were going on. Some were furbishing up their arms, or mending their old armor; others were providing new weapons for themselves, or new harness for their steeds; knights, squires, pages, and grooms, all found enough to do, and all looked forward with eager impatience to the day that was set for the march. In the smithies the bellows roared and the fires glowed; and smiths and armorers worked day and night, forging swords and spear points, and riveting armor plates and rings of mail. And even in the kitchens there was an unwonted hurrying to and fro, and the sound of busy voices and busier hands; while in the halls and the castle-chambers many a brave-hearted lady sat stitching and embroidering rich garments for her lord.

The time of the Easter festival came at last. Grass was springing fresh and green in the meadows. The trees were putting forth their leaves. In the wildwood the voice of the cuckoo and the song of the warbler were heard. The ice had disappeared from the river, and the snow had melted in the valleys: the roads were once more passable. It seemed a fitting time for the beginning of new schemes and of bold undertakings. And early one April morning the great army, with Charlemagne and his peers at its head, filed out of the city, and began its march toward the Rhine. And Roland, proud and happy as a knight with spurs, was allowed to ride in the train of Duke Namon.

When the Saxons heard of the coming of the Franks, they hastily crossed again into their own country, and shut themselves up in their towns and strongholds. But Charlemagne followed them without delay; nor did the wide, deep Rhine hinder him long. Through all their land he carried fire and sword; nor did he spare any one through pity. For he was a Christian: while the Saxons were Pagans, and worshipped Thor and Odin; and many of them had never heard of the true God. It is said, that, a little while before this time, an English priest named St. Liebwin had gone alone into the very heart of Saxony for the purpose of carrying the gospel of Christ to that benighted folk. Boldly he stood up before them when they came to worship in their false temples, and, holding the cross in his hands, he upbraided them.

"What do ye?" he said. "The gods that ye worship live not, they understand not, they see not. They are the works of your hands. They can help neither you nor themselves. Wherefore, the only true and good God, having pity on you, has sent me unto you to warn you of the trouble which shall come upon you unless ye put away your false gods. A prince, wise, strong, and unsleeping, shall come among you, and he shall fall upon you like a torrent. At one rush he shall invade your country; and he shall lay it waste with fire and sword, and spare none."

Great was the anger of the Pagan folk when they heard this bold speech of St. Liebwin. Some threatened to tear him to pieces in front of their temples: others ran in haste to the woods, and began to cut sharpened stakes with which to slay him. But one, more wise than the rest, a chief named Buto, stood up before them, and cried out, "Do not act rashly in this matter! It is against our laws, and contrary to our custom, to mistreat or abuse ambassadors. We have always received them kindly, hearkened to their messages, and sent them away with presents. Here is an ambassador from a great God; and should we slay him?"

The words of the chief softened the anger of the Saxons, and they allowed St. Liebwin to return unharmed across the Rhine. But they still clung to their false gods, and thought no more of his warning until after Charlemagne had overrun their country, and carried dire distress among them.

Among the places which fell into the hands of the French was the stronghold of Ehresburg, near which was a temple of the Saxons,—a spacious building, wide and high, and ornamented with thousands of trophies taken in battle. In the midst of this temple stood a marble column on which was the figure of an armed warrior holding in one hand a banner, and in the other a balance. On the breastplate of the figure was engraven a bear; and on the shield which hung from his shoulders was painted a lion in a field full of flowers. This figure was the idol known in history as Irmin, and was the image of the war-god of the Saxons. Charlemagne caused the temple of Irmin to be torn down and destroyed, and he buried the idol and its column deep in the earth. But so great was the building, and so large was the image, that the whole army was employed three days in their destruction.

By this time midsummer had come. The sun shone hot and fierce in a cloudless sky. There had been no rain since the early spring, and the ground was parched and dry. There was no water in the brooks; the springs ceased flowing; and ere long the river itself became dry. The leaves of the trees withered for want of moisture; the grain would not ripen in the fields; the meadows and pastures were burned up with the heat and the long drought. Warriors who had never turned their backs upon a foe trembled now at the thought of death from thirst and starvation. Horrible indeed was the fate which threatened the French army, and Charlemagne ordered a quick retreat towards the river Rhine. Yet both men and horses were weak with fasting, and exhausted by the oppressive heat; and the march was slow and painful. They reached the dry bed of an unknown stream, and could go no farther. The soldiers groped among the rocks, and tried in vain to find some trace of moisture in the sand. Every mind was burdened with despair. Not one among the knights but that would have given his richest fief for a drink of cold water.

All at once a storm cloud was seen in the south. Rapidly it rose higher and higher above the horizon. The lightnings flashed; the roar of distant falling rain was heard. A great hoarse shout went up from the parched throats of ten thousand warriors. They were saved. Soon the bed of the river was filled with a torrent of rushing, foaming water; and men and beasts hastened to quench their thirst. And good Archbishop Turpin, taking the crucifix in his hand, stood up before the host, and thanked Heaven for this timely deliverance. And all joined in solemnly singing praises to God; and all devoutly believed that they had been thus blessed because they had overthrown the idol of Irmin, and destroyed his temple. The very same day the Saxons sent to Charlemagne begging for peace, and offering to do him homage, and pay him tribute. And the king took hostages from them from among the noblest families in the land, and then recrossed the Rhine into his own country.

ADVENTURE IV

THE KNIGHT OF THE SWAN

ONE day Roland stood at the window of a castle overlooking the Rhine, while Charlemagne and Duke Namon sat on the balcony outside, enjoying the pleasant breeze that was wafted to them from the not far-distant sea. All at once the clear-ringing sound of a bell reached their ears. At first it seemed far away; but it came slowly nearer and nearer, until the whole air seemed filled with the sweet, simple music. By this time all eyes in the castle were turned in the direction whence the sounds seemed to come. The windows and doors, the battlements and the towers, were crowded with knights and ladies, squires, pages, and menials, all charmed by the sweet tones, and all anxious to know by what strange power they were produced.

"What seest thou down the river?" asked the king of the watchman on the tower.

"My lord," answered the watchman, "I see nothing save the waving of the reeds in the wind, and the long ripple of the waves on the shelving banks."

Still louder and clearer rang the bell; still nearer and nearer it seemed to come. All Nature appeared to be listening.

"Watchman," cried the king again, "seest thou yet any thing?"

"I see," answered the watchman, "a mist, like a little silver cloud, resting upon the water, and coming slowly toward us. But I cannot distinguish aught else."

Sweeter and sweeter grew the sounds, like the music of angel voices in the air. The hearts of the listeners stood still; they held their breath; they feared to break the wondrous spell.

"Watchman," cried the king, "what seest thou now?"

"My lord," answered now the watchman, "I see a white swan floating on the water; and on its neck there is a crown of gold; and behind it is a silver boat made like the shell of a scallop, which it draws by a silken cord; and in the scallop sits a knight in full armor. But the device on his shield is a strange one, and I cannot tell from what land he comes. In the bow of the boat hangs a little bell; but I know not whether the sound which so ravishes our ears is made by its ringing, or whether it is the song of the swan."

And now the swan and the strange little boat were plainly seen by all the inmates of the castle. Slowly they drew nearer and nearer to the quay. At last the boat came alongside of the landing place, and stopped. The music, too, ceased as soon as the swan left off rowing. Then certain of the king's men stepped down to the water-side; and one whose name was Nibelung, and who had come from the unknown Northland, gave the stranger his hand, and helped him from the scallop. And the swan turned about, and swam away in the direction whence he had come, drawing the empty shell-boat behind him. And the strange, sweet music, which began again as soon as the swan commenced rowing, grew fainter and still more faint, until at last it died away in the far distance, and was never heard again.

The strange knight, who was ever afterward known as the Knight of the Swan, was led into the presence of the king. But he spoke not a word to any one; and although he seemed right nobly bred, and courteous, it was soon plain to all that he was quite dumb. Before the king there stood warriors from every land,—Frenchmen, Italians, Greeks, Persians, Goths, Saxons, and Danes; and he commanded each of these to speak in his own tongue to the stranger. But the Knight of the Swan answered not a word, nor seemed to understand what they said to him. Then Roland saw that a blue ribbon was tied around the stranger's neck, and that to it was fastened a small roll of parchment.

"My lord," said he to the king, "perhaps this roll will tell who he is, and why he comes in this strange manner to you."

"Take the parchment," said the king, "and see if any thing is written thereon."

And Roland unloosed the ribbon from the stranger's neck, and opened the roll, and read these words: "My name is Gerard Swan, of the race of Lohengrin. I seek a home with you, and a wife, and a fief of lands."

"Right welcome are you, Sir Gerard of the Swan!" said the king, taking his hand. "You shall have all for which you have come, and much more."

Then Nibelung, by the king's command, unarmed the knight, and carried his sword and shield and rich armor to the guard room. And the clothing which the stranger wore beneath his armor was of the most princely kind,—of purple velvet embroidered with gold. And he had upon his hand a ring of curious workmanship, in which was set a cross that glittered like the rays of the sun. And the king took off his own mantle of crimson silk and rich ermine, and threw it over the knight's shoulders.

And a banquet was held that day in token of rejoicing for

the victories so lately won; and the Knight of the Swan sat at the right hand of the king.

"Why does my uncle show so great honor to a stranger?" asked Roland afterward.

"He is a godsend," said Duke Namon. "Wherever he is, there will Heaven's favor be; and whatever cause he may espouse, it will prosper."

"He looks, indeed, like a strong-hearted knight," thought Roland.

Not many days after this, Charlemagne and his warriors returned to Aix. And the Knight of the Swan proved himself to be in all things upright and trustworthy. He soon learned to talk; and, next to Duke Namon, he was long looked up to as the ablest of the king's advisers. And so highly did Charlemagne esteem him, that he gave him his sister, the Princess Adalis, in marriage, and made him Duke of Ardennes. But no man durst ever ask him whence he came, or to what race he belonged.

ADVENTURE V

OGIER THE DANE

On the day that Roland was fourteen years old, he was allowed to lay aside his page's dress, and don the garb of a squire. Very proud was he of this new honor, and faithfully did he try to merit it. He was now no longer a boy, whose chief duties were to serve the ladies of the household, and to wait on his master at table. He was regarded as a youth perfecting himself in the use of arms, and making himself ready for the active business of knighthood. He learned how to handle all kinds of weapons, and very expert did he become in the use of the sword and the heavy lance. He practised himself in every manly art, and learned to endure every sort of hardship. And there was no one in Charlemagne's court, nor, indeed, in all France, who could excel him in the feats of skill and strength in which the young men of those days prided themselves.

About this time there came to dwell in the household of Duke Namon a youth, some three years older than Roland, named Ogier. He was a Dane, and had come to France as a hostage. Very tall he was, and straight as a mountain pine; and men said that a handsomer youth had never been seen. His father was Godfrey, king of Denmark, known everywhere as one of the bravest and most daring of the Northmen: he lived in a strong-built castle on the shore of the sea, and had long boasted that he acknowledged no man as his peer, not even the mighty Charlemagne of France. Many years had

Godfrey ruled over the rude and danger-loving people of Denmark; and the swift-sailing dragon ships of the jarls and vikings who owned him as their master were known and feared in every sea and on every coast, from Jutland to Cornwall and Finisterre. And it was whispered that the Danish king had even hoped to rival Charlemagne in power, and that he had dreamed of making himself, some day, the master of all Europe.

And this is the story that men tell of the childhood of Ogier. When he was but a babe in his mother's arms, there was heard one day, in his father's castle, the sweetest music that mortals ever listened to. Nobody knew whence the bewitching sounds came; for they seemed to be now here, now there: yet every one was charmed with the delightful melody, and declared that only angels could make music so heavenly. Then suddenly there came into the chamber where Ogier lay six fairies, whose beauty was so wonderful and awful, that none but a babe might gaze upon them without fear. And each of the lovely creatures bore in her hands a garland of the rarest flowers, and rich gifts of gold and gems. And the first fairy took the child in her arms, and kissed him, and said,—

"Better than kingly crown, or lands, or rich heritage, fair babe, I give thee a brave, strong heart. Be fearless as the eagle, and bold as the lion; be the bravest knight among men."

Then the second fairy took the child, and dandled him fondly on her knees, and looked long and lovingly into his clear gray eyes.

"What is genius without opportunity?" said she. "What is a brave heart without the ability to do brave deeds? I give to thee many an opportunity for manly action."

The third fairy laid the dimpled hands of the babe in her own white palm, and stroked softly his golden hair.

"Strong-hearted boy, for whom so many noble deeds are waiting, I, too, will give thee a boon. My gift is skill and strength such as shall never fail thee in fight, nor allow thee to be beaten by a foe. Success to thee, fair Ogier!"

The fourth fairy touched tenderly the mouth and the eyes and the noble brow of the babe.

"Be fair of speech," said she, "be noble in action, be courteous, be kind: these are the gifts I bring thee. For what will a strong heart, or a bold undertaking, or success in every enterprise, avail, unless one has the respect and the love of one's fellow-men?"

Then the fifth fairy came forward, and clasped Ogier in her arms, and held him a long time quietly, without speaking a word. At last she said,—

"The gifts which my sisters have given thee will scarcely bring thee happiness; for, while they add to thy honor, they may make thee dangerous to others. They may lead thee into the practice of selfishness, and base acts of tyranny. That man is little to be envied who loves not his fellow-men. The boon, therefore, that I bring thee is the power and the will to esteem others as frail mortals equally deserving with thyself."

And then the sixth fairy, the youngest and the most beautiful of all, who was none other than Morgan le Fay, the Queen of Avalon, caught up the child, and danced about the room in rapturous joy. And, in tones more musical than mortals often hear, she sung a sweet lullaby, a song of fairyland and of the island vale of Avalon, where the souls of heroes dwell.

And, when she had finished singing, Morgan le Fay crowned the babe with a wreath of laurel and gold, and lighted a fairy torch that she held in her hand. "This torch," said she, "is the measure of thy earthly days; and it shall not cease to burn until thou hast visited me in Avalon, and sat at table with King Arthur and the heroes who dwell there in that eternal summer-land."

Then the fairies gave the babe gently back into his mother's arms, and they strewed the floor of the chamber with many a rich gem and lovely flower; and the odor of roses and the sweetest perfumes filled the air, and the music of angels' voices was heard above; and the fairies vanished in a burst of sunbeams, and were seen no more. And when the queen's maidens came soon afterward into the chamber, they found the child smiling in his mother's arms. But she was cold and lifeless: her spirit had flown away to fairyland.

And Ogier, though left thus motherless, was carefully tended and reared, and became, not only the pet of the king's household, but the hope of all Denmark. The wisest men were lured from other lands, and employed as teachers of the young prince; and he was instructed in all the arts, and in all the learning, of the times. And he grew to be a strong and handsome youth, tall and comely, and skilful in every manly exercise. No knight in all his father's domains could ride so well as he; none could wield the sword with greater skill, or handle the lance more easily; and no one was more courteous, more kind to his friends, more terrible to his foes, than Ogier. And the Danes looked forward with secret pleasure to the time when he should become their king. But he had scarcely passed the years of a page and been made a squire in his father's household, when there came a great change to him, and his life's outlook was sadly altered. His father had married a scheming, heartless woman, who hated Ogier, and who sought to drive him away from Denmark in order that her own son, Guyon, might be the heir to the kingdom. And she daily poisoned the king's mind by persuading him that Ogier was plotting against him, and planning to seize his kingdom. And King Godfrey, when he saw with what favor the people looked upon his son, grew strangely jealous and cold, and treated him harshly and ofttimes cruelly. But Ogier, nothing daunted by ill fortune, or by the frowns of his father, or by the taunts of his evil-minded step-mother, held on his way, and allowed neither malice nor despair to interfere with his happiness, or to make him forgetful of his duties.

At about the time when Ogier was sixteen years old, the news first came to Charlemagne of the greatness of the Danish king, and of his project to set up a rival kingdom in the North. And he vowed that the Danes too, as all the neighboring nations had already done, should acknowledge him their sovereign lord, and pay him tribute. He sent, therefore, an embassy of a hundred knights, under Ganelon of Mayence, to demand of King Godfrey a promise of homage and fealty, as the holder of a fief from France. King Godfrey received the messengers kindly, and entertained them in the most kingly manner for seven days. And, when they had told him their errand, he led them through the different apartments of his strong castle, and showed them the well-built walls, and the variety of weapons, and the great store of provisions, that he had laid in, in readiness against a siege. And he said, "Tell

Charlemagne that there are a hundred such castles in Denmark, and that not one has ever been surprised or taken by a foe."

Then he caused to pass before them the flower of his army, —ten thousand knights, clad in complete armor, and mounted on matchless steeds of war.

"Tell Charlemagne," said he, "that what you have seen is but a small part of my strength, and that, if he wishes to fight for the mastership, I am ready to meet him."

"On what conditions?" asked Ganelon. "You would best make them liberal, for Charlemagne seldom grants, and never asks terms."

"On these conditions," answered the king,—"that the vanquished shall embrace the religion of the victor, and become his vassal."

"It is well," said Ganelon. "I will carry your answer to Charlemagne."

Then the king gave rich presents to the messengers, and sent them back again into their own country.

When Charlemagne heard the boastful message that was brought to him by Ganelon, he at once called together an army of fifty thousand men, and marched northward to chastise the audacious Dane. A great battle was fought, and King Godfrey was terribly defeated. The ten thousand knights, of whose bravery he had boasted, were found to be no match for the better trained and more skilful warriors of France. The Danish army was routed, and the king himself was taken prisoner.

"What now sayest thou about the mastership?" asked Charlemagne in great anger. "What now wilt thou give for thy life?"

"I will abide by the conditions on which I at first offered to fight you," answered Godfrey. "I will become a Christian, and be your vassal; and, if I may hold the fief of Denmark, I will pay you a yearly tribute of whatever sum you may demand."

Then Charlemagne, who was ever lenient to a fallen foe, willingly made peace with the Danish king, and, after he had been baptized, made him Duke of Denmark. But he asked, that, in proof of his sincerity, Godfrey should give up as hostages four of the noblest youths about his court. This the humbled Dane agreed to do; and by the advice of his wife he gave his own son, the matchless Ogier, as one of the four. And not long after this, Charlemagne and his host returned home.

It chanced that Duke Namon of Bavaria saw the Danish prince, and was much pleased with his open countenance, his noble form, and his courtly manner; and he hastened to get leave of the king to have the young man in his own household, not as an underling or a servant, but as a worthy and honored squire. And it was thus that Ogier and Roland came to dwell beneath the same roof. And their friendship waxed daily stronger and stronger, until in the end they exchanged tokens, and pledged each other as brothers in arms. Nevertheless, Roland still remembered Oliver with the same brotherly love as of yore, and allowed not his affection for Ogier to make him forget his earlier vows of brotherhood.

Ogier grew daily stronger and more handsome, and more skilful in every feat of arms, and more graceful in every deed of courtesy. And none of the youths about the French court, not even Roland, could equal him in the games wherein their strength and endurance were tried. But as months and months went by, and his father allowed him still to be held as a hostage and a prisoner in a strange land, his heart sometimes burned with impatience, or sometimes grew sad with a weary longing for freedom.

In the meanwhile, Duke Godfrey, the father of Ogier, was too busy plotting treason against his liege lord Charlemagne to have much thought for his son; and indeed, so great was his feeling of jealousy toward Ogier, that he had no wish to have him ever return to Denmark. His wife was very anxious that the Danish crown might be left to her own son, Guyon; and she at length persuaded her husband to withhold from Charlemagne the tribute which had been promised; for she hoped that the French king would become so angered by this neglect that he would put the hostages to death.

And now four years had passed, and Charlemagne had not received a penny of tribute from Godfrey; nor had the Danish duke come once to his court to do him homage, as he had agreed. Often had the king threatened to punish the Dane for his neglect. But his wars in Italy and with the Saracens had claimed all his time, and the affairs of Denmark were allowed to rest without much attention. And Godfrey went on strengthening his castles, and building a fleet, and training his fighting men; and he persuaded himself that he would yet outwit and get the better of the king. But one day Charlemagne, as he sat at table with his peers around him, chanced to remember the slighted tribute, and the homage so long due him from Duke Godfrey.

"While all my enemies are humbled in the dust," said he, "this Dane is the only man who dares neglect his duty. He shall be reminded at once of his broken promises, and of the debt which he owes us."

And he immediately despatched an embassy of four trustworthy knights, with a retinue of squires and servitors, to the court of Denmark to demand that the tribute so long overdue should be paid without further delay.

ADVENTURE VI

HOW THE ARMY CROSSED THE ALPS

It was near the time of the solemn festival of Easter,—the time when Nature seems to rise from the grave, and the Earth puts on anew her garb of youth and beauty. King Charlemagne was at St. Omer; for there the good Archbishop Turpin was making ready to celebrate the great feast with more than ordinary grandeur. Thither, too, had gone the members of the king's household, and a great number of lords and ladies, the noblest in France. There were the queen, the fair Fastrada, and Charlemagne's two sons Charlot and Louis, and his sisters Bertha and Alice, and his daughters Belissent and Emma. And there also were many of the peers of the realm,—Duke Namon, and Ganelon, and Malagis the wizard, and Alcuin the English schoolmaster, and Gerineldo the king's scribe, and Roland, and Ogier the Dane. And with many fond anticipations all awaited the coming of the festal day, and the new season of active duty and labor which it would usher in.

But there came fleet messengers to St. Omer, bearing to Charlemagne news as unlooked-for as it was disagreeable. The ambassadors whom he had sent last autumn to claim the homage and the tribute due from Duke Godfrey of Denmark had come home with shaved faces and tonsured heads. Barely had they escaped with their lives from the traitorous Dane. And they had brought this word from Godfrey. "Tell your king," said he, "that the lord of Denmark is no man's thrall, and that never will he do homage, or pay aught of tribute, to any foreign tyrant."

Great was the wrath of Charlemagne, and he declared at once that Ogier the Dane, and his three comrades, should be put to death; for, according to the terms made with Godfrey, the young men were now for-hostaged, and their lives were justly forfeited. And in spite of the sage advice of Duke Namon, and the prayers of the queen herself, the king caused the four hostages to be thrown into the dungeon of St. Omer; and he threatened, that, as soon as Eastertide was past, they should be brought out, and hanged in the sight of all the people. Then word was sent to Paris and to Aix, and to all the chiefs and lords in France, calling every one who was able to bear arms to rally around the king's standard, and be ready on a moment's notice to move against the traitorous Duke of Denmark. And when, at length, Easter morning broke, and the sun rose clear and bright in a cloudless sky, its rays fell upon the armor and banners of a mighty host encamped at St. Omer, and expecting on the morrow to begin the march to the North.

But a new surprise awaited Charlemagne. Scarcely had the good archbishop pronounced a blessing upon the devout multitude assembled at the Easter service, when two messengers came in hot haste, and demanded to speak with the king. They had come from Rome, and they bore letters from Pope Leo. Sad was the news which these letters brought, but it was news which would fire the heart of every Christian knight. The Saracens had landed in Italy, and had taken Rome by assault. "The pope and the cardinals and the legates have fled," said the letters; "the churches are torn down; the holy relics are lost; and the Christians are put to the sword. Wherefore the Holy

Father charges you as a Christian king to march at once to the help of the Church."

It needed no word of Charlemagne to arouse the ardor of his warriors. Every other undertaking must be laid aside, so long as Rome and the Church were in danger. The design of marching against the Danes was given up for a time; and the heralds proclaimed that on the morrow, at break of day, the army, instead of advancing northward, would move southward toward Italy.

"What shall we do with Ogier and the other Danish hostages?" asked Ganelon, smiling, and hoping that the king would carry out his threats, and have the young men put to death.

"It is no fit time to deal with them now," answered the king. "Let the three who are of lower rank lie in prison where they are. But as for Ogier, the prince, do you take charge of him, and bring him with you to Rome. See that he does not escape; and, when we have driven the Pagans out of the city, we shall have him hanged as a traitor in the sight of the whole host."

The morning after Easter dawned, and the great army waited for the signal to march. The bugles sounded, and the long line of steel-clad knights and warriors began to move. Charlemagne rode in the front ranks, ready, like a true knight, to brave every difficulty, and to be the first in every post of danger. Never did a better king wear spur. Roland, as was his wont on such occasions, rode by the side of Duke Namon, carrying that knight's shield and the heavier parts of his armor; and, as became a trusty squire, he thought not of his own pleasure, but of the comfort of him whom he served. Nor did he consider his own safety or his own honor to be matters of concern, so long as Duke Namon was his lord. But Ogier the Dane rode in the rear of the host, with Ganelon's squires; and, being a prisoner, he was not allowed to carry any arms, or to move out of sight of the young men who guarded him.

Great was the haste with which the army moved, and very impatient were the warriors; for the whole of France lay between them and fair Italy, and they knew that weeks of weary marching must be endured, ere they could meet their Pagan foe in battle, and drive him out of the Christians' land. Many days they rode among the rich fields, and between the blooming orchards, of the Seine valley; many days they toiled over unbroken forest roads, and among marshes and bogs, and across untrodden moorlands. They climbed steep hills, and swam broad rivers, and endured the rain and the wind and the fierce heat of the noonday sun, and sometimes even the pangs of hunger and thirst. But they carried brave hearts within them; and they comforted themselves with the thought that all their suffering was for the glory of God and the honor of the king, for their country's safety and the security of their homes. And every day, as they advanced, the army increased in numbers and in strength: for the news had been carried all over the land, that the Saracens had taken Rome, and that Charlemagne with his host was hastening to the rescue; and knights and noblemen from every city and town and countryside came to join his standard, sometimes alone and singly, and sometimes with a great retinue of fighting men and servitors. And when at last they had passed the boundaries of France, and only the great mountains lay between them and Italy, Charlemagne could look behind him, and see an army of a hundred thousand men.

And now messengers came to him again, urging him to hasten with all speed to the succor of the pope.

But the Alps Mountains lifted themselves up in his pathway, and their snowy crags frowned threateningly upon him; their steep, rocky sides arose like walls before him, and seemed to forbid his going farther; and there appeared to be no way of reaching Italy, save by a long and circuitous route through the southern passes. In the hope that he might find some shorter and easier passage, Charlemagne now sent out scouts and mountaineers to explore every valley and gorge, and every seeming mountain pass. But all came back with the same story: there was not even so much as a path up which the mountain goats could clamber, much less a road broad enough for an army with horses and baggage to traverse. The king was in despair, and he called together his counsellors and wise men to consider what should be done. Duke Namon urged that they should march around by way of the southern passes; for, although a full month would thus be lost, yet there was no other safe and well-known land-route to Italy. Ganelon advised that they should turn back, and, marching to Marseilles, embark from thence on ships, and undertake to reach Rome by way of the sea.

Then the dwarf Malagis came before Charlemagne, bearing in his hand a book, from which he read many spells and weird enchantments. Upon the ground he drew with his wand a magic ring, and he laid therein the hammer of Thor and the sword of Mahmet. Then, in a loud, commanding voice, he called upon the sprites, the trolls, and the goblins, with whom he was familiar, to come at once into his presence. And the lightning flashed, and the thunder rolled, and smoke and fire burst forth from the mountain peaks, and the rocks and great ice-fields were loosened among the crags, and came tumbling down into the valley. And dwarfs and elves, and many an uncanny thing, danced and shouted in the mountain caves; and grinning ogres peeped out from the deep clefts and gorges; and the very air seemed full of ghostlike creatures. Then the wizard called by name a wise but wicked goblin, known among the Saracens as Ashtaroth; and the goblin came at once, riding in a whirlwind, and feeling very angry because he was obliged to obey.

"Tell me now," said Malagis, "and tell me truly, whether there is here so much as a pathway by which Charlemagne may lead his army through the mountains."

The goblin was silent for a moment; and a dark cloud rested upon his face, and his look was terrible. But the wizard, in no wise daunted, returned his glance, and in the tones of a master bade him clear up that clouded look, and answer the question he had asked. Then Ashtaroth curbed his anger, and spoke.

"On what errand would the French king cross the Alps?" he asked. "Seeks he not to harm my friends the Saracens?"

"That is, indeed, his errand," answered Malagis.

"Then, why should I do aught to help him?" asked the goblin. "Why do you call me from my rest, and bid me betray my friends?"

"That is not for thee to ask," said Malagis. "I have called thee as a master calls his slave. Tell me now, and tell me truly, is there here any pass across the mountains into Italy?"

"There is such a pass," answered the goblin gravely; "but it is hidden to eyes like mine. I cannot guide you to it, nor can any of my kind show you how to find it. It is a pathway which only the pure can tread."

"Tell me one thing more," said Malagis. "Tell me one thing, and I will let thee go. How prosper thy friends the Saracens at Rome?"

"They have taken all but the Capitol," was the answer. "They have slain many Christians, and burned many buildings. The pope and the cardinals have fled to Spoleto. If Charlemagne reach not Italy within a month, ill will it fare with his friends."

Then Malagis, satisfied with what he had heard, unwound the spell of his enchantments; and amid a cloud of fire and smoke the goblin flew back again into the mountains.

And now the good Turpin came forward, with a crosier in his hand, and a bishop's mitre on his head, and a long white robe thrown over his shoulders, scarcely hiding the steel armor which he wore beneath. And he lifted up his eyes to heaven, and prayed. And the sound of his voice arose among the cliffs, and resounded among the rocks, and was echoed from valley to valley, and re-echoed among the peaks and crags, and carried over the mountain tops, even to the blue sky above. And the king and those who stood about him fancied that they heard sweet strains of music issuing from the mountain caves; and the most bewitching sounds arose among the rocks and gorges; and the air was filled with a heavenly perfume and the songs of singing-birds; and a holy calm settled over mountain and valley, and fell like a blessing upon the earth. Then the Alps no longer seemed obstacles in their way. The steep cliffs, which had been like mighty walls barring their progress, seemed now mere gentle slopes, rising little by little toward heaven, and affording a pleasant and easy highway to the fair fields of Italy beyond.

While Charlemagne and his peers gazed in rapt delight upon this vision, there came down from the mountain crags a beautiful creature such as none of them had ever before seen. It was a noble stag, white as the drifted snow, his head crowned with wide-branching antlers, from every point of which bright sunbeams seemed to flash.

"Behold our leader and our hope!" cried Turpin. "Behold the sure-footed guide which the Wonder-king has sent to lead us through narrow ways, and over dangerous steeps, to the smiling valleys and fields of Italy! Be only strong and trustful and believing, and a safe way shall open for us, even where there seemed to be no way."

Then the vision faded slowly away from the sight of the peers; and the mountain walls rose up before them as grim and steep as ever; and the snow-crowned crags looked down upon them even more angrily than before, and there seemed no road nor pathway which the foot of man could follow. But the wondrous white stag, which had filled their minds with a new-born hope, still stood in plain sight on the lowermost slopes of the mountain.

The king, without once taking his eyes from the Heaven-sent creature, mounted his war steed, and sounded the bugle which hung at his girdle; and the great army, confiding in the wisdom of their leader, began to move. The white stag went first, steadily following a narrow pathway, which led upward by many steep ascents, seemingly to the very clouds; and behind him rode Charlemagne, keeping ever in view his radiant, hopeful guide, and followed by the long line of knights and warriors, who, cheered by his earnest faith, never once feared the end. Higher and higher they climbed, and more and more diffi-

Charlemagne crossing the Alps.

cult became the way. On one side of them arose a steep wall, shutting out from their sight more than half of the sky: on the other side, dark gorges and yawning gulfs descended, threatening to bury the whole army in their bottomless depths. And by and by they came to the region of snow and ice, where the Storm-king holds his court, and reigns in everlasting solitude. And, looking back, they could see sweet France, lying spread out as a map before them, its pleasant fields and its busy towns seeming only as specks in the dim distance. But when they looked forward, hoping there to see a like map of fair Italy, only the rocks and the ice, and the narrow pathway, and the desolate mountain crags, met their sight. And they would have become disheartened by the difficulties before them, and have turned back in utter despair, had not the bright form of their guide, and the cheerful countenance of Charlemagne, inspired them with ever-renewed hope. For seven days they toiled among the dangerous steeps; and on the eighth a glorious vision burst upon their view—the smiling plains of Italy lay before them. At this sight a great shout of joy went up from the throats of the toil-worn heroes, and the good archbishop returned thanks to Heaven for their deliverance from peril. And, a few hours later, the whole army emerged into the pleasant valleys of Piedmont, and encamped not far from Aosta.

Very wonderful indeed had been this passage over the Alps; and, what was more wonderful still, not a man, nor a beast, nor any part of the baggage, had been lost. After he had rested and dined, the king called before him his minstrels and jongleurs, and bade them sing their merriest songs, and play their gayest tunes on the harp, the viol, and the guitar. And the heart of the king was softened by the sweet strains of music, and by the feelings of thankfulness which filled his soul; and he felt no longer any malice toward those who had done him wrong, nor any hatred toward his enemies. Then one among the minstrels, an old man who had been a bard among the Saxons, and who knew all the lore of the North-folk, tuned his harp, and sang a song of the old Pagan days, and of the bold, free life of the Danish sea-kings.

When the minstrel ceased, the king, who had been strangely touched by the lively melody, looked around upon his peers, and asked,—

"Is there not with us a young Danish prince, one Ogier, the son of the rebel Godfrey? Methinks that he, too, can make fine music on the harp."

"My lord," answered Duke Namon, "the young man, as you doubtless remember, is for-hostaged; and he is now a prisoner in charge of Duke Ganelon."

"Let him be brought hither," said the king.

A few minutes later, Ogier, erect and proud, and as fearless as a young lion, was led into the presence of Charlemagne and the peers; and by his side walked his brother-in-arms, young Roland. He took the harp from the minstrel's hands; and, as his fingers swept lightly over the strings, he sang a song that he had learned in his father's court in Denmark. And all who heard him agreed that they had never listened to sweeter music.

"Young man," said the king, "thou singest well. I would fain reward thee, and hence I grant thee a reprieve. I give thee thy life until we again return to France."

Then Roland, as the nephew of the king, boldly begged that he would grant a full pardon to Ogier. But he would not. Never, said he, should feelings of pity turn him aside from the path of justice. Should he spare the life of one person for-hostaged, the value of hostages as pledges of good faith would no longer be regarded. Then Duke Namon asked the king, that as a personal favor, he would allow Ogier to remain with him during the rest of the march: he wished him to care for his nephew, a noble knight who was in his train, and was sick. To this request the king readily assented, and Ogier was re-instated in the service of his former loved master. And Roland and the other squires with Duke Namon, welcomed him most heartily to his old place of honor among them.

ADVENTURE VII

KNIGHTED ON THE BATTLEFIELD

SCARCELY had the army rested from the fatigues of the march across the Alps, when messengers came the third time from the pope, praying Charlemagne to hasten his coming. "The heathen triumph! The Christians are put to the sword! The Holy Father charges thee as the champion of Christendom to come quickly to his aid!" At once the camp at Aosta was broken up, and the great host advanced by hasty marches on towards Rome. And Roland and Ogier the Dane rode side by side, and lamented that they were not yet armed knights, and could not take any active part in the battle which was soon to be fought.

"I have not long to live," said Ogier; "and the heaviest thought that weighs upon my mind is, that I shall die without having distinguished myself in arms, and without having done aught for the glory of the king or the honor of knighthood."

"It shall not be," answered Roland. "You shall not die thus early and thus shamefully. I will again intercede with my uncle the king, and I will save you. And ere many years we both shall be knights, armed and belted and spurred, brothers-in-arms and peers of the king, worthy to do our part in battle with the unbelievers, and in all honorable undertakings."

The French arrived at Sutri. Roland saw with pleasure the familiar haunts of his boyhood. He pointed out to Ogier the rocky cleft on the hilltop, where, years before, he had watched for the coming of Charlemagne's host. And, when the old castle came in view, many memories, pleasant and painful, rushed into his mind. Oliver's father, Count Rainier, had long ago removed to Genoa, and the place was now held by strangers; nor did Roland see a single face in the town that he remembered as having known in the days of his childhood.

A short distance beyond Sutri, they met the Pagan host who had come out of Rome to give them battle. Charlemagne decided to attack them at once. Duke Namon, as the worthiest of the peers, led the vanguard of the French; but Roland and Ogier staid in the rear with the other squires, much grieving that it was not allowed them to bear arms, and that they could take only the part of lookers-on in this great contest. The golden standard of the king, the sacred Oriflamme, was carried by one Alory, who claimed it as the right of an Italian; he being a native of Apulia.

Roland and Ogier climbed a hill in order the better to view the fight. Duke Namon, with the bravest knights of France and their Italian allies, followed the standard to the attack. At the first assault the Pagans were worsted: they seemed to fall back in confusion, and Duke Namon pressed upon them right valiantly. Then the foe rallied again; they stood stubbornly; they rushed savagely upon the bearers of the golden standard. Alory and his cowardly companions from Lombardy were frightened: they had not the fearless hearts which are born of Northern blood. They turned, and fled for their lives. Full of joy now were the Pagans to see the Oriflamme in flight: full of shame and bewilderment were the French. In vain did Duke Namon strive to turn the tide: he was hemmed in by giant foes on every side. He fought manfully, but against such odds, that he was soon taken prisoner. Many other knights, the bravest among the French, were overpowered. Charlemagne himself was hard beset. His lance failed him, he was unhorsed; and yet most valiantly did he defend himself.

Roland and the Dane could no longer hold themselves aloof. They saw Alory and his coward Lombards coming up the hill in shameful flight. They called the squires around them, and urged them to rally to the fray like heroes.

"But how shall we fight without arms?" asked the faint-hearted.

"Fight with whatever comes to hand!" cried Roland. "A sharpened stake wielded by a brave man is better than a lance in the hands of a coward. Let us die here for the king and for France rather than turn our backs to the foe."

Alory and his Lombards were now very near.

"Believe me," cried Ogier, "if God have part or parcel in this day's work, these cowards shall take hence neither horse nor arms!"

"Shame be on any that shall fail thee!" answered the squires.

As Alory rode up, they seized his horse by the bits: they stopped him in his shameful flight.

"Have you lost the day?" asked Ogier.

"Where is the king?" asked Roland. "Where is Duke Namon? How have you left the French?"

"The king is taken," answered Alory. "The infidels hold the field. The French are slain."

"Thou liest!" cried the squires. "Had ye not failed in battle, all would have been well."

Without another word, Ogier felled Alory with a blow of his fist, for arms had he none. The other squires followed his example, and dragged the craven Lombards from their saddles. They despoiled them of their armor, they seized their arms, and mounted their steeds. Ogier took the golden standard in his hands; the golden cords fluttered around his wrists; the charger which he bestrode champed the bit, impatient to return to the field.

"Follow me, ye who are not cowards!" he cried.

The squires hastily formed in ranks, ready for the onset. He who could find no lance was content with a sharpened stake, with the splintered branch of an apple-tree or an ash. Very eager was every one for the fray. They tore their clothing into shreds with which to make pennons: they cared little for shields or war coats.

By this time Charlemagne had freed himself from the Pagans who beset him, and had again mounted his war-horse. Only a hundred knights were left with him now; all the others had been slain, or taken prisoners, or had sought safety in flight. But the king would not leave the field. The Pagans were already gloating over their victory. They were thinking of the day when they should see the Christian knights eaten by lions in the arena at Rome: they did not dream of any danger. Suddenly Ogier and Roland and the troop of squires swept down upon them like a whirlwind upon a field of growing corn. Never were Pagan folk so taken by surprise. Roland attacked the chief who held Duke Namon prisoner: he split his shield in twain, and burst his coat-of-mail asunder. The French knights were all set free. The squires hastily donned the armor of the slain Saracens, and followed in swift pursuit their panic-stricken foes. Never was rout more unexpected or more complete.

In the mean while Charlemagne, seeing the flight of the enemy, stopped not to learn the cause, but followed recklessly in their wake. His hauberk was broken, and his shield was pierced with many lance-thrusts; but his good sword Joyeuse was in his hand, a very terror to his foes. He sees Corsuble, the Saracen king, flying over the plain, and, unmindful of danger, he gives pursuit. A moment more, and Corsuble's head will roll in the sand. But no! Two Pagan knights, very giants in stature, rush to the rescue. Charlemagne's horse is slain beneath him, and he himself is stretched helpless upon the ground. And now the Saracens, content with having rescued their own chief, and anxious to save themselves, would have ridden onward, had not the golden eagle on Charlemagne's casque betrayed his rank. They hesitated. It would never do, they thought, to leave the deed but half done. Hastily they dismounted to give the fallen king his death-blow. Never had his life been in so great peril. But Ogier had seen him fall, and he rushed with the speed of a falcon to his aid. The golden standard which the young squire held in his hands hindered him from drawing his sword; and one would have thought him but a poor match for the two well-armed Saracens. But he came so swiftly, that he was upon them ere they were aware. One of them was ridden down by his horse, and rolled ingloriously in the sand: the other received such a stunning blow with the staff of the Oriflamme, that he fell senseless to the ground. Then Ogier helped the king to disentangle himself from his fallen steed, and saw him safely mounted on the horse of one of the Saracens.

"Ah, Alory, thou brave knight!" said Charlemagne, not recognizing the squire in disguise, "I have blamed thee wrongfully. I thought that I saw thee flying disgracefully from the field. But I was wrong, and thou shalt be rewarded for thy bravery."

Ogier said not a word, but, giving spurs to his steed, he rode onward in eager pursuit of the flying foe.

Complete was the defeat of the Saracens: in great haste and fear they retreated to Rome, and left the French the masters of the field. Then Charlemagne blew his bugle, and called around him his peers and the knights whom the battle had spared. And the good Turpin laid aside his helmet and his sword, and putting his mitre on his head, and holding a crosier in his hand, he sang the solemn *"Te Deum Laudamus;"* and all the mighty host joined in praising God. While they were yet singing, Ogier the Dane came humbly forward, and laid the Oriflamme, all torn, and covered with dust, at Charlemagne's feet. And with him came Roland and the other squires, walking awkwardly in their misfit armor; and all knelt reverently before the king. And Charlemagne spoke kindly to them, and again thanked Ogier for his bravery, again calling him Alory. And the archbishop held his hands above them, and blessed them. Then young Roland, bursting with impatience, threw off his helmet and Ogier's; and the other squires laid aside their armor. Great was the astonishment of the king and his knights when they learned that the day had been won, and their own lives and honor saved, through the valor of mere squires. And the king folded Ogier in his arms, and thanked Heaven that he had not hanged him last Easter. And Duke Namon, with tears of joy in his eyes, embraced both the young men, and called down the choicest blessings on their heads for the honor which they had done him by that day's gallant deeds and the signal service which they had rendered the cause of Christendom.

Then, turning to Charlemagne, he asked, "What is to hinder, my lord, from investing these young men with the honors of knighthood?"

"They richly deserve it," answered the king. "Let us make ready at once for the ceremonies. Such valor must not long be unrewarded."

Great was the rejoicing now among the French; for all the knights knew Roland and Ogier, and loved them. Only two—Ganelon of Mayence, and Charlot the son of the king, their hearts burning with jealousy and unreasoning hate—stood aside, and would not join in the general gratulations. When every thing was in readiness, the young men again knelt before the king. The good archbishop, after a solemn service, spoke briefly of the duties of the knight, and warned them of the difficulties and temptations in their way. Then, taking the swords which had been prepared for them, he blessed them, and laid them upon the rude altar which had been hastily built for the occasion. When this had been done, the king stepped forward, sword in hand, and, smiting each of them three times upon the shoulder, he said, "In the name of God and St. Michael I dub thee knight: be valiant, loyal, and true!" Then the peers who stood about arrayed them in the knightly garb which had been brought for them. Duke Namon, who had been the guardian and most faithful friend of both Roland and Ogier, laced their golden spurs upon their ankles. Turpin blessed their white armor, and invested each in his coat of mail. Duke Richard of

Normandy buckled on their breastplates; and Guy of Bourgogne presented them the arm-pieces and the gauntlets. Then came Charlemagne with the swords which he had taken from the altar. To Ogier he gave a plain steel blade bearing the inscription, WEAR ME UNTIL YOU FIND A BETTER. But to his nephew Roland he gave a wondrous weapon with jewelled hilt, and a fire-edge gleaming like the lightning's glare. And Roland, as he took it, read these words, engraved with many a fair device upon the blade, I AM DURANDAL, WHICH TROJAN HECTOR WORE.

The oath of chivalry was now taken by the new-made knights. Each swore that he would be faithful to God, and loyal to the king; that he would reverence all women; that he would ever be mindful of the poor and the helpless; that he would never engage in an unrighteous war; that he would never seek to exalt himself to the injury of others; that he would speak the truth, and love mercy, and deal justly with all men. And Charlemagne blessed them, and promised to love them as his sons; and they, in turn, vowed to love and honor him as their father in knighthood. And then, having donned their helmets, they mounted their steeds, which stood in readiness, and rode away full-made knights.

The next morning, as Charlemagne rested in his tent, he bethought him of the shameful conduct of Alory.

"Where now," said he, "is the cowardly Apulian who so nearly ruined our cause yesterday?"

"My lord," answered Duke Namon, "he was sorely bruised by the blow with which the Dane hurled him from his saddle. This, together with fear and shame, has made him hide himself from the sight of all true knights."

"Let him be found," said the king, "and let meet punishment be awarded him for his treason and his cowardice."

Not long afterward Alory, having been dragged from his hiding-place, was brought into the presence of the king. When asked to plead his excuse for his craven conduct, he was dumb: he could say nothing in his own defence. Then the peers adjudged him disherited, and forbade him ever again to show his face in the king's court, or ever again to mingle in the company of true knights. But Roland and Ogier, when they heard the sentence, begged leave to speak in his favor.

"It is not the part of a freeman," said they, "to take pains to forjudge his peer; nor should he deal harshly or unmercifully with another's weaknesses. If all who flee from battle were disherited, greatly thinned would be our ranks. If a man has been gifted with the heart of a hare, he cannot exchange it for that of a lion. Lombards know not how to carry the Oriflamme of France, neither have they business to meddle with great battles. We pray that Alory be forgiven, and that he be not intrusted again with duties too great for him."

Well pleased were the peers with these sensible words of the new-made knights; and they freely forgave the craven-hearted Apulian, not for his own sake, but for the sake of Roland and Ogier the Dane.

ADVENTURE VIII

HOW OGIER WON SWORD AND HORSE

On the banks of the Tiber, not more than a league from the city of Rome, the French encamped, and waited for the Saracens to sally out and attack them. But the Pagans were too wise to risk another battle in the open field. They had ravaged and laid waste all the country around; they had harvested the corn, and carried the grain into the city; they had cut down the vineyards and the orchards; they had seized all the cattle, and driven them within the walls; they had stored away great supplies of provisions, and made ready for a long siege. The Franks, on the other hand, never having thought but that they could support themselves by foraging, were without food. They were in no condition to carry on a siege against an enemy so well provided. The king was in great trouble. He saw clearly, that, unless he could strike a decisive blow very soon, hunger—a foe stronger than the Pagan horde—would force him to withdraw. Many of his fighting men, too, had lost the enthusiasm which they had felt while the enemy were still at a distance. They began to complain of being kept so long away from their homes and from France; and some of the weaker-minded knights, led by the crafty Ganelon, had gone so far as to plot rebellion, and were planning secretly how they might betray Charlemagne, and leave fair Italy in the hands of the Saracens. It was plain to every one, that unless the Pagans could be persuaded to come out from behind the walls, and risk another open battle, the Franks would soon find themselves in desperate straits, and be obliged to give up their undertaking.

While Charlemagne and his peers paused, and considered what it was best to do, young Charlot, the rash and foolish son of the king, was trying to carry out a plan of his own. With two thousand young men, hot-headed and hare-brained like himself, he had secretly left the camp at nightfall, and marched toward the city, intending by a bold dash upon the enemy to carry succor to the Christian garrison who still held the Capitoline Fortress. But the watchful Saracens were not to be caught napping. As the young prince and his men cantered carelessly along the highroad, thinking how on the morrow the whole world would ring with the praises of their daring, they did not know that Chief Karaheut, the bravest of the Pagan leaders, with five thousand picked men, was waiting in ambush for them. All at once, like so many fierce tigers, the Pagans rushed out upon the unsuspecting and unready band of Charlot. Short would have been the fight, and mournful would have been the end, had not the sound of the first onset reached the tent where Charlemagne and his peers sat in council. The air resounded with the yells of the exultant foe and the din and crash of arms. Quickly were Roland and Ogier and their brave comrades in the saddle. Very swiftly did they ride to the rescue. Chief Karaheut, when he saw them coming, called off his men, and withdrew in order toward Rome; and Charlot, crestfallen and ashamed, with the remnant of his band, rode back to the Christian camp. Very angry was Charlemagne at the unwise conduct of his son: furious was he that the Pagans had won the right to say that they had worsted any part of his host in battle. Scarcely could his barons hinder him from striking the foolhardy Charlot with his mace. But Roland, whose words always had great weight with the king, persuaded him to forget his anger. It was not the French who had been worsted in the late fight: it was only a band of rash young men, irresponsible, and unworthy of attention. Not many suns should rise ere the boastful Saracens should know the true strength, and feel the full force, of the Christian arm.

The next day, about noon, as the king sat in his master-tent, with all his peers around him, it was announced that a messenger had come from Corsuble, the Saracen king. It was Chief Karaheut himself. He came to Charlemagne's camp, riding on a mule, and accompanied only by two squires. He was unarmed, and very richly dressed. A turban of red satin embroidered with gold was upon his head; a gold-buttoned mantle of purple silk was thrown over his shoulders; around his neck was a collar of rich ermine. Right nobly sat he on his mule; right royally did he salute the king.

"In the name of all that the Franks hold dear," he said, "I greet great Charlemagne. I greet, too, the knights and barons who sit beside him; but above them all I greet Ogier the brave Dane."

The king and his peers heard this greeting in silence; but, when the name of Ogier was mentioned, the jealousy of young Charlot waxed so great, that he could scarcely hold his tongue.

"Who are you?" asked Charlemagne; "and what is your errand?"

"I am Karaheut," answered the Saracen proudly. "I am the bearer of a message from great Corsuble, the king of the faithful. He bids you leave him in peaceful possession of this city of Rome which he has taken in honorable war, and which is his more than yours. Ten days he will give you to take your army and all that is yours out of Italy. If you go not, then he will meet you in battle, and will spare you not; neither will he have mercy upon any who hold the name of Christian."

"Never have I turned my back upon unbelievers," haughtily answered the king. "We are ready for fight. Tell your master that we fear not the issue. God will be the judge betwixt us."

Chief Karaheut bowed courteously. "Yes, surely," said he, "God will be the judge. But why risk the lives of so many worthy men? Were it not better to settle the matter without so much bloodshed? If you will not withdraw peaceably, King Corsuble allows me to make this offer to you. Let the bravest man among you meet me in single combat, and let the issue of that fight decide who shall be the master of Italy. If I conquer, Rome shall be ours, and you shall return at once across the Alps. If I am beaten, the hosts of the faithful will at once embark, and sail back to their old homes beyond the sea, leaving you in Rome."

"That seems a fair offer," said Charlemagne, "and right willingly do we accept; for we like not to spill blood unnecessarily. Choose you now the bravest man among us, and let the issue be left in the hands of God."

Karaheut, without more ado, pulled off his glove, and cast it down at the feet of the Dane. Ogier at once stood up, and accepted the challenge. But Charlot, ever foolish and ever vain, took him by the arm, and drew him aside.

"Ogier," whispered he, but so loudly that he was heard by the bystanders, "Ogier, it is very unwise for you, a mere boy, thus to accept the gauntlet of battle, while your betters are passed by without notice. Your place is in Denmark, dressing leather and pressing cheese, and not in company with the heroes of France. And, if I forget not, your father still owes fourpence of tribute to Charlemagne, and your head has been pledged as security. The Saracen's glove was not intended for such as you. Stand aside, and I will do the battle."

Chief Karaheut's anger waxed very hot, for he despised the base-hearted Charlot. "Great king," cried he, "methinks you have little to do to let your son thus browbeat and insult your barons before your face."

"The Pagan speaks wisely," said Duke Namon; and all the knights, save Ganelon, assented. "For you we left our pleasant homes, our loving wives, our children, our lands, and our fiefs; and now your son openly insults us. Were it not for fear of breaking our knightly vows, and being guilty of unfaith toward God, we would turn our faces at once toward France."

Charlemagne saw the justice of these complaints; and, turning to Charlot, he reproved him harshly for his disrespect to Ogier and the barons. But the shallow-pated prince excused himself, and still insisted on fighting the Saracen—if not Karaheut, then some other Pagan warrior of rank equal to himself. He wished to make amends for last night's disgraceful mistake. In the end it was agreed that there should be two combatants on each side, that Ogier should fight with Karaheut, and that Charlot should have for his opponent Prince Sadone, the son of the Saracen king. It was further arranged, that the combat should take place on the morrow, in a grassy meadow near the banks of the Tiber, and that the fighting should be with swords and on foot. Then Karaheut rode back again to Rome.

The next day, at the rising of the sun, Ogier and Charlot mounted their steeds, and rode away toward the place that had been appointed for the combat. With great care had they armed themselves. Charlot wore at his side his father's own sword, the trenchant blade Joyeuse, with the carved hilt of gold; and his coat-of-mail was of the truest steel. The Dane, too, was well equipped, but only as a common knight; and the sword which he carried was that which the king had given him on investing him with knighthood.

Chief Karaheut and young Sadone already waited for them at the meadow. Most royally were the Pagans armed. Karaheut's shield was of steel inlaid with gold and engraved with many strange devices and many words of mystic meaning. On the rim of his helmet burned five gem stones, bright as little suns, or as torches in the darkness of the night. By his side hung the world-famous sword called "Short." This sword was the work of a giant smith named Brumadant, and, next to Joyeuse and Durandal, was the best that had ever been wrought. Twenty times over had Brumadant melted and welded this blade; and he had tempered it in the blood of dragons and at the forge-fires of the elves. When he had finished it, he tried it upon a block of marble. The huge stone was split asunder from end to end: but, in drawing out the sword, a palm's length of the blade was broken off; and this is why it was always called "Short." And Karaheut prized it above every thing else, for it was a very terror to all his foes. Sadone was equipped, as became a king's son, fair and courteously: his helmet sparkled with jewels, and his breastplate and shield were of the brightest polished steel. His sword was a famous blade that had been brought from the North. Men said that it had been wrought by Wayland, the master-smith of the Saxons, and that it had been worn by many of the doughtiest heroes of the Northland.

Together the four knights rode across the meadow, choosing a fit place for the combat. They chatted together pleasantly, as friends long-tried and true, rather than as foes making ready to meet each other in deadly fight. Having reached a smooth, grassy knoll, Ogier and Karahuet dismounted; and while their steeds wandered about over the green, cropping the grass and the rich herbage, they began to make ready for the duel. But Charlot and Sadone, not altogether pleased with this spot, rode onward, seeking a better. Suddenly, from the wood, thirty Pagan horsemen swept down upon them: they were men whom Corsuble had treacherously hidden there in order to seize the Christian knights. Karaheut was the first to see them, and he cried out to the Dane to defend himself. Charlot put spurs to his horse, and galloped with all speed back to Charlemagne's camp. But Ogier, on foot, and armed only with his sword, was no match for so many horsemen. Valiantly for a time, however, did he defend himself, and more than one stout Saracen was unhorsed. Yet soon his sword was broken, and he was forced to yield himself a prisoner; and, before Charlemagne could send him aid, the treacherous Pagans had carried him to Rome, and taken him into the presence of their king.

In King Corsuble's garden, beneath an olive tree, they stripped the Danish hero of his armor. Turks and Persians crowded around to see him, as if he were some wild beast of the desert. Some were for putting him to death at once. Others cried out, "Fie, for shame! Let him go back to his own folk! Never should it be said that we deal thus treacherously with our foes." Chief Karaheut begged the king to set him free.

"It is a dishonor to our religion," said he, "thus to break

our plighted faith with the Christians. It is contrary to all the laws of knighthood."

"I hold no faith with the Christian dogs," angrily answered the king. "My own will is higher than all the laws of chivalry. It is to this vile Dane that we owe our defeat of the other day. To-morrow he shall be hanged in the sight of all our people."

When Karaheut heard this answer, he went away in great grief and anger, declaring that never would he allow so base and dishonorable a deed to be done. And he called his men together, and bade them be ready on the morrow to rebel against the king, who had shown himself unworthy of their fealty.

And now Glorianda, the daughter of King Corsuble, came down the garden walk to see the peerless young hero of the North. Very handsome was the princess—straight of body, and fair of face. Well clad was she in the costly cloth of Greece, with a tunic of purple embroidered with gold, and over it a silken mantle. On her feet she wore narrow shoes of Cordova, colored and adorned with Moorish gold. Hot shone the sun; and instead of a wimple she wore a jaunty hat on her head. Blue were her eyes; her mouth was small, and sweet as a babe's. A fair barbarian was she,—so fair, that no man on earth could be tired of seeing her, even if he gazed forever. When she saw the hero Dane, so comely and tall and strong, and heard that he was doomed to die a felon's death on the morrow, she was very sad. And she prayed her father to spare his life. But King Corsuble's heart was harder than flint.

"Say not a word!" he cried. "I have vowed that the dog shall die, and so it shall be."

The next morning, at break of day, Chief Karaheut went again into the presence of Corsuble to beg him to have mercy on Ogier. But the king was furious, and more determined than ever.

"He shall live until the setting of this day's sun," said he, "but not a moment longer. And, if you dare speak to me again in his favor, you shall hang with him."

Then Karaheut went out of the palace, and mounted his steed, and galloped with all haste out of the city and past the guards, who dared not question him, and stopped not until he reached the Christian camp, and stood once more in front of Charlemagne's master-tent.

"Great king," said he, "hearken to me! I have come to yield myself your prisoner. You shall not say that I have betrayed you, or that I have been false to my word. I am here for you to deal with me even as my own people shall deal with Ogier."

The knights and barons were filled with wonder.

"Here, indeed, is a gentle Pagan!" cried they.

"By my troth, he is the worthiest of heroes!" said Charlemagne. "Never have I seen a truer knight, nor one more loyal, or more perfect in every knightly virtue."

The day began to wane. The sun was sloping far toward the west. Ogier, in his prison cell, had well-nigh given up all hope of escape. Suddenly he heard a great uproar in the street below,—the sound of tramping feet and of lusty cheers. He peered out through the grating of his window, and saw that the noise was made by a company of strange Pagans marching toward the king's palace. They were travel-stained, and seemingly weary with long journeying, and were dressed in a garb different from any that Ogier had ever seen. He asked his jailer who these strange people were, and was told that they were the bravest warriors of all Paynimry, just come from India to the succor of King Corsuble.

"And who is the black giant who rides before them on that wondrous horse?" asked Ogier.

"That is Brunamont, the King of Maiolgre, the great island of the sea," answered the jailer; "and the horse which he bestrides is the famed steed Broiefort."

"Never saw I a nobler charger," said Ogier. "Methinks I would rather own him than be master of a city."

Great was King Corsuble's delight at the timely coming of his allies; and he quite forgot that the Danish hero lay in his prison tower, awaiting his doom. He thought only of how he might best welcome and entertain the giant king of Maiolgre. So he made a great feast in his palace-hall; and all the noblest of his warriors, save Karaheut, were there. And Brunamont, hideously ugly and black, sat in the seat of honor by his side. And the wine went freely round, and both king and guests were very merry.

"Ah, my sweet friend!" said Corsuble, embracing the giant: "thou hast come in the very nick of time. The Franks are now at our mercy, and we shall soon drive them out of Italy. Then it will be an easy matter to cross the mountains after them, and drive them out of France also. And thou, dear Brunamont, shalt not go unrewarded. Thou shalt have France for thy portion, and thou shalt be my son-in-law. Here is my daughter Glorianda, the peerless pearl of Paynimry: she shall be thy wife. —Arise, Glorianda, and salute thy future husband!"

Glorianda arose, as she was bidden; but she had no word of salutation for the grim king of Maiolgre.

"My lord," said she to Corsuble, her father, "it is not the

custom for a maiden who is betrothed to one prince to be given to another, and that without her consent. You know that I am plighted already to Chief Karaheut, and I will be the wife of none other."

"Ha!" cried the king half-merrily, half-angrily. "When did it become the custom among us for a maiden to choose whom she would marry? Karaheut is a traitor. And who is there here to hinder me from giving thee to whomsoever I please?"

"If Karaheut were only here, he would save me," said Glorianda. Then she bethought her of Ogier the Dane, lying in prison, and doomed to death; and she went on, "but he is not here, and I have no champion. Nevertheless, there is that young Christian whom you have in jail, who I am sure will take the place of the absent Karaheut, and defend me against this injustice. Let him be my champion; and, if Brunamont overcome him in fair combat, then I will submit."

King Corsuble was pleased with this proposal; and the swarthy Brunamont, who had never been beaten in battle, was only too glad to show his prowess by contending in single combat with the pale-faced Northman.

When word was brought to Ogier in prison, that he had been chosen as the champion of the Princess Glorianda, he was highly pleased. "I would rather die, fighting the Pagan monster with my fists," said he, "than suffer the disgraceful punishment of a felon." And he sent one of Karaheut's squires to bear the news to his friends in the Christian camp. When Karaheut heard that the Dane was to fight in his place against the giant Brunamont, he begged Charlemagne to allow him to go and see the combat; and he pledged himself, that, in case

Ogier should not gain his freedom, he would come back, and again yield himself prisoner. Charlemagne consented; and Karaheut lost no time in returning to the city. There he armed the Dane in his own armor, and gave him as a present the noble sword Short,—the blade which Ogier both desired and feared more than all things else on earth.

"Take this sword," said he, "and it shall prove a firm friend to thee. If thou dost but conquer in this battle, it shall be thy reward."

Very thankful was Ogier; and his heart grew big with hope as he took the jewelled hilt in his hand, and read the inscription on the blade, I AM CORTANA THE SHORT. HE WHO HAS THE RIGHT ON HIS SIDE NEED NOT FEAR THE MIGHT OF THE WRONG-DOER.

The place appointed for the combat was a treeless island in the middle of the River Tiber. The banks on either side were lined with thousands of men from both armies, anxious to witness the fray. Ogier was the first to take his place. His friends on the farther bank of the river feared greatly the result of the combat. They felt, that, however bravely he might fight, his strength would be no match for that of the grim giant who had already overcome and slain more than twenty valiant kings. They had not learned that skill is stronger in the end than mere brute force. They beckoned to Ogier to throw himself into the river, and swim across to them.

"Ogier," they cried, "come to the host! It is your only chance of escape. Save your life while you may."

But Ogier shook his head.

"Not for a whole valley full of gold," said he, "would I do a deed so cowardly!"

And now came Brunamont to the combat, riding the famed steed Broiefort. How Ogier longed to have that noble animal for his own! Never had there been a more goodly horse. Black as midnight was he, with a silver star in the middle of his forehead; and men said that he could climb the steepest mountain without tiring, or run three whole days without panting or stopping.

"Great Father," said Ogier, raising his hands to heaven, "thou who didst form all the world, if it please thee, give me the victory to-day!"

But his thoughts were on the horse.

Brunamont dismounted, and with long strides advanced toward Ogier. Scornfully he laughed at his foe; and he brandished his sword about his head, and thought to make quick work of this combat. But sad was his mistake. The good blade Short leaped suddenly out of its scabbard, and the light of its gleaming edge flashed hither and thither like the play of the lightning in the summer's cloud. The first stroke cut the sword of Brunamont in twain, and left the giant but half armed. The second stroke cleaved his iron helmet; and, although it missed his brain, it sheared off his left ear, and laid the whole side of his face bare. Brunamont, who had never before felt fear, waited not for the third stroke. He turned and fled, thinking only of how he might save his life. He leaped into the river, hoping to swim across to his Pagan friends; but the current was deep and swift, and his heavy armor dragged him down, and the waters soon made for him a grave.

Ogier took to himself the horse Broiefort, for he considered that he had fairly won him; and there was nought that now is or ever was that he coveted so much. Charlemagne at once led his army across the river, and attacked the astonished and disappointed Saracens. Great was the rout of the unbelievers; and many of their bravest warriors were slain, or taken prisoners. And on the morrow King Corsuble, defeated and crestfallen, withdrew from Rome, and with his whole army embarked, and set sail across the sea. And Charlemagne, after seeing the pope happily restored to his place, returned to France.

ADVENTURE IX

ROLAND'S ARMS

ROLAND had now come to the years of manhood. Among all the knights and warriors in Charlemagne's court he was accounted the best. Save only Ogier the Dane, he excelled them all in every deed and feat of arms, in knightly courtesy, in respect for authority, in kind consideration for the poor and friendless. And every one, except Prince Charlot and Ganelon of Mayence, praised and loved him; for he was indeed a knight without fear and without reproach.

Great care was taken by Charlemagne to provide armor for his nephew, fitting for one who was destined to be a hero. From the far south a helmet was brought,—a wondrous casque most wondrously wrought. Men said that it was the handiwork of Vulcan, the lame blacksmith of the golden age,—the age when the gods still lived, and mingled with mankind. It was made of steel, inlaid with gold and pearls, and bound around with brass. It was engraved, inside and outside, with strange mottoes and battle-scenes, and legends of knightly valor. Above its crest waved an ostrich plume, and in front sat a golden eagle. Only two such helmets did Vulcan make,—one for Trojan Hector, the godlike hero of that ancient day; and the other for the noblest knight of later times.

The war coat which Roland wore had been brought from the far North, and was such as the men of France had never before seen. They said that it was the work of Wayland, the master-smith of the Teuton folk. So curiously had it been wrought, and so rare was the temper of its steel, that no thrust of lance, nor stroke of sword, could harm him whom it incased. The metal of which it was made had been digged from the earth by the cunning dwarf-folk, who lived in the hill caves of the North while yet the race of men-folk was young. It had been smelted in the mountain furnaces of the giants. Twelve months had Wayland worked day and night at his forge, beating it into shape, and tempering it, as he only knew how. And, when he had finished it, he had given it to Beowulf, the Anglo-Saxon hero, the slayer of the monster Grendel and of the fire-breathing dragon of the North. When or how it had been brought to France, I know not. But, when Roland first donned it, it is said that men whispered among themselves, and said, "What need has he of such rare armor? Better give it to some one whose body is not already proof against harm." For it was believed that Roland bore a charmed life, and that like Achilles of old, and like Siegfried, no weapon could touch or harm him save in a single small spot of his body,—some said midway between his shoulders; others said on the bottoms of his feet.

The arms which our hero bore were in every way equal to the armor which protected him. His shield was of three plates of steel, copper, and gold, bound together with bolts of brass; and on it were emblazoned the quarterings of red and white,—the armorial bearings by which he was distinguished. His favorite lance was a mountain ash, weighty and tough, a very beam in length, and so heavy, that none but Roland, or Ogier the Dane, could poise it. The golden spurs which he wore as the sign of his knighthood had been given him by Morgan the Fay, the fairy queen of Avalon; and I have been told that they were the same that had been worn by the famed King Arthur when he and his knights of the round table lived amongst men.

But the sword which Roland carried at his side was the noblest piece of all. The world had never seen a more wonderful blade than Durandal. Not Siegfried's Balmung, nor King Arthur's Excalibur, nor Charlemagne's Joyeuse, nor Ogier's Short, could be compared with it in beauty and true worth. It was the sword which Hector, the mighty prince of Troy, had wielded so valiantly in battle with the Greeks. From Vulcan's forge it had come, where the lame smith-god had tempered it in the flames of Tartarus. Neither wood, nor stone, nor any metal, could turn its razor edge: no war coat, nor helmet of steel, could withstand its stroke. On one of its bright blue sides were many mystic letters carved,—words which the Trojans knew, but which had long ago been forgotten, and which none but soothsayers could now make out. Malagis the dwarf read them: "LET HONOR BE TO HIM WHO MOST DESERVETH IT." On the other side were the words which I have elsewhere quoted,—"I AM DURANDAL, WHICH TROJAN HECTOR WORE,"—written in Latin. It is said by some, that once, when Charlemagne was in the valley of Mauriveine, an angel—or more likely a fairy—gave this sword to him, and told him to gird it on a young knight who had never known fear or reproach. Others say, that, after the death of Hector at the hands of the wrathful Achilles, this wondrous blade had been taken and kept by fair Penthiselea, Queen of Persia; and that from her it had been handed down, age after age, from one generation to another, to be wielded by the worthiest of Persia's Pagan princes; and that at last Charlemagne had wrested it from the unbelievers, and kept it to endow his loved nephew. Let it be as it may, we know that the king gave it to Roland when he invested him with knighthood, and that Roland proved himself well worthy of the gift.

Next to the sword Durandal, the thing which Roland prized the most was an ivory horn which he wore hung from his neck by a golden chain. This horn had been made from the tooth of a sea-horse, or, what is more likely, the tusk of a unicorn; and it was set thick with pearls and priceless gem-stones, and inlaid with silver and gold. Old stories are not quite clear as to how or where Roland got this wondrous horn; but I have heard that it, too, was a gift from the king. Charlemagne had long prized it as a rare treasure, not only on account of its great beauty and its workmanship, but also because of the wonderful music which was said to issue from it when blown by any one who was strong enough to sound it. Yet nobody in Charlemagne's time had ever heard it. The stoutest knights who came to Paris or to Aix were challenged to blow upon it, and the king promised to give the beautiful instrument to him who could first make the slightest sound come out of it. And, although some had split their lungs in trying, no one had ever succeeded in making a single note. On an idle day in winter, the king by chance bethought him of challenging Roland to blow.

"Dear nephew," said he, "you have never yet been beaten in tourney or in fight, nor have you ever failed in any thing you have undertaken. I have here something that will test your strength. It is the horn of my grandfather, the great Charles the Hammer. In his days, when men were stronger and seemingly more valiant than now, the most wondrous sounds were made to come out of it. I have heard it said that these sounds had all the sweetness of angels' songs coupled with the deafening din of the thunder's crash. And, indeed, some slanderers once whispered that it was the sound of this horn, rather than his own valor or that of his fighting men, that won for Charles the Hammer that grand victory over the Saracens at Poictiers which has made his name so famous. But men have grown wondrous weak of lungs, and not a knight in all France can blow the horn now."

Roland took the ivory bugle in his hands, and admired its rare beauty. Then he put it to his mouth and blew. A sound more wonderful than any man then living had ever heard came forth, and filled the hall and the great palace, and rolled out through the gates into the streets and over the country, and was carried from city to castle, and from castle to countryside, and through the forests, and over the mountains, until the whole land, for leagues and leagues around, echoed and re-echoed with the wondrous vibrations. Never were folk more astonished than those who heard this sound. Men, women, and children stood in utter amazement, holding their hands to their ears, afraid to listen, and yet wishing to hear. Some thought that the heavens were falling, and that the end of the world had come. Others wondered what kind of thunder this was, which, with all its deafening clangor, was sweeter than music. The king, with hasty gestures, begged Roland to stop blowing; but, after he had ceased, the sound continued for a long time to reverberate among the castle towers, and from hill to hill, and from earth to sky, like the distant rolling of the thunder after a summer storm has passed over our heads.

"The horn is yours," said the king, delighted and amazed. "You have fairly won the horn of Charles the Hammer, and no one can ever gainsay your right to it. But I give it to you only on condition that you shall never blow it, save in battle and in time of the utmost need."

That same evening, as Charlemagne and his household sat in the well-warmed hall of the palace, and beguiled the hours with music and mirth, a minstrel sang to them the Song of the Lorrainers; and he told them of the gallant sons of Hervi, of Garin, and Bego of Belin, who, he said, was the last knight who had carried the ivory bugle of Charles the Hammer.

The Story

Charles the Hammer was dead, and his young son Pepin was king of France. Bego of Belin was his dearest friend, and to him he had given all Gascony in fief. You would have far to go to find the peer of the valiant Bego. None of King Pepin's nobles dared gainsay him. Rude in speech and rough in war, though he was, he was a true knight, gentle and loving to his friends, very tender to his wife and children, kind to his vassals, just and upright in all his doings. The very flower of knighthood was Bego.

Bitter feuds had there been between the family of Bego and that of Fromont of Bordeaux. Long time had these quarrels continued, and on both sides much blood had been spilled. But now there had been peace between them for ten years and more, and the old hatred was being forgotten.

One day Bego sat in his lordly castle at Belin; and beside him was his wife, the fair Beatrice. In all France there was not a happier man. From the windows the duke looked out upon his broad lands and the rich farms of his tenants. As far as a bird could fly in a day, all was his; and his vassals and serving-men were numbered by the tens of thousands. "What more," thought Bego, "could the heart of man wish or pray for?" His two young sons came bounding into the hall,—Gerin, the elder born, fair-haired and tall, brave and gentle as his father; and Hernaudin, the younger, a child of six summers, his mother's pet, and the joy of the household. With them were six other lads, sons of noblemen; and all together laughed and played, and had their boyish pleasure.

When the duke saw them, he remembered his own boyhood days and the companions who had shared his sports, and he sighed. The fair Beatrice heard him, and she said, "My lord, what ails you, that you are so thoughtful to-day? Why should rich duke like you sigh, and seem sad? Great plenty of gold and silver have you in your coffers; you have enough of the vair and the gray,* of hawks on their perches, of mules and palfreys and war steeds; you have overcome all your foes, and none dare rise up against you. All within six days' journey are your vassals. What more would you desire to make you happy?"

"Sweet lady," answered Bego, "you have spoken truly. I am rich, as the world goes; but my wealth is not happiness. True wealth is not of money, of the vair and the gray, of mules, or of horses. It is of kinsfolk and friends. The heart of a man is worth more than all the gold of a country. Had it not been for my friends, I would have been put to shame long ago. The king has given me this fief, far from my boyhood's home, where I see but few of my old comrades and helpers. I have not seen my brother Garin, the Lorrainer, these seven years, and my heart yearns to behold him. Now, methinks, I will go to him, and I will see his son, the child Girbert, whom I have never seen."

**The vair and the gray,*—furs used for garments, and in heraldry. Vair is the skin of the squirrel, and was arranged in shields of blue and white alternating.

The Lady Beatrice said not a word, but the tears began to well up sadly in her eyes.

"In the wood of Puelle," said Bego, after a pause, "there is said to be a wild boar, the largest and fiercest ever seen. He outruns the fleetest horses. No man can slay him. Methinks, that if it please God, and I live, I will hunt in that wood, and I will carry the head of the great beast to my brother the Lorrainer."

Then Beatrice, forcing back her tears, spoke. "Sir," said she, "what is it thou sayest? The wood of Puelle is in the land of Count Baldwin, and thou knowest that he was slain by thee in those unhappy wars long time ago; but I have been told that he left a son, who has sworn to avenge him. The wood is also in the march of Fromont the chief, and he owes thee a great grudge. He would be too glad to do thee harm. I pray thee do not undertake this hunt. My heart tells me,—I will not hide the truth from thee,—my heart tells me, that if thou goest thither thou shalt never come back alive."

But the duke laughed at her fears; and the more she tried to dissuade him, the more he set his mind on seeing his brother the Lorrainer, and on carrying to him the head of the great wild boar of Puelle. Neither prayers nor tears could turn him from his purpose. All the gold in the world, he said, would not tempt him to give up the adventure.

So on the morrow morning, before the sun had fairly risen, Bego made ready to go. As this was no warlike enterprise, he dressed himself in the richest garb of knightly hero,—with mantle of ermine, and spurs of gold. With him he took three dozen huntsmen, all skilled in the lore of the woods, and ten packs of hunting hounds. He had, also, ten horses loaded with gold and silver and costly presents, and more than a score of squires and serving-men. Tenderly he bade fair Beatrice and his two young sons good-by. Ah, what grief! Never was he to see them more.

Going by way of Orleans, Bego stopped a day with his sister, the lovely Helois. Three days he tarried at Paris, the honored guest of the king and queen. Then pushing on to Valenciennes, which was on the borders of the great forest, he took up lodging with a rich burgher called Berenger the gray.

"Thou hast many foes in these parts," said the burgher, "and thou wouldst do well to ware of them."

Bego only laughed at the warning. "Didst thou ever know a Gascon to shun danger?" he asked. "I have heard of the famed wild boar of Puelle, and I mean to hunt him in this wood. Neither friends nor foes shall hinder me."

On the morrow Berenger led the duke and his party into the wood, and showed them the lair of the beast. Out rushed the monster upon his foes; then swiftly he fled, crashing through brush and brake, keeping well out of the reach of the huntsmen, turning every now and then to rend some too venturesome hound. For fifteen leagues across the country he led the chase. One by one the huntsmen lost sight of him. Toward evening a cold rain came up; and they turned, and rode back toward Valenciennes. They had not seen the duke since noon. They supposed that he had gone back with Berenger. But Bego was still riding through the forest in close pursuit of the wild boar. Only three hounds kept him company. The beast was well-nigh wearied out, and the duke knew that he could not go much farther. He rode up close behind him; and the fierce animal, his mouth foaming with rage, turned furiously upon him. But the knight, with a well-aimed thrust of his sword, pierced the great beast through the heart.

By this time, night was falling. The duke knew that he was very far from any town or castle, but he hoped that some of his men might be within call. He took his horn, and blew it twice full loudly. But his huntsmen were now riding into Valenciennes; nor did they think that they had left their master behind them in the wood. With his flint the duke kindled a fire beneath an aspen tree, and made ready to spend the night near the place where the slain wild boar lay.

The forester who kept the wood heard the sound of Bego's horn, and saw the light of the fire gleaming through the trees. Cautiously he drew nearer. He was surprised to see a knight so richly clad, with his silken hose and his golden spurs, his ivory horn hanging from his neck by a blue ribbon. He noticed the great sword that hung at Bego's side. It was the fairest and fearfullest weapon he had ever seen. He hastened as fast as he could ride to Lens, where Duke Fromont dwelt; but he spoke not a word to Fromont. He took the steward of the castle aside, and told him of what he had seen in the wood.

"He is no common huntsman " said the forester; "and you should see how richly clad he is. No king was ever arrayed more gorgeously while hunting. And his horse—I never saw a better."

"But what is all this to me?" asked the steward. "If he is trespassing in the forest, it is your duty to bring him before the duke."

"Ah! it is hard for you to understand," answered the forester. "Methinks that if our master had the boar, the sword, and the horn, he would let me keep the clothing, and you the horse, and would trouble us with but few questions."

"Thou art indeed wise," answered the steward. And he at once called six men, whom he knew he could trust to any evil deed, and told them to go with the forester.

"And, if you find any man trespassing in Duke Fromont's wood, spare him not," he added.

In the morning the ruffians came to the place where Duke Bego had spent the night. They found him sitting not far from the great beast which he had slain, while his horse stood before him, and neighed with impatience, and struck his hoofs upon the ground. They asked him who gave him leave to hunt in the wood of Puelle.

"I ask no man's leave to hunt where it pleases me," he answered.

They told him then that the lordship of the wood was with Fromont, and that he must go with them, as their prisoner, to Lens.

"Very well," said Bego. "I will go with you. If I have done aught of wrong to Fromont the old, I am willing to make it right with him. My brother Garin, the Lorrainer, and King Pepin, will go my surety."

Then, looking around upon the villainous faces of the men who had come to make prisoner of him, he bethought himself for a moment.

"No, no!" he cried. "Never will I yield me to six such rascals. Before I die, I will sell myself full dear. Yesterday six and thirty knights were with me, and master huntsmen, skilled in all the lore of the wood. Noble men were they all; for not one of them but held in fief some town or castle or rich countryside. They will join me ere long."

"He speaks thus, either to excuse himself or to frighten us," said one of the men; and he went boldly forward, and tried to snatch the horn from Bego's neck. The duke raised his fist, and knocked him senseless to the ground.

"Never shall ye take horn from count's neck!" he cried.

Then all set upon him at once, hoping that by their numbers they might overpower him. But Bego drew his sword, and struck valiantly to the right and to the left of him. Three of the villains were slain outright; and the rest took to their heels and fled, glad to escape such fury.

And now all might have been well with Duke Bego. But a churl, armed with a bow, and arrows of steel, was hidden among the trees. When he saw his fellows put to flight, he drew a great steel bolt, and aimed it at the duke. Swiftly sped the arrow toward the noble target; too truly was it aimed. The duke's sword fell from his hands: the master vein of his heart had been cut in twain. He lifted his hands toward heaven, and prayed:—

"Almighty Father, who always wert and art, have pity on my soul.—Ah, Beatrice! thou sweet, gentle wife, never more shalt thou see me under heaven.—Fair brother Garin of Lorraine, never shall I be with thee to serve thee.—My two noble boys, if I had lived, you should have been the worthiest of knights: now, may Heaven defend you!"

After a while the churl and the three villains came near him, and found him dead. It was no common huntsman whom they had killed, but a good knight,—the loyalest and the best that ever God's sun shone upon. They took the sword and the horn and the good steed; they loaded the boar upon a horse; and all returned to Lens. But they left Bego in the forest, and with him his three dogs, who sat around him, and howled most mournfully, as if they knew they had lost their best friend.

The men carried the great boar into the castle of Lens, and threw it down upon the kitchen hearth. A wonderful beast he was: his sharp, curved tusks stuck out full a foot from his mouth. The serving-men and the squires crowded around to see the huge animal; then, as the news was told through the castle, many fair ladies and knights, and the priests from the chapel, came in to view the sight. Old Duke Fromont heard the uproar, and came in slippers and gown to ask what it all meant.

"Whence came this boar, this ivory horn, this sword?" he inquired. "This horn never belonged to a mere huntsman. It looks like the wondrous horn that King Charles the Hammer had in the days of my father. There is but one knight now living that can blow it; and he is far away in Gascony. Tell me where you got these things."

Then the forester told him all that had happened in the wood, coloring the story, of course, so as to excuse himself from wrong doing.

"And left ye the slain man in the wood?" asked the old duke. "A more shameful sin I have never known than to leave him there for the wolves to eat. Go ye back at once, and fetch him hither. To-night he shall be watched in the chapel, and to-morrow he shall be buried with all due honor. Men should have pity of one another."

The body of the noble Duke Bego was brought, and laid upon a table in the great hall. His dogs were still with him, howling pitifully, and licking his face. Knights and noblemen came in to see him.

"A gentle man this was," said they; "for even his dogs loved him."

"Shame on the rascals who slew him!" said others. "No freeman would have touched so noble a knight."

Old Duke Fromont came in. He started back at sight of him who lay there lifeless. Well he knew Duke Bego, by a scar that he himself had given him at the battle of St. Quentin ten years before. He fell fainting into the arms of his knights. Then afterward he upbraided his men for their dastardly deed, and bewailed their wicked folly.

"This is no poaching huntsman whom you have slain," said he, "but a most worthy knight,—the kindest, the best taught, that ever wore spurs. And ye have dragged me this day into such a war that I shall not be out of it so long as I live. I shall see my lands overrun and wasted, my great castles thrown down and destroyed, and my people distressed and slain; and as for myself I shall have to die—and all this for a fault which is none of mine, and for a deed which I have neither wished nor sanctioned."

"And the words of Duke Fromont were true," added the story-teller as he brought his story to an end. "The death of Bego of Belin was fearfully avenged by his brother the Lorrainer and by his young sons Gerin and Hernaud. Never was realm so impoverished as was Fromont's dukedom. The Lorrainers and the Gascons overran and laid waste the whole country. A pilgrim might go six days' journey without finding bread, or meat, or wine. The crucifixes lay prone upon the ground; the grass grew upon the altars; and no man stopped to plead with his neighbor. Where had been fields and houses, and fair towns and lordly castles, now there was nought but woods and underbrush and thorns. And old Duke Fromont, thus ruined through no fault of his own, bewailed his misfortunes, and said to his friends, 'I have not land enough to rest upon alive, or to lie upon dead.' "

ADVENTURE X

A ROLAND FOR AN OLIVER

CHARLEMAGNE held high festival at Paris. It was in thanksgiving for the victories with which his arms had everywhere been blessed. Once more the foes of Christendom had been driven from Christian soil; once more did peace and prosperity seem to smile upon France. And the king had summoned the worthiest barons and warriors of his realm to award to each some fitting recompense for his services and good faith.

Among the knights who had come to Paris was old Count Gerard, the grandfather of Oliver, and one of the most powerful barons of France. He had come to renew his homage for his ancient fief of Viana; and he hoped that the king, as a reward for his lifelong services, would grant him now the vacant fief of Burgundy. But, from some reason best known to himself, Charlemagne failed to invest him with the wished-for dukedom. Some say that it was all the result of an awkward accident. The count, they say, after doing homage for Viana, stooped, as was the custom in those times, to kiss the king's foot. But, greatly to his chagrin, he stumbled, and his lips touched the foot of the queen, who was sitting by the side of Charlemagne. The knights who stood around were much amused, and could not forbear laughing at the unlucky count; but the king, in anger, told him that the fief of Burgundy had already been granted to a younger and more courteous knight, and that he must content himself with Viana until he had learned better manners. Count Gerard, boiling over with rage, turned upon his heel, and strode out of the palace. He called his men together, mounted his horse, and set out with all speed for Viana.

It matters not whether this story be true or not, we know that Count Gerard rebelled against the king, and declared, that, for the affront which Charlemagne had offered him, he would no longer be his man, nor pay him tribute. He shut himself up in the stronghold of Viana, which he victualled and strengthened with great care, and made ready for a long and a close siege. He sent also to his brother Miles of Apulia and to his son Rainier of Genoa, craving their help. Miles came with a thousand men bearing shields; and Rainier, with two thousand crossbow-men. With Rainier came also his son Oliver, boldest of warriors, and his daughter Alda, beautiful as a Persian peri, brave as a Saxon valkyrie.

Great indeed was the siege which Charlemagne placed around Viana: none ever saw the like before. And he vowed that he would never leave it, nor give up the contest, until the proud Gerard should be humbled in the dust before him. For nine weeks he besieged the stronghold, and allowed no one to come in or to go out; and yet so well supplied was the garrison with all things needful for life and comfort that they cared but little for the blockade. Neither besiegers nor besieged spared any pains to annoy one another. If Charlemagne's warriors dared approach too near the walls, they were driven back by a shower of arrows from the crossbows of the sharp-sighted Genoans. If the men of Viana ventured outside of the gates, or beyond the moat, a troop of fleet horsemen drove them back at the point of the lance. Sometimes the besieged would make a bold sally, and attack their foes in the open plain; sometimes the besiegers would try to take the stronghold by storm. But day after day went by, the summer passed, and autumn came, and the war seemed no nearer at an end.

Sometimes the Lady Alda stood upon the ramparts, and cheered the besieged, or helped to throw down stones and other missiles upon the heads of those who were trying to scale the walls. And once, dressed in full armor, she ventured out at the head of the Vianese, and boldly charged upon the besiegers. One day, Roland, seeing the fair lady standing upon the wall, rode up within call, and asked her her name.

"My name is Alda," she answered, "and my grandfather is the Count Gerard."

"And my name is Roland," said the hero, "and my uncle is King Charlemagne. Never have I seen a warrior-maiden fairer or nobler than thou. Never will I cease to love and to woo thee, though it should be at the cost of my life."

The next morning Roland fully armed, with his hawk perched on his wrist, rode down toward the Rhone. In the garden, beneath the walls of the fortress, he saw a mallard sitting. Thinking to have some sport, he loosed the hawk from his arm. High into the air the creature sprang; round and round above his head it circled, looking down in search of prey. It saw the mallard in the garden, and, quick as an arrow, darted down upon it. But, after it had struck the unoffending bird to the ground, it seemed not at all anxious to come back to its master. In vain did Roland whistle and call: as if knowing that it was beyond his reach, it sat on the branch of an apple tree, and quietly plumed its feathers. A knight in the castle, seeing the hawk, and wishing to have it for his own, came out into the garden to call it. He was armed from head to foot, and his visor was closed, and a long red plume waved from his helmet's crest. The bird heard his call, and flew to him, and alighted upon his wrist. A noble bird it was,—the falcon which Roland petted and prized more than any other.

Roland spurred his steed, and rode as near to the walls as a prudent fear of the crossbow-men would allow. "Sir knight," cried he very courteously, "give me back my bird, and you shall have fifteen pounds of gold!"

"Nay," answered the Knight of the Red Plume. "Not for a hundred pounds would I give him to you. I have taken him fairly, as the spoils of war, and I mean to keep him. No usurer shall buy me with gold."

Then Roland again put spurs to his horse, and, heeding not the threats of the crossbow-men upon the battlements, he rode boldly across the field, and paused not until he stood within ten paces of the strange knight, and close to the castle wall. But the visors of both warriors were closed, and neither could see the other's face.

Very courteously, as became a well-taught knight, Roland asked the other his name.

"Vassal," answered he, "my name is my own, and I give it not to strangers or to foes. You may call me the Knight of the Red Plume."

"Friend," said Roland, "I seek no quarrel with you. Give me my bird,—carry it no farther,—and we shall part in peace, to meet, perhaps, as foes another time."

"Ah, indeed!" answered the stranger-knight with a sneer. "Truly, you should be my henchman. A brave man you seem to be! If you will serve me a year and a day, you shall be knighted, and shall have either land, or fee, or burgh, or castle, as your valor shall deserve."

Roland was deeply angered by these taunting words, and he drew his sword half out of its scabbard. But then he remembered that he had vowed not to cross weapons that day with any foe.

"Vassal!" cried he, rising in his stirrups, "I pray you that for love you give me the bird; and I promise you that if, after to-day, you ask aught of satisfaction from me, it shall be as you wish."

"The hawk is yours," answered the knight, loosing the bird, and handing it to Roland. "Willingly I give it you. But remember your promise."

"Truly it shall not be forgotten," answered Roland.

And the two knights parted.

Week after week passed by, and still the wearisome siege continued. Some say that Charlemagne was encamped around Viana for seven years, but I think it could not have been more than seven months. Nevertheless, the whole country, for leagues on every side, was laid waste; and what had once been a blooming garden was now in a fair way to become a desert. The vineyards had been destroyed; the orchards had been cut down; the houses of the country-folk had been burned and destroyed. Great, indeed, was the distress caused by this quarrel between the king and the count; but the distress fell upon neither king nor count, but upon the innocent and the helpless. Ah, how cruel is war!

The king allowed neither wind nor rain to turn him aside from his purpose, or to make him forget his vow; and all winter long his men sat by their camp fires, and surlily guarded the approaches to Viana. At length, however, Eastertide drew on apace; and the woods began to grow green again, and the flowers sprang up in the meadows, and the birds sang soft and sweet. And many knights bethought them then how idly and vainly their time was being spent in this fruitless war against one of their own number; and they longed to ride away in quest of other and more worthy adventures. The king tried hard to press the siege and to bring it to a speedy close, but in vain. The watchful and valiant crossbow-men held the besiegers at bay, and obliged them to keep their accustomed goodly distance from the walls.

One day a party of strange knights rode into the camp, and asked to see the king without delay. They came from the mountain land which borders France on the south; and they brought stirring news,—news which aroused the zeal of every loyal Christian warrior. Marsilius, the Pagan king of Spain, they said, had crossed the Pyrenees with a great host of Saracens, and was carrying fire and sword and dire distress into the fairest provinces of Southern France. Unless Charlemagne should come quickly to the help of his people, all Aquitaine and Gascony would be lost, and the Pagans would possess the richest portion of his kingdom.

The king was much troubled when he heard these tidings, and he called his peers together to ask their advice. All declared at once in favor of raising the siege of Viana, of making some sort of peace with Gerard, and marching without delay against the invaders. But Charlemagne remembered, that, before undertaking the siege of Viana, he had vowed not to desist until Count Gerard was humbled in the dust at his feet.

"I have an oath in heaven," said he, "and I must not break it. This traitor Gerard shall not be spared."

"Which were better," asked Duke Ganelon mildly,—"to forget a vow which was made too hastily, or to sit here helpless, and see all Christendom trodden under the feet of accursed Saracens?"

"It seems to me," said sage Duke Namon, "that the present business might be speedily ended by leaving it to the judgment of God. Count Gerard knows nothing of the straits that you are in: he cannot have heard of this invasion by the Saracens; and he will gladly agree to any arrangement that will bring your quarrel with him to an honorable end. Let two knights be chosen by lot, one from each party, and let the combat between them decide the question between you and Count Gerard."

Charlemagne and his peers were much pleased with this plan; and a messenger with a truce-flag was sent into the fortress to propose the same to Count Gerard. The men of Viana were not only heartily tired of fighting against the king, but they foresaw that, if the siege were kept up much longer, they would be obliged to surrender for want of food; for their provisions were already beginning to run low. So they very gladly agreed to leave the whole matter to the decision of Heaven; and, as they numbered among them some of the bravest and most skilful swordsmen in Christendom, they had little doubt but that the judgment would be in their favor.

When the messenger came back to Charlemagne with Count Gerard's answer, the king and his peers at once drew lots in order to determine which one of their number should be their champion. The lot fell upon Roland; and to him was assigned the danger and the honor of maintaining the dignity and authority of the king, and of deciding a question which many months of warfare and siege had failed to settle.

Early the following morning Roland was ferried over to an island meadow in the Rhone, where the knight who had been chosen by the Vianese folk to oppose him was already waiting. He was surprised to see that it was the Knight of the Red Plume,—the same with whom he had talked in the garden beneath the castle walls. Roland was well armed; but instead of his own shield he carried another, which the king had given him—one wide and thick, but new and untried; yet his good sword, Durandal the terror, slept in its sheath by his side, and with it alone he would have felt sure of victory. The Knight of the Red Plume had armed himself with the greatest care. His war coat had been wrought by the famed smith, the good Jew Joachim, and was said to be proof against the stroke of the best-tempered sword. The hauberk which he wore was the one which King Æneas, ages before, had won from the Greeks on the plains of Troy. His buckler was of fishskin from the great salt sea, stretched on a frame of iron, and hard enough to turn the edge of any common sword.

On one bank of the river stood the friends of Roland, anxious to see how the young hero would acquit himself, and yet not at all fearful of the result. On the other side were Count Gerard and Miles and Rainier, and the bravest knights and the fairest ladies of Viana. And among these last, the fairest of all was Alda, the daughter of Rainier, and the sister of Oliver. Very beautiful was she to look upon. A coronet of pearls encircled her brows; golden was her hair, which fell in rich ringlets on her shoulders; blue were her eyes as the eyes of moulted falcon; fresh was her face, and rosy as dawn of a summer's day; white were her hands, her fingers long and slender; her feet were well shaped and small. The red blood had risen to her face. Eagerly she waited the beginning of the fray. Roland, when he saw her, trembled as he had never trembled before an enemy.

The signal for the onset is given. The two knights put spurs to their steeds, and dash toward each other with the fury of tigers and the speed of the wind. The lances of both are shivered in pieces against the opposing shields, but neither is moved from his place in his saddle. Quickly, then, they dismount, and draw their swords. How Durandal flashes in the light of the morning sun! Now does the helmet which the good Jew Joachim made do good service for the red-plumed knight. The fair Alda is overcome with fear. She hastens back to the castle. She goes to the chapel to pray, and falls fainting at the foot of the altar.

Never before has there been so equal a fight. For more than two hours the two knights thrust and parry, ward and strike; but neither gains the better of the other. At last, however, the sword of the red-plumed knight is broken by a too lusty blow upon Roland's helmet: his shield, too, is split from top to bottom. He has neither wherewith to fight, nor to defend himself, yet he has made up his mind to die rather than to be vanquished, and he stands ready to fight with his fists. Roland is pleased to see such pluck, and he scorns to take advantage of his foe's ill plight.

"Friend," said he right courteously, "full great is your pride. and I love you for it. You have lost your sword and your shield, while my good Durandal has neither notch nor blemish. Nephew am I to the king of France, and his champion I am to-day. Great shame would be upon me, were I to slay an unarmed man when he is in my power. Choose you now another sword—one to your own liking—and a more trusty shield, and meet me again as my equal."

Roland sat down upon the grass and rested himself, while the red-plumed knight bade his squires bring him another sword from the castle. Three swords were sent over to him,—that of Count Gerard, that of Rainier the Genoese, and Haultclear, a blade which the Jew Joachim had made, and which in old times had been the sword of Closamont the emperor.

The knight chose Haultclear. Roland rose from the grass, and the fierce fight began again. Never were weapons wielded with greater skill; never was there a nobler combat. The sun rose high in the heavens, and the noontide hour came; and still each knight stood firmly in his place, thrusting and parrying, striking and warding, and gaining no vantage over his foe. After a time, however, the patience of the red-plumed knight gave out. He grew furious. He was anxious to bring the combat to an end. He struck savagely at Roland; but the stroke was skilfully warded, and Haultclear snapped short off near the handle. At the same time Durandal, coming down with the force of a thunderbolt, buried itself so deeply in the shield of the red-plumed knight, that Roland could not withdraw it.

Both knights were thus made weaponless; but neither was vanquished. Wrathfully they rushed together to seize each other, to throw each other down. Moved by the same thought, each snatched the other's helmet, and lifted it from his head. Some say that a bright cloud and an angel came down between them, and bade them cease their strife; but I know not whether this be true, for, as they stood there, bareheaded, and face to face, memories of their boyhood came back to them. Both were struck dumb with astonishment for a moment. Roland saw before him his loved brother-in-arms, Oliver. Oliver, now no longer the red-plumed knight, recognized his old friend Roland. Then they rushed into each other's arms.

"I yield me!" cried Roland.

"I yield me!" cried Oliver.

Great was the wonder of Charlemagne and his peers when they saw their champion thus giving up the fight when victory seemed assured. Equally great was the astonishment of the Vianese and of Oliver's kinsmen. Knights and warriors from both sides of the river hastened to cross to the island. They were eager to know the meaning of conduct seemingly so unknightly. But when they came nearer, and saw the men, who had fought each other so long and so valiantly, now standing hand in hand, and pledging anew their faith as brothers-in-arms, every thing was made clear. And with one voice all joined in declaring that both were equally deserving of the victory. And Ogier the Dane stood up, and said, that, although the question between Charlemagne and Gerard was still unsettled, yet Roland and Oliver had acquitted themselves in all things as became true knights.

"Let him who would gainsay it speak now, or forever hold his tongue!" he cried.

But in all the host there was not one who wished to break lances with Ogier, or to risk his displeasure by disputing his word.

Then the folk of Viana went back to their castle prison,

A Roland for an Oliver.

and their foes returned to their tents; and each party began anew to plan means by which this tiresome and unprofitable war might be brought to an end.

Another week, and a fortnight, passed by, and every day messengers came to Charlemagne, telling of the ravages of Marsilius the Moor, and begging him to hasten to the aid of his people. Very willingly would he have gone, and left Viana in peace, had it not been for the remembrance of his vow.

"I cannot go," said he, "until this rebel Gerard is humbled upon his knees before me."

One by one his knights, tired of inaction, and preferring to wage war against unbelievers rather than against men of their own faith and nation, stole quietly from the camp, and rode away toward the Pyrenees. It seemed as if the king would be left, after a while, to carry on the siege of Viana alone; yet he never faltered in his determination to perform his vow to the very letter.

One day some huntsmen brought word to Charlemagne that a fierce wild boar had been seen in Claremont wood, and that he was now hiding in a thicket not far from Viana. Ever eager for the chase, the king at once mounted his horse, and, followed by his men and his hounds, he hastened to the wood. It was not long until the grim beast was driven from his lair; and the king, as was his wont, gave chase. Duke Gerard and his knights, watching from the towers of Viana that morning, had seen the kingly hunting party ride out into the wood.

"Let us have a hand in this hunt," said Rainier of Genoa. "We might hunt for royal game; and, could we but take the king, we might end this war on our own terms."

Count Gerard and the other nobles were pleased.

"I know a secret underground passage," said the count, "which leads directly from the castle to the wood. Once there, we might lie in wait in the thickets, and waylay the king as he passes by."

The knights at once girded on their armor, hung their shields to their necks, and took their bows and arrows in hand. Then, led by two trusty squires, who lighted the way with torches, they filed through the long, dark tunnel, and came out in the midst of a briery thicket in the wood of Claremont. The sound of the baying hounds told them that the game was not far away; and soon, as good fortune would have it, the hunted beast, furious with rage, rushed past them. Very close behind him came Charlemagne, riding upon his favorite hunting-steed and so intent upon spearing the boar that he neither saw nor thought of any thing else. The huntsmen and most of the hounds had been left far behind.

"Now is our time!" cried Rainier. And, quick as thought, five well-armed knights rushed out of the thicket, and seized the king's charger by the reins, and called upon him to surrender. Having only the weapons of the chase, and being set upon so unexpectedly, Charlemagne was no match for his stout assailants. Quickly he was seized, and dragged from the saddle: firmly but gently was he held by his captors. Then Aymery of Narbonne, bloodthirsty, and at heart a traitor, whispered to Count Gerard, and advised him to kill the king.

"With him out of our way," said he, "we shall be free; our fiefs shall be our own; and no man shall claim homage or tribute from us."

But the count pushed him aside with scorn.

"Shame on thee!" he answered. "May it not please God that ever king of France be killed by me: of him I will hold my castle and my lands!" And he knelt humbly before the captive king.

Charlemagne's heart was touched by the words of loyalty and good faith which fell from the lips of the count.

"Gerard of Viana," he cried, "all this trouble between thee and me is ended and forgotten. If thou hast harmed me, I freely forgive thee. No penny of tribute shalt thou pay for land, or fief, or castle. Only for the sake of my vow, renew thy homage."

Then Gerard ungirt his sword from his side, and uncovered his head, and knelt again before the king; and he placed both his hands between those of the king, and said,—

"From this day forward I become your man of life and limb, and of all wordly worship; and unto you I will be loyal and true, and I will bear you faith for the lands and the castles and the houses that I claim of you. And to no other lord will I grant obedience, save at your behest."

Then the king raised him gently from the ground and kissed him, and answered,—

"Count of Viana, my man shalt thou be in life and limb and worldly worship; and to thee do I grant the lands, the fiefs, and the castles of Viana, to have and to hold without any payment of tribute, or any other service save that which is given in honorable war."

Then the other knights, in the order of their rank, came and knelt likewise before the king; and each in his turn promised to be his man,—first Rainier of Genoa, then Miles of Apulia, then Oliver, and lastly the headstrong Aymery of Narbonne. And the king forgave each one all the wrong that he had ever done him, and gave back to each all the lands and fiefs and tenements and all the honors that he had held before.

"And now," said Charlemagne to Count Gerard, "I will go with you, and sup with you to-night in your lordly castle of Viana."

Great was the wonder of the Vianese when they saw the king enter their halls, not as the prisoner, but as the friend and guest, of the count. And great, indeed, was the joy when it was known that peace had been made, and that the wearisome siege was at an end. In the broad feast hall, a rich banquet was spread, and the night was given up to feasting and music and merrymaking. And among the knights who sat at the table there was none more noble or more handsome than Oliver. And among the ladies who added grace and beauty to the glad occasion not one was so fair as Oliver's sister, the matchless Alda.

But in the tents of the besiegers that night there was much disquietude and bewilderment. The huntsmen had sought in vain for Charlemagne in the wood; and, when they could not find him, they came back to the camp, thinking that he had become wearied of the chase and had returned. On their way they had found his horse grazing among the herbage, with the reins lying loose on his neck. Great now was their uneasiness. Roland put himself at the head of fifty horsemen, and scoured the country for miles around. But as the darkness of night began to settle over the earth, they were forced to return, sadder and more perplexed than ever, to the camp. Many were the guesses which were hazarded regarding this strange disappearance of the king. Some thought that the wild boar, which was known to be very large and fierce, might have turned upon him, and torn him in pieces in the wood. Others suggested that mayhap he had followed the example of his barons, and ridden away from this dull siege to the more active war against the Saracens; but this did not seem at all probable. The greater number were agreed in believing that he had been waylaid and taken prisoner by the men of Viana. And all were for placing themselves under the leadership of Roland, resolved, that on the morrow they would make one grand assault on the castle, and carry it, if possible, by storm.

The next morning, what was the astonishment of the besiegers to see the gates of Viana thrown wide open, and the men, to the number of two thousand, march out with music playing, and banners flying, as if it were a gay holiday! But greater still was their wonder when they saw that the knight who rode so grandly in the van by the side of Count Gerard was their own loved king. Roland, who at first was fearful that the Vianese were plotting some treachery, had hastily drawn up his warriors in line of battle, ready to defend the camp. But Charlemagne, as soon as he had come near enough to be heard, explained that peace had been made, and that Count Gerard and the barons who were with him in Viana had renewed their homage, and that all past differences had been forgotten.

After this the king held his court for seven days in the castle of Viana; and the men who had so lately been foes stood together in the halls as sworn friends, loyal and true. And the days were given over to merrymaking. And Roland and Oliver, the long separated brothers-in-arms, sat together in the hall and at the feast table, and talked of what had befallen them since the day when they plighted their faith to each other among the hills of Sutri. And, before the week had passed, Roland and Alda, the sister of Oliver, were betrothed.

ADVENTURE XI

REINOLD OF MONTALBAN

Marsilius the Saracen had carried fire and sword into the fairest provinces of Southern France. He had pillaged the cities, and burned the towns, and ravaged the fields, and what had once been the pleasantest and most prosperous of Charlemagne's domains he had turned into a smoking desert. The distressed people had sent message after message to the king, begging him to send them help; but he was too intent upon besieging Viana, and too determined to redeem his vow by humbling the haughty Count Gerard in the dust before him. And as day after day passed by and the Pagans still continued to burn and destroy, the unhappy folk began to lose all hope, and to fear that they had been forgotten, and abandoned to the ruthless fury of their Saracen foes. What, then, was their joy, when the news was carried from mouth to mouth that the siege of Viana had been raised, and that Charlemagne and his knights were riding to their aid!

Over hill, and through valley, and across desert wastes, rode the kingly company; and no one cared for weariness, or for pain, or for hunger, so long as the Pagan folk threatened their land, and they were marching to the rescue. But, among all the knights and barons in the French host, none were more impatient than the three brothers-in-arms,—Roland, and Oliver, and Ogier the Dane. And when they reached that part of the land which had been ravaged by Marsilius, and saw the smoking ruins and deserted farmlands, and distress and death on every hand, they could no longer restrain themselves. They longed for a chance to take vengeance upon the hated unbelievers.

"The army moves too slowly," said Roland to his comrades. "Every day adds to the distress of our people and to the fiendish triumph of our foes. Let us ride on faster. We are mounted better than those who follow us; and while they are toiling among these hills and over these ill-conditioned roads, we may, perhaps, overtake and give battle to some part of the Pagan host."

Not a moment did his brother knights hesitate; not a word of dissent did they speak. They put spurs to their steeds, and with a few trusty followers were soon far in advance of the main army, determined, if possible, to come up with the enemy, and offer them battle.

Marsilius the Moor had no sooner heard of the peace made at Viana, and of the coming of Charlemagne and his warriors, than he ordered an immediate retreat into Spain; and he was now well on his way back to the passes of the Pyrenees. Day after day Roland and his comrades followed in the wake of the flying foe. Sometimes, on climbing to the top of a hill, they could see the banners of the Pagan rearguard far in advance of them. Sometimes, when a breeze came to them from the west, they could hear the tramp of the Moorish horse, or the rough cries of the Moorish soldiery. But, ride as fast as their steeds would carry them, they could not overtake the enemy, who, it seems, were mounted as well as they. And at last, when the great mountain wall of the Pyrenees rose up in front of them, the Pagan host had already entered one of the passes, and had crossed safely over into Spain. The heroes were greatly disappointed because the foe had thus escaped them; yet they deemed it the better part of valor to give up the pursuit, and to ride back to Charlemagne and his host, who were still advancing among the hills and valleys of Southern Gascony.

The king received the news of the escape of Marsilius with a much better grace than they expected.

"I am glad that he is well out of our way," said he; "for now I shall have but one foe to deal with, instead of two."

They asked him what he meant.

"Five leagues from here," said he, "is the stronghold of Montalban, where my rebel nephew, Reinold, has taken refuge, with his brothers and all the discontented barons of Southern France, and from whence he gives aid and comfort to our Pagan foes. I will not rest until I have razed Montalban to the ground, and punished my nephews as they deserve."

Not long afterward the host came in sight of the marble walls of Montalban, glistening in the sunlight like a white star on the mountain tops. But who was this rebel, Reinold, who dwelt in this princely castle on the borderlands of France? I will tell you.

In the earlier years of Charlemagne's reign, the noblest among the barons at his court was Duke Aymon of Ardennes. Aymon had married Aya, the sister of Charlemagne; and he had four sons—Allard, Guichard, Richard, and Reinold—and a daughter named Bradamant. Upon a time Charlemagne held a high festival, and ordered that all his noblest vassals should come and do him homage. All who had been summoned were there, save Sir Bevis of Aigremont, the brother of Duke

Aymon. The king was very angry that one of his barons should neglect the duty of renewing his homage. He vowed that he would not only take away all the fiefs and estates of Sir Bevis, but that he would have him hanged as a traitor. Duke Namon, ever far-sighted and just, persuaded him to try peaceful measures first, and to send an embassy to the absent knight, summoning him the second time. Charlemagne sent, therefore, his own son, Lothaire, with four hundred chosen warriors, to demand the renewal of homage from Sir Bevis. But Sir Bevis had resolved that he would no longer be the vassal of the king, and that he would hold his fiefs in his own right and by his own strength. So he caused Lothaire to be waylaid in the forest of Ardennes, and slain. Very great was the anger and the grief of Charlemagne when the news of this treacherous act was brought to him. Without any delay he summoned his host, and marched in full force against Aigremont. But Duke Aymon and his four sons did not follow the standard of the king. They preferred to join themselves with the rebel Sir Bevis; and this was the beginning of the great trouble which arose between them and Charlemagne. Not long after this, a battle was fought, and the rebels were routed with great slaughter; and Sir Bevis and Duke Aymon came barefooted into the presence of the king, and humbly craved his mercy. Charlemagne agreed to pardon them if they would come to Paris and renew their homage. But Ganelon, ever bent upon mischief, upbraided the king for his forbearance toward his enemies.

"Much love had you for your son Lothaire!" said he. "His blood, spilled in the wood of Ardennes, still calls for vengeance upon his murderers. But his father is deaf: he cannot hear those cries."

And he persuaded the king to waylay and kill Sir Bevis while on his way to Paris. Duke Aymon and his sons, therefore, again took up arms against Charlemagne, and a long and cruel war between them followed.

Now, Duke Aymon had a wonderful horse, named Bayard, —the noblest steed in all the world. Very large and strong was he; and he could run with the speed of the winds; and he was very wise and knowing. One day this horse was missed from his stall; and although the duke ordered all the country around the castle to be searched, no one remembered having seen the missing steed, and he was not to be found anywhere. Very sad was Duke Aymon. He would liever have lost a thousand men, or even the best of his castles, than this horse. While he was musing over his misfortunes, the dwarf Malagis, who was his cousin, and always a firm friend of his house, stood before him.

"Ah, cousin Malagis!" said the duke. "Thou art the very man I wished most to see. Thou hast the gift of witchcraft, and thou canst tell me where my Bayard is."

"Indeed I can!" answered the dwarf. "I saw him carried off last night by goblins. And he is now hidden and imprisoned in the smoky caverns of Mount Vulcanus."

"And can nothing be done to bring him back?" asked the duke. "Without my horse I am ruined."

"I will bring him back to you," said the wizard. And before the duke could say a word, he had walked out of the gate, and was hastening across the country toward Mount Vulcanus.

After a toilsome journey of many days, Malagis came to the great smoky mountain of Vulcanus; and without fear or hesitation he climbed down the broad chimney-way, and stood in the smoke-begrimed caverns and halls where King Vulcan, the lame blacksmith of the Golden Age, still held his court, although most of his kith and kin had died long before. Very courteously did Malagis greet the ruler of these doleful regions.

"Who art thou?" asked Vulcan. "How darest thou, who art only a puny mortal, come thus into the presence-chamber of the immortals?"

"My name is Malagis," answered the dwarf, "and among men I am known as a great wizard. But they think nothing of my art. Little praise get I for all my wisdom."

"Men are by nature thankless," said Vulcan.

"So they are," answered Malagis. "And for that same reason I have left their abodes, and have come to live with you, and to offer my services to you."

"What can you do?" asked Vulcan.

"Try me and see," answered the wizard.

"Very well, then," said the old master smith. "I will give you a task that will put your cunning to the test. A fortnight ago the mountain goblins, who are the only servants I have nowadays, brought me a steed, the most wonderful that was ever seen. The famed horses of olden times were but very tame creatures compared with him. He is wiser than the Centaurs, swifter on foot than Pegasus was on the wing, fiercer and wilder than Bucephalus, nobler than the fabled Greyfell. Very fain would I ride out into the great world mounted on the back of this steed, but he will not let me come near him. Now, if you want to show your skill as a magician, do you go to my stables, bridle and saddle this untamable steed, and bring him here that I may mount him."

"My lord," said the cunning dwarf, "I will try what I can do with him."

When Malagis entered the stables, the fierce horse ran toward him, angrily snapping and kicking. But the wizard whispered, "Bayard, thy master Aymon wants thee." At once the creature stopped. All the fierceness of his nature seemed to leave him. He rubbed his nose gently against the dwarf's shoulder, and whinnied softly, as if in answer to what had been spoken. The next moment Malagis sprang upon the back of Bayard.

"To Duke Aymon!" he cried.

At one bound the horse leaped out of the enclosure, and was soon racing, with the speed of the wind, through the mountain passes and the valleys, and the forests and morasses, joyfully hastening back toward the well-known wood of Ardennes. When the master smith, Vulcan, saw how he had been outwitted, he summoned his goblin host, and sent them in pursuit of the daring wizard. Forth from the smoking chimney of the mountain they rushed; swiftly through the air they were borne, riding on the back of a huge storm cloud. The winds roared, lightning flashed, the thunder rolled, the air seemed full of evil creatures. But Malagis rode fearlessly onward, swifter than the storm cloud, swifter than the wind, and paused not once until he reached Duke Aymon's castle. In the mean while the duke had met with many sad misfortunes. He had been beaten in battle, and his best men had been slain. Some in whom he had trusted as friends had deserted him. He was on the point of giving up the struggle, and throwing himself upon the mercy of Charlemagne. Great, then, was his joy when he saw the faithful Malagis return with Bayard.

"My wise, trusted cousin!" he cried. "My noble war steed! Once more fortune smiles upon me."

The flight of Malagis.

And fortune did smile upon him. The neighboring barons came to his help, and many a stronghold and many a fair province of France acknowledged his mastership. At length Charlemagne, tired of the profitless war, offered to make peace with Duke Aymon. He promised to give back to his rebellious vassal all the fiefs, all the lands and castles and burghs, that he had held before, and to receive him again at court with all the honors due to a brother-in-law of the king.

"And what compensation will he offer for the death of my brother Sir Bevis?" asked the proud duke.

"He will pay thee four times the weight of the murdered Bevis in gold," answered the king's messengers.

"It is not enough," answered Aymon. "My brother was a gentle and right noble baron, and no paltry blood-fine such as is paid for the death of a common knight will suffice. Let the gold be six times the weight of the slain Sir Bevis. On no other terms will I make peace."

When Duke Aymon's answer was carried to Charlemagne, the king for a long time hesitated, for he liked not the payment of so heavy a blood-fine. But at last, through the advice of the wise Namon, peace was concluded; and Aymon and his four sons, now all stalwart young knights, were restored to their old places of trust and honor. But Aymon could not rest in idleness; neither did he love peace. He longed to do some great deed of arms that would make his name known and feared among men. So at last, when he could no longer endure the life of inaction which he was obliged to lead in France, he crossed over the Pyrenees into Spain, and engaged in warfare with the Moors.

For many years no news of Duke Aymon was carried back

to France, and the Princess Aya and her four sons mourned him as dead. But one day there came a messenger to Ardennes, saying that the long-absent duke was lying ill at an inn in Gascony, and that he prayed to see once more his wife and children. Without delay, Aya and her sons hastened to his side. They found not the stalwart warrior as they had last seen him, but a feeble old man, gray-bearded, tanned, and weather-beaten. Yet Aya recognized in him her long-errant husband, and the three elder sons embraced him tenderly as their father. But Reinold stood back, doubtfully hesitating.

"Who is this worn-out warrior?" asked he. "Methinks he cannot be my father; for Duke Aymon is a hero, and this is but a man of common mould."

"Young man," said Aymon, sitting upright in his bed, "if you remember not my face, look upon this ring, which your mother gave me in the days of our youth; look, too, upon these scars, which were given me in battle, and which you certainly cannot have forgotten."

"And think you that I would be deceived?" asked Aya. "Never was there a nobler duke than your father."

"Yes, mother," cried Reinold, "I know him now." And he seized his father in his arms, and squeezed him so heartily, that the old warrior was glad to be released.

Duke Aymon brought great wealth from Spain, and divided it equally among the Princess Aya and his three eldest sons. But to Reinold he gave as his portion the horse Bayard and the sword Flamberge. With kind nursing and constant care, his strength came back, and in a few weeks he was well enough to return with his family to his old home in Ardennes.

Not long after this the king held a great tournament at

Aix; and the bravest warriors, the noblest knights, and the fairest ladies of the land, were there. To this tournament went the four sons of Aymon, glorying in their strength and skill; and save Roland, and Ogier the Dane, there were none who dared hold a lance to them, or make trial with them of any knightly feats of arms. The young men about the court looked upon them with feelings of bitter jealousy; and Charlot the king's son, and Bertholais his nephew, plotted how they might bring them to grief. And Ganelon the mischief-maker, when they asked his advice, said,—

"Challenge one of the brothers to a contest. If you gain the better of him, it will be easy to slay him as if it were by accident."

"That would be too great a risk," answered Charlot. "The sons of Aymon have not their equals in the lists, and not one of them has yet been worsted. The praises of the hated Reinold are in the mouths of all those who attended the tournament yesterday, and they say that his brothers are as skilful and as strong as he."

Ganelon smiled, and stood for a moment silent. Then he said, "It is not likely that they excel in all kinds of games. A good jouster is not commonly a good chess-player. Now, what I advise you to do is this: do you, Bertholais, send a challenge to Allard, the eldest of the brothers, to play a quiet game with you, and let each of you wager his head on the result. You have never been beaten at chess, and it is not possible that you should be. By this means you may rid yourselves of one of the brothers, and at the same time disgrace the others."

Charlot and Bertholais were delighted with the cunning words of Ganelon, and at once sent a challenge to Allard. But

Allard was loath to play a game on conditions such as those. He was not afraid for his own sake; but he said, that, if he should win, he would not wish to harm the head of his cousin Bertholais.

"Thou art a coward!" said Charlot. "Thou fearest for thine own head!"

Then at last the young hero, much against his will, agreed to play with Bertholais.

They sat down at the table to play. On one side stood the three umpires chosen by Allard: they were Roland, Ogier the Dane, and Duke Namon. On the other side stood the friends of Bertholais,—Charlot, Ganelon, and young Pinabel of Mayence. The chessmen with which Allard played were of silver, but those of Bertholais were golden. Five games were played; and, much to the astonishment of all, the boastful Bertholais was checkmated in every one. Then Allard arose from the table.

"I shall not claim the stakes," said he mildly. "I played only for the sake of my own life and good name. And on no account would I harm the head of the prince my cousin."

Bertholais was boiling over with wrath. He seized the chessboard, and struck Allard in the face with all his might. Blood flowed from the mouth and nose of the hero, and ran down upon his clothing. Yet, not wishing to provoke a greater quarrel, he turned about, and left the room. As he crossed the courtyard, he met his brother Reinold. Great was the wrath of Reinold when he heard what had happened.

"Saddle your horses, and be ready to ride with me!" he cried to his brothers and friends.—"Allard, my good fellow, I will have the stakes for which you played!"

Boldly he walked into the presence-chamber of the king.

"I have come," said he, "to claim the blood-fine that is due for the death of my uncle Bevis. Six times his weight in gold was promised, but it has never been paid."

It was now Charlemagne's turn to be angry. He said not a word; but he pulled off his steel gauntlet, and threw it into the face of the too bold Reinold.

"If thou wert not the king," said the knight, "thou shouldst fight me on that challenge."

As he left the hall, he met the unlucky Bertholais. He drew his sword Flamberge, and with one stroke severed the prince's head from his body. A great uproar arose in the palace, but no one seemed to know what to do.

"Seize the villain!" cried Charlemagne. "He shall be hanged as a vile thief and murderer."

But his brethren were in the courtyard, already mounted; and Bayard was there, waiting to carry him, swifter than the wind, out of harm's way. At once there was a great hue and cry. A thousand men-at-arms, mounted on the fleetest steeds, gave chase. Reinold might have escaped, but he would not leave his brothers. Outside of the city they were overtaken. A desperate fight took place. All the followers of the four brothers were either slain or taken prisoners; and all their horses, save Bayard alone, were killed. Seeing matters in so desperate a strait, Reinold bade his brothers mount behind him on Bayard's long back. Quickly they obeyed him; and the noble horse galloped away with the speed of a storm cloud, bearing his fourfold burden far beyond the reach of Charlemagne's avengeful anger.

For seven years did the four brothers wander as outlaws

in the wood of Ardennes. Their father, Duke Aymon, was loyal to the king, and would not give them aught of comfort or of aid. Great was their poverty and distress, and they suffered much from hunger and cold and wretchedness. But the wonderful horse Bayard was their best friend: he kept as big and as fat as ever, and thrived as well on dry leaves as other horses do on oats and corn. At last the brothers, tired of living where every man's hand seemed to be raised against them, escaped from the wood of Ardennes, and came into the border land of Spain. There they sought the friendship and protection of a Moorish chief named Ivo. Right gladly did the Pagans receive them, for the fame of their daring had gone before them. They were taken into the household of Ivo, and for three years they served him loyally and well. And so great was the favor with which the Moor looked upon Reinold, that he gave him his only daughter Clarissa in marriage, and the richest lands among the Pyrenees as a fief. And Reinold built on one of the hills a beautiful and strong fortress of white marble which he called Montalban. And there he gathered around him a great number of warriors, knights, and adventurers,—Pagans, as well as Christians,—and set himself up as the king of the country round about. And oftentimes he had given aid to the Moors in their wars against Charlemagne.

And now the king had resolved, if possible, to humble his outlawed nephews, and to punish them for their crimes and rebellious doings. And it was for this reason, that, as we have seen, he halted in his pursuit of Marsilius and his host, and made ready to besiege Montalban.

ADVENTURE XII

MALAGIS THE WIZARD

For a whole month the host of Charlemagne lay encamped in the neighborhood of Montalban. But the proud white castle which shone so clear upon the mountain top was so strongly fortified, and the roads which led to it were so steep and narrow, that it was impossible to reach even its outer walls. Nor could they by any means shut up the garrison, or hinder them from getting food and recruits from their Pagan friends on the other side of the mountains.

"It is folly to besiege the eagle in his eyry," said Roland.

"You speak wisely," answered the king. "And while we are here idly watching this stronghold, where four rebels lie secure, a score of other traitors are plotting mischief in other parts of our kingdom. To-morrow we will try a stratagem; and, if then we fail, we will give up this undertaking, and hie us back to Paris."

The next morning the watchman who stood above the gates of Montalban saw the French army on the move. A long line of steel-clad warriors, with the golden Oriflamme at their head, filed slowly past the foot of the mountain, and turned down the valley road which led back into France.

"Up, Reinold!" cried Allard. "Our enemies have abandoned the siege! Outwitted and ashamed, they go back to their homes. Let us saddle our steeds, and follow in their wake, and harass them on the road."

"Do no such thing!" said the dwarf Malagis. "They would draw you away from your safe stronghold, and lead you into an ambush. Let them march away quietly; and, when they see that you are too wise to fall into their trap, they will return into France, and annoy you no more. The king has enough to do to attend to his affairs at Paris, without wasting the whole summer here."

Through all their troubles, Malagis had been the firm friend of his cousins, the four sons of Aymon. And he was able sometimes to be of great use to them; for men looked upon him as a being of more than human power and knowledge, and he was allowed to pass from place to place, and from camp to camp, without question and without hinderance. Sometimes he was with Charlemagne, sometimes he was with the brothers; but oftener he was wandering hither and thither in company, as men believed, with his kinsfolk,—the wood sprites and the mountain goblins.

"Thou sayest wisely, my elfin cousin," said Reinold. "But, now that our foes have left us once more in quiet, there is one duty that I must do without delay. It is full ten years since I saw my mother, the Princess Aya. Above all things else in life, I long to see her once more; and I know that her tender heart yearns to meet her wayward sons again. I will dress me in a pilgrim's garb; and I will go now to the old home at Dordon, and make myself known to her."

"We will go with you!" cried all three of his brothers.

A few days after this, four humble pilgrims stood at the gate of the castle at Dordon. So poor they were, that there was scarcely a whole thread of cloth on their backs; and they seemed footsore with their long journeying, and weak from much fasting. They begged, that, for the love of Him who died on the cross, they might be given a crust of bread, and be allowed to rest for the night on the hard stones of the kitchen floor. The gentle Aya, when she was told how they stood at the gate, bade them to be brought into her presence. Much affrighted was she at their haggard faces, and bold, determined looks.

"These are no common pilgrims," said she; and yet her heart was strangely moved toward them. And she gave them food and clothing, and saw that every thing was done that could add to their comfort.

"This I do," said she, "for the love of God, the Gentle Father, who I pray may save my sons from danger and death. For I have not seen them these ten years."

"How is that?" asked one of the pilgrims. "Tell us about your sons."

Then Aya began to tell the story of the sad misfortunes that had driven her sons into exile and caused her so many years of anxiety and sorrow. But, as she spoke, the tallest of the four pilgrims withdrew his cowl from his head, and displayed a strange scar in the middle of his forehead. The princess started with surprise.

"Reinold!" she cried. "Fair son, if it be indeed thou, tell it me at once."

The great heart of the hero was too full for speech. He wept. The gentle mother knew now that these were her sons who stood before her. Weeping with great joy, she fell into Reinold's arms: tenderly they kissed her a hundred times over. Not one of them could speak a word, for aught that lives.

And the princess made a feast for her sons in the banquet

hall. And she set before them all that was rarest and best in the way of meat and drink,—venison and fish and fowl, and white wine and red in a great cup. And she herself waited on them at table. While they were eating, Duke Aymon came home from hunting.

"Who are these men who eat like lords, but who are dressed like holy pilgrims?" he asked as he walked suddenly into the banquet room.

The Princess Aya, weeping, answered,—

"They are your sons, the long-lost heroes of our house. They have braved every danger to see their mother once again. And I have given them shelter this one night, and food such as the sons of Duke Aymon should eat. When the morning dawns they will go away, and I know not if in all my life I shall see them again."

The iron-hearted duke was in truth pleased to see his sons, but with him duty was stronger than love. He tried to forget that he was a father, and to remember only that he was a knight, and a loyal vassal of the king. Roughly he spoke to the young men.

"Out upon you, you traitors!" he cried. "My castle is no abiding place for men who make war upon Charlemagne and his knights. You are no sons of mine. No favors shall ye seek of me."

Right angry was the courteous Reinold to hear these words from his father's lips. He sprang from the table. Had any other knight spoken thus, he would have made him rue it. But he checked his fiery temper.

"Baron," said the hero, "it is hard to hear one who should keep us and help us, through bad report as well as good, talk thus harshly and unreasonably. It is maddening to know that you thus disherit us for the sake of the most selfish of kings."

Duke Aymon's love now got the better of his loyalty. For a time he could not speak for weeping. Then he said, "Reinold, very worthy son of baron art thou. I know not thy peer on earth. But for my oath's sake I dare not give you aught of aid or comfort."

And very sorrowfully the duke turned away, and left the hall. And he mounted his steed, and rode away. And he came not back to Dordon until he heard that the king had pardoned his sons.

After he had gone, Reinold and his brothers laid aside their pilgrim garbs, and dressed themselves in apparel befitting their rank. And their mother gave them of her gold and silver, which she had in great abundance. And messengers were sent out into the city and into the countryside, to make it known to all men who were dissatisfied with the king and his doings, that the four sons of Aymon were resting for the night in their father's castle.

"Let all who would aid them against the tyranny of Charlemagne," said the messengers, "arm themselves, and join them, without delay."

At dawn the heroes rode boldly out of Dordon, and behind them followed seven hundred noble knights who had vowed to see them safe again in their mountain home of Montalban. On their way they were overtaken by the dwarf Malagis, who had with him four sumterloads of gold and silver. He had just come from the king's court at Paris. But, when he was asked where he had gotten the treasure which he brought, he said,—

"The mountain goblins and the wood sprites have sent a part of their secret hoard to the heroes of Montalban."

When Charlemagne learned that the sons of Aymon had so boldly visited their mother at Dordon, and that they had gone back to their mountain stronghold with so great a following, his wrath waxed very hot, and he called his peers together to ask their advice. Duke Namon and Roland were in favor of peace.

"Grant the four knights your forgiveness," said they, "and you will gain four very powerful vassals, who will be of great help to you in your wars against the Saracens."

But Ganelon, the cunning mischief-maker, arose and said, "The king will scarcely humble himself by making terms with traitors. It would be better to try one more stratagem at least, ere we acknowledge ourselves outwitted by them. Now, there is the old Moorish chief, Ivo, the father-in-law of Reinold. He loves nothing so much as money. He would sell his own children for gold. If we could only gain his friendship, he might be persuaded to betray the four brothers into our hands."

Charlemagne was delighted with this cunning suggestion: it pleased him better than the wiser plans for peace which Roland and Duke Namon had proposed. Secret messengers were at once sent to Chief Ivo with rich presents of gold and jewels, and promises of much more, if he would betray the four sons of Aymon. Ganelon was right when he had spoken of Ivo's great love of money. He listened eagerly to the offers of the king's messengers; and his heart grew black, and his long fingers itched for the promised rewards. And, without a single twitch of conscience, he agreed to sell Reinold and his brothers, and their mountain fortress, to the king.

One day the faithless Ivo went to Montalban, as he had been wont to do, to see his daughter Clarissa, and to talk with the hero brothers. He had just come from Paris, he said, and he brought glad news.

"Would you like to make peace with your uncle the king?"

"Nothing would gladden our hearts more," said Reinold. "It is hard to live thus outlawed and hunted down by our own kinsmen and those who should be our friends."

Then Ivo, with smooth, lying words, told them that the king had offered to let all bygones be bygones, and to receive them into the highest favor at his court, if they would only prove their sincerity by a single act of submission.

"What is it?" asked they. "We will sacrifice every thing except our lives and our knightly honor, in order that there may be peace between us and the king."

"It is only this," said the cunning Ivo. "It is that you dress yourselves in the garb of pilgrims, like that which you wore when you visited your mother at Dordon, and that, barefooted and unarmed, you ride to the fortress of Falkalone, and there do homage to the king, begging his forgiveness."

"That is easily done," said Reinold. "It is not half so hard a penance as we have suffered these ten years past. You may tell the king that we will do as he desires, for we are sadly tired of this strife."

A few weeks after this, a messenger came to Montalban, bringing word that the king with his peers had come to the castle of Falkalone, and that he waited there the submission of Reinold and his brothers. The four knights at once made ready to obey the summons. They donned their pilgrims' garbs, and, barefooted and unarmed, mounted the donkeys which were to carry them across the mountains. Then Clarissa, the wife of Reinold, prayed them not to go.

"My father, Chief Ivo," said she, "would stoop to any deed of treachery for the sake of gold. And my heart tells me that he is luring you to Falkalone to betray you. I beg you not to go thus unarmed into the lion's power."

But Reinold would not listen to his fair wife.

"An ungrateful daughter you are," said he, "thus to accuse your father of the basest crime of which a warrior can be guilty. I have ever found him trustworthy, and I will not now believe him to be false."

With these words he turned, and rode out through the castle gate, not even bidding Clarissa good-by. Richard and Guichard followed him, but Allard tarried a few moments in the courtyard.

"Take these good friends with you," said Clarissa; "you will have need of them, if I mistake not." And she handed him four swords, among which was Reinold's Flamberge.

Allard thanked the lady; and, taking the good weapons, he hid them carefully beneath his penitent's robe. Then giving whip to his donkey, he followed his brothers down the steep mountain road which led toward Falkalone.

As the heroes were passing through a narrow glen not more than a league from Falkalone, they were set upon by a party of horsemen who lay in ambush there. Then it was that Reinold thought of fair Clarissa's warning words, and bitterly he repented that he had not hearkened to her advice. But Allard quickly divided the swords among them; and, when Reinold saw his old friend Flamberge once more in his hand, his fears vanished, and he stood boldly on guard against his foes. But how could four men, mounted only on donkeys, and armed only with swords, defend themselves from the onset of three-score steel-clad knights on horseback? Allard, Guichard, and Richard were soon overthrown, and made prisoners. What would Reinold not have given for a stout lance, and his trusty war steed Bayard, at that moment? Yet bravely he fought, and more than one of his foes bit the dust. At last night came on; and, while the others were groping in the dusk, he turned his donkey about, and, as he knew the road well, he made his way safely back to Montalban.

Reinold expected that Charlemagne would again lay siege to his mountain castle, and try to gain by force what he had partly failed to gain by guile. He therefore doubled the guards on the walls, and sent out companies of armed men to watch every turn of the narrow road which led from the valley up to the fortress; and on the rocks and high places he caused great heaps of stones and other missiles to be piled, ready to be thrown down on the heads of any foes who should dare approach too near. But, at the very moment when the king was ready to begin the assault on Montalban, messengers came to him from Paris, bringing news which made it necessary for him to return home without further delay.

"Let the three rebels whom we have taken," said he, "be carried back with us in chains to Paris. As soon as our leisure serves us, they shall be hanged like so many thieves. Their fate will be a warning to all other traitors."

Then Reinold, when he heard it, resolved that he would at all hazards save the lives of his brothers. So he mounted his good steed Bayard, and set out alone for Paris. One day, at the noontide hour, he stopped to rest in the cool shade of a great oak. The sun shone very hot; the grass upon which he reclined was green and soft; the bees hummed drowsily among the leaves overhead; every thing was so calm and still, that, before Reinold knew it, he had fallen asleep. And Bayard, pleased with the pasturage which spread around, left his master's side, and wandered hither and thither, grazing the sweetest clover and the freshest leaves of grass. It so happened that some country folk who were passing that way saw the horse; and one of them, who had been at Dordon, said,—

"See there! I verily believe that steed is Bayard."

But the others laughed at him.

"At any rate," said he, "he is a rich prize. See the goldred saddle on his back, the golden stirrups at his sides, and the silken reins that rest upon his neck. He belongs to no common knight. I mean to take him to Paris, and claim a reward for having found him. He would be a handsome gift to present to the king."

Now, this man was no common countryman, or he would not have dared think of touching so rare and rich a prize; nor could he, without the help of magic, have come near the horse. But he had seen something of the world; and in his youth he had lived some time with an old wizard, from whom he had learned something of witchery and enchantment. So, as he drew near the grazing horse, he mumbled many strange, uncouth words, and scattered a fine white powder to the winds. Yet, even with all these precautions, it was with the greatest difficulty that he caught hold of the reins of Bayard, and seated himself on his back. The horse at once set off at a full gallop toward Paris; and so swift was his passage, that early the next morning he stood in the courtyard of the king's palace.

When word was brought to Charlemagne, that Bayard, the matchless steed of the Montalban hero, was at the door, he could not believe it. But when he went out, and saw for himself that horse, the like of which there was none on earth, his joy was greater than if it had been Reinold himself.

"Verily, this horse is worth more than a province!" said he.

And he at once conferred the honor of knighthood upon the countryman, loading him with rich presents of gold and silver, and giving him as a fief the lands and castles of the dead Duke Gilmer of Vermandois.

Now let us go back to Reinold, whom we left sleeping in the shade of the friendly oak. When he awoke, the sun was sloping far down toward the west. He had never before slept so long and so carelessly by the roadside. He arose and looked around. His steed was nowhere to be seen. He called him, at first softly, then very loudly, "Bayard!" He listened to hear the shrill whinny with which the horse always answered his call. And when no sound came back save the echo of his own anxious voice, then Reinold knew that Bayard was lost, and he threw himself in despair upon the ground.

"What need to live longer," said he, "when I have lost every living being that I loved? False fealty, force, and fraud have deprived me of a father's love, of a mother's caresses, of my brothers' companionship. I have not kith nor kin to whom I may go for sympathy and fellowship. And now my horse, whom I loved as a fourth brother, has been stolen from me."

As he spoke, his eyes fell upon his golden spurs, the symbol of his knighthood. He seized them in his hands, and wrenched them from his ankles.

"What need of these, when Bayard is gone!" he cried. "Without a horse, I am no longer a knight."

"Good-day to you, my lord!" said a shrill, harsh voice at his elbow.

He looked up, and saw a little old man, bent almost double with the infirmities of age, standing very close to him, and gazing at him with a strange, quizzical look on his little dried-up features. The old man was dressed in the garb of a begging pilgrim, his long white beard fell in tangled masses halfway to his feet, and his twinkling gray eyes were almost hidden beneath his heavy white eyebrows.

"Good-day to you, my lord!" he said a second time, bowing very low.

"It may be a good day to you, old man," said Reinold. "But, as for me, I have scarcely known a good day in all my life."

"My lord," said the pilgrim, "why should your heart lose hope? Do but give me a present as a token of your faith, and I will pray Heaven to help you. Prayer is the poor man's defence, and it has sometimes relieved the rich and the great from their distresses."

"Your prayers may do me much good," answered Reinold; "but I have no faith in them, nor indeed in aught else. Yet no beggar has ever gone away from me empty-handed. Here are my spurs, the priceless gifts that my mother buckled to my ankles on the day that I was dubbed a knight. Take them: I shall never wear them again."

The pilgrim took the spurs, and, bowing low, said, "My lord, these spurs may be worth ten pounds; but my prayers are worth much more. Have you nothing else to give?"

Reinold's down-heartedness began now to give place to anger. "A fig for your prayers!" answered he. "If it were not for your gray hairs, I would give you a sound drubbing for a present."

"Ah, good sir," said the old man, "it is not thus that Christians give alms to pious pilgrims. If every one of whom I have begged had beaten me, the churches and the convents would have been but poorly furnished. But some have shared their last crust with me, and great has been their reward. Therefore, I ask thee again, if thou hast any thing to spare, give it me."

Then Reinold took off his mantle,—a beautiful garment of velvet, embroidered with silk and gold,—and gave it to the pilgrim.

"Take this," said he. "It is the last gift of my wife, the charming Clarissa, the fair Pagan, whose love for me is, I fear, greater and more sincere than I deserve."

The old man folded the mantle carefully, and put it in his wallet. Then, with another low bow, he said, "My lord, have you nothing else that you would give me for the sake of kind remembrance?"

Reinold's wrath now got the better of him. Fiercely he drew Flamberge from his scabbard. He seized the pilgrim by the beard. "Wouldst thou rob me?" he cried. "Even thy age shall not save thee!"

The old man quietly pushed back his hood. His long beard fell off in Reinold's grasp. He looked at the hero with a smile.

"Good Sir Reinold," said he, "wouldst thou slay thy cousin Malagis?"

It was indeed the wizard dwarf Malagis, who, for some reason best known to himself, had chosen to come before Reinold in this disguise.

"Cheer up, brave cousin!" said he. "Faith and hope have brought about greater wonders than the wizard's wand ever accomplished. But despair has never yet gained a victory. Your brothers are prisoners in the king's castle, and Bayard is on his way to Paris. But, if you will trust me, all will yet be well."

He then took from his wallet an old gown, like that which he himself wore, and bade Reinold put it on over his armor, instead of the rich mantle which he had just given away. He unlaced his helmet, and hid it in a clump of shrubs, and, instead of it, he drew over his head a ragged gray hood, which hid more than half his face beneath its folds. A false beard and a few touches of paint were all that was needed now to change the hero into the likeness of a pious pilgrim.

"Malagis," said Reinold, embracing the wizard, "thou art truly a godsend! I believe in thee."

A few days after this, two pilgrims, old and lame, limped through the streets of Paris, begging alms of the good people whom they met. They stood on the bridge over the Seine, and watched a grand procession of lords and ladies crossing the river, on their way to a tournament which was to be held in the meadows on the other side.

"Put on your spurs, cousin," said the wizard; "for, believe me, you will soon need them."

By and by a great shouting was heard; and the king was seen riding toward the bridge, with Roland and the other peers in his train. In front of him was the great war steed Bayard, led by four stout grooms. The horse was most richly apparelled. The bridle was of silver and gold, with reins of fine sable and silk-covered leather; the saddle was wonderfully wrought of leather and cloth and rare metals; and over all were trappings of crimson velvet bordered with cloth-of-gold, on which fair ladies' fingers had deftly embroidered the white lilies of France. It was hard to tell which the people applauded more,—the grand old king who sat so proudly on his own charger, or the noble steed who walked before him like the monarch of his kind.

"They are leading the horse to the lists," said a monk who stood near. "The knights are there to make trial of their skill in mounting and riding him, and he who succeeds best is to have him as a present from the king."

"When will kings cease to give away the things that do not belong to them?" asked Malagis.

All at once the horse was noticed to stop. He had seen the poor pilgrims on the bridge. With a sudden toss of the head he jerked away from the grooms; and, neighing joyfully, he ran forward, and laid his head on Reinold's shoulder.

"Never saw I such a horse as Bayard," said Roland to the king. "He seems to scorn our company, and to like those ragged beggars better than knights and noblemen."

"Come, Bayard," said the king, riding forward and laying his hand on the reins. "Thou shouldst be more choice of thy comrades."

"And is this, indeed, Bayard?" asked one of the pilgrims. "How lucky we are to happen here at this moment!"

Then, turning to Charlemagne, he said, "Most gracious king, I pray you to grant us a boon. This my poor brother has been deaf and dumb and blind these many days, and there is in life no joy for him. He wanders with me from place to place in great distress; and, do what he will, he can find no relief. But yesterday a wizard told me, that, if he could be allowed to ride even ten steps on the great steed Bayard, he should be healed."

The king and his courtiers laughed.

"I have half a mind to let him try," said Charlemagne; "for, although I have heard of miracles, I have never yet seen one."

"Even if he should not be healed," said Roland, "it would be equally a miracle. It would be as wonderful to see a cripple ride the great Bayard as to see the blind restored to sight."

Then, by the king's command, the grooms lifted the supposed pilgrim into the saddle. Men wondered why the horse should stand so gently, and allow himself to be backed by the awkward, ragged beggar, when he had refused to let the noblest barons put feet in his stirrups. But their wonder grew to astonishment when the dumb pilgrim spoke the word "Bayard!" and the horse, with his rider sitting gracefully in the saddle, dashed across the bridge and galloped away more swiftly than horse had ever before been known to gallop. The king and all his peers put spurs to their steeds, and followed. But in less than a minute the wonderful Bayard was out of sight, and none of his pursuers saw him again. More swiftly than a bird could fly through the air, he sped southward over hill and dale and forest and stream, and stopped not once until he had carried his master safely back to Montalban.

"Fools that we are!" said the king. "Again have we been outwitted by that villain Reinold and his cunning cousin Malagis. If ever the wizard comes within my reach, he shall suffer for this."

But Malagis had taken care to slip away during the confusion; and, though the king ordered that search should everywhere be made for him, he was not to be found in Paris.

That same night a little man dressed in gray made his way, silent and unseen, to the prison tower of the king's castle. The guards before the doors were asleep, and the sentinels who stood on the ramparts above nodded at their posts. He touched the great oaken doors. The iron bolts flew back with a faint click; the chains were unfastened without a rattle; the doors turned silently on their hinges. Some men say that the cunning wizard, for it was Malagis, did all this through magic: others say that he had bribed the watchmen. Be this as it may, he had no trouble in finding his way to a narrow dungeon, where the air seemed heavy and cold, and the water oozed and trickled through the ceiling, and the horrible gloom of the grave seemed to brood over all. There three men were chained to the wall. They were Allard, Guichard, and Richard. When they heard him enter, they supposed it was the jailer, come to lead them out to their death. And they were glad, for death in any shape would have been better than life in such a place. The wizard touched them, and their chains fell from their limbs. He must have had the jailer's keys.

"Up, cousins!" he cried. "You are saved. I am Malagis. Follow me."

Silently they groped their way out of the prison. At the castle gate four fleet horses, ready saddled, waited for them. They mounted them, and, ere the morning dawned, were many leagues away from Paris, riding straight for Montalban.

Very angry was the king when he learned, next day, that

he had been again outwitted, and that the sons of Aymon had escaped. He vowed that he would not rest, nor cease his efforts, until he had dined in the broad feast hall of Montalban. And he called together his host, and marched with all haste back, for the third time, to the country of the Pyrenees.

The mountain stronghold was surrounded on every side by the men of Charlemagne. Every road and every pass leading to it were carefully guarded. The king knew that he could never reach the walls, or hope to carry the place by assault, and therefore that the only way to capture it was to starve the garrison into surrender. Yet week after week passed by, and neither party seemed to gain any advantage over the other. Once a company of knights, under Reinold, made a sally into the plain below, and had a brief passage-at-arms with some of Charlemagne's men. Roland and Reinold measured their lances with each other; and Roland, for the first and only time in his life, was unhorsed.

"Ah, good cousin!" cried Reinold, "that was your horse's failure, and no fault of yours."

And he at once called off his men, and rode back to the castle. Roland was very much grieved at the disgrace of his fall: but, instead of feeling angry, he cherished the warmest feelings of friendship for his gallant cousin; and he vowed, that, if ever the king should forgive Reinold, he would love him next to Oliver, and Ogier the Dane.

It happened one night, that Malagis—as, indeed, he had often done before—went out as a spy into Charlemagne's camp. The soldiers were sleeping quietly in their tents; and, as the wizard crept stealthily from one place to another, he threw a white sleeping-powder into the air, which caused even the most

The beleaguered castle.

watchful sentinels to close their eyes. Thus he made his way into the very heart of the camp; and, without any fear of awakening the sleepers, he stood in the door of the king's tent. Suddenly, and to his great surprise, he felt himself seized by the collar, and lifted from the ground. He looked around, and saw that he was in the strong grasp of Oliver, who, from some reason which the wizard could never understand, was not made drowsy by the sleeping-powders. Malagis earnestly begged the knight to set him free. But Oliver would not listen to a word. He aroused the sleepers in the tent, and carried the struggling dwarf into the king's presence.

"Ah, thou cunning wizard!" cried the king, "I have thee at last! And, even though the unseen powers be on thy side, thou shalt not get off easily."

Then he ordered Malagis to be bound and carried out of the camp and thrown from the top of a precipice.

"My lord," said the wizard, "I have but one favor to ask of you. Let me live long enough to sit once more with you and your peers at the banquet table."

"It shall be as thou desirest," said the king; "but thy life shall not be much the longer thereby."

Then he ordered a feast to be made ready at once, and he sent out and invited the noblest of his barons to come and eat with him. It was midnight when the king and his knights sat down to supper, and much did they enjoy the good food and the rich wine which were placed before them. But soon they began to feel drowsy. One by one they closed their eyes, and fell back in their seats fast asleep. In a short time not a single person in all the camp, save Malagis, was awake. His eyes twinkled merrily; and he could not help jumping upon the table, and dancing about in glee, as he saw how the magic powder had again cast a spell of slumber over all. Then he stepped softly to the side of the sleeping Charlemagne; and, after giving him an extra pinch of the snuff, he lifted him on his shoulders, and carried him out of the tent. It was a great burden for the little man to carry, but we must believe that his magic increased his strength tenfold as he toiled up the narrow mountain paths with his kingly burden on his back.

When he reached the castle, the gate was opened; and he carried the king, still fast asleep, into the broad hall. Great was the astonishment of Reinold and his brothers when they saw what kind of a prisoner the dwarf had brought them.

"Your troubles are at an end, my cousins," said he. "You may now make peace on your own terms."

The king was carried to the best guest chamber in the castle, and every thing was done that could add to his comfort. But he did not awaken until noon the next day. You may imagine his surprise when he opened his eyes, and found himself, not, as he supposed, in his tent, but in a sumptuous castle, furnished as grandly as his own palace. For a long time he would not believe but that it was all a dream; and not until Reinold and Malagis came into his presence, and told him where he was, and how he came there, did he recover from his bewilderment. At first he was very angry, and harshly upbraided them for their treason. But Reinold did not once forget the courtesy that is due from a knight to his king. As Charlemagne was very hungry after his long sleep, he was persuaded to sit down with the sons of Aymon at the banquet table, and partake of the choice food and the rare wines with which Montalban was well supplied. But when the brothers spoke to him of peace, and prayed that he would let bygones be bygones, and receive them again into his kingly favor, he grew angry and morose, and bade them open the castle gates, and let him go back to his friends, who were anxiously seeking him in the valley below.

"Never will I make peace with you!" he cried.

"It shall not be said that I have dealt harshly with the king," said Reinold. "He shall have his freedom; and, if our kindness has no power to touch his heart, then we must still defend ourselves in Montalban."

And the king went out of the castle, and back to his own camp, without a word of forgiveness for his unhappy nephews.

As Reinold passed through the courtyard soon afterward, he saw Malagis the wizard burning a great heap of papers and boxes and odd mixtures, and making strange motions and gestures over them, as the flames consumed them.

"What are you doing, cousin?" he asked.

"I am burning all the tools of my trade," said Malagis sadly. "The wizard's art is thrown away upon such men as you. I am going to leave Montalban, never to return again. Had you been wise, you would have kept the king a prisoner, and forced him to grant you peace."

After Charlemagne had gone back to his camp, he began to think more seriously about this long and profitless war with his nephews.

"Why not bring it to a close by granting them your forgiveness?" asked Roland.

"But my oath," said Charlemagne. "I dare not forget my oath."

"True," answered Roland. "But what was your oath?—that you would not make peace, nor grant your forgiveness, until you had dined in the banquet-hall of Montalban?"

"That was my oath, and it shall be remembered."

"But have you not dined to-day in the banquet-hall of Montalban?"

The king was silent, and he went and shut himself up alone in his tent. The next day he sent a messenger to the heroes of Montalban, offering to make peace with them on their own terms, to grant them full pardon for all past offences, and to restore to them all the honors, fiefs, and dignities which were theirs by right. And thus the sorrowful wars with Duke Aymon's sons were ended.

ADVENTURE XIII

THE PRINCESS OF CATHAY

It was the season of Pentecost, and Charlemagne was holding a great feast and a high tide of rejoicing at Paris. The city was dressed in holiday attire; and there was much banqueting, and music and dancing, and jousting, and many gallant deeds at arms. And the noblest men and the fairest women in Christendom had gathered there to do honor to the king and to share in the glad festivities. For, strange as it may seem, Charlemagne was now, for the first time in his reign, at peace with all the world. Neither foes abroad nor traitors at home dared lift up their heads, or show their hands.

On the last day of the feast a grand tournament was held in the meadows; and the king and his peers, and the lordly strangers who were visiting at the court, were there. Some merely sat in the galleries as spectators: others entered the lists as contestants in the noble passage-at-arms. There might have been seen Roland and Oliver, and Ogier the Dane, and Reinold of Montalban, and wise old Duke Namon, and evil-eyed Ganelon, and even the cunning wizard Malagis. There, too, were the queen and her train of high-born dames, and the fairest damsels that the sun of France had ever shone upon. But fairer than all others was the matchless maiden Alda, the betrothed of Roland. And most worthy among the strangers was a young English knight named Astolpho,—a poet by birth, and fairer of face and speech than he was skilful in the use of arms. There, also, were several Pagan princes, who had come to Paris either to see and admire the splendor and the power of the Christian king, or to spy out the weak points in his government, and determine what his real strength might be. Chief among these was a dark-faced giant named Ferrau, a prince of Saragossa, who was said to be the ablest and bravest of all the Saracen knights in the train of King Marsilius of Spain. But no one of all the great company who met to view the tournament there in the Seine meadows could excel Roland in grace and strength and skill. Many were the feats at arms that he performed that day, and in more than one combat was he hailed the victor.

Late in the afternoon, when the heralds had announced the cessation of the day's amusements, and the folk were about to leave the place, the sound of a bugle was heard outside of the lists. And when, by the king's command, the barriers were thrown open to admit the new-comer, whoever he might be, there came a strange procession through. Four giants, taller by half than the tallest man in Charlemagne's court, presented themselves, and came directly toward the king. Their faces were dark and fierce; and they looked down upon the knights, who made way for them, with an ill-hidden expression of scorn. Behind them, on a milk-white palfrey, rode a young lady. A princess she seemed, and the most beautiful that Charlemagne or his knights had ever looked upon. She was dressed in the fashion of the Far East, and upon her head was a diadem of pearls; and the palfrey upon which she sat was trapped to the foot in blue velvet, bordered with crimson cloth-of-gold. And by the side of the strange lady there rode a noble knight, clad in a war coat of polished brass, upon a war steed harnessed in white cloth-of-gold, bearing a device of eyes full of tears. And neither knight nor lady looked to the right or to the left, but followed their huge guides straight toward the place where the king sat.

When Charlemagne first saw the giants coming so boldly in on foot, he was on the point of ordering them driven from the lists. But when his eyes rested on the rare beauty of the strange princess who followed them, and on the proud form of the knight, her companion, he allowed them to come very near to him in order that he might the better see them, and speak with them.

"Who are you?" he asked. "And why come you here at this late hour of the day, unheralded and unknown?"

The four giants made humble obeisance to the king, but said not a word. The knight sat upright on his charger, his eyes fixed upon the ground before him, his face immovable as that of a statue, seeming neither to hear nor to see aught that was going on around him. But the lady rode forward until she was directly in front of the high seats. And she courtesied reverently to the king; and, lifting her peerless eyes toward him, she said,—

"Right high, right worthy, and right mighty king, I am Angelica. My father is King Galafron, the ruler of far-off Cathay; and he is, next to you, the mightiest monarch in the world. This young knight who rides by my side is my brother Argalia, than whom few braver men are known. By the leave of our kingly father we have journeyed from the rising sun to the western sea, viewing the wonders of nature, and the power of men, and the might of Christendom. And we seek a knight without fear and without shame, who will dare meet my brother in honorable act of arms."

At these words several of the knights sprang up, eager to offer the gage of battle to the new-comer. But Charlemagne motioned them to be quiet; and the Princess Angelica went on:—

"We have heard, most noble king, that you are at peace with all the world, and for that reason we have been the more bold to come into your country. And we had hoped to be here to take part in the passage-at-arms to-day, but were delayed in the journey. And now, since the hour is too late for any further jousting, allow me to challenge you and the bravest of your knights to meet my brother Argalia in single combat with lance to-morrow at the foot of the Stair of Merlin."

"We most certainly accept the challenge," said the king, smiling.

"But listen to the conditions," said the princess. "Whoever is unhorsed by my brother becomes his lawful prisoner, and is held by him as a hostage until he is ransomed. But, should any knight overcome my brother in fair fight, that knight may, if he choose, claim me as his wife, and all my dowry as his reward. For the Fates have written that this can be done only by the greatest hero in the world."

All the men who stood near and heard this challenge were astonished at the strangeness of the terms which were offered, and yet they were all the more eager to engage in combat with the young prince. For, the longer they looked upon the matchless form and features of Angelica, the more they were enraptured with her heavenly beauty.

"We accept the conditions," said the king graciously. "To-morrow morning the worthiest warriors in my realm shall meet thy brother in a trial of arms at the Stair of Merlin. If any man fail, he forfeits his freedom. But remember the reward that is promised the victor!"

"It is well," answered the princess. "We shall remember."

Then, saluting the king reverently, she turned her palfrey about, and with her brother followed her giant escort out of the lists.

And now a great dispute arose among the knights. Each one was anxious to be the first to try his strength and skill in the joust with the Prince of Cathay. Charlemagne, seeing that the question could be settled in no other way, declared that the whole matter should be left to chance, and ordered that lots should be drawn. Thirty-one knights offered themselves, and not one felt any doubt but that the palm of victory in the coming contest would be his. Each wrote his name on a bit of parchment, which he dropped into Roland's helmet. Then the slips were drawn out one by one by a blindfolded page, and the names were read in their order by Archbishop Turpin. The first name was that of the English knight, Astolpho. Everybody smiled when it was read,—some in disdain, others in ridicule. And some were so unmannerly as to hint that the fair-haired foreigner would succeed better in a tourney with minstrels, with the harp as his weapon instead of the lance.

"Has he ever been known to unhorse his opponent?" asked one.

"Never," was the answer. "But he has been known to tumble from his own steed at the mere sight of a lance."

The second name drawn was that of the dark-browed Pagan chief, Ferrau. There was a low murmur of disappointment among the knights; for the fierce Moor was noted, not only for his great strength, but for his skill also in every feat of arms. And all felt that Argalia must indeed acquit himself well if he would come out whole and well from a combat with so valiant a foe.

"It seems as if these heathen foreigners are to snatch all the honors out of our hands," said Oliver.

"It shall not be!" answered Reinold, biting his lips in anger.

The third name was that of Ogier the Dane, and there was a general sigh of relief.

"Another foreigner!" said Duke Ganelon disdainfully.

"And yet he is a more loyal Frenchman than thou," answered Roland, turning sharply upon the old traitor, and gazing so fiercely into his face that he was glad to slink away from the place.

The fourth name was that of Reinold of Montalban; and the fifth was that of the king himself. Oliver's name was the tenth. But Roland, who was burning with impatience to distinguish himself in a combat like this, was left until the very last: his name was the thirty-first. Among all the knights who had offered themselves as combatants in the act of arms which was about to take place, not one, save Ferrau the fierce Moor, was satisfied with the lots.

That evening Malagis the wizard opened his book of enchantments, and sought to find out therefrom what fortune the Fates had in store for him and his friends. But he desired most to know what would be the end of the jousting on the morrow, and whether aught of honor should accrue to his cousin Reinold of Montalban. As he looked in his book, strange, weird creatures came and danced before him. Fairies and hobgoblins, good and bad, flocked into his chamber, and courtesied and bowed, and saluted him as their master. And every one seemed anxious to tell him something, and waited only for his questions, or for his gracious leave to speak. Did you ever think, my children, that there is magic in every book, and that when you open the pages, good fairies or wicked elves come and whisper to you? The words are the mysterious creatures that salute the magician who reads; and they tell him of the wonderful past, and lay bare for him the secrets of the present and the future.

Among the ghostly visitors who came at the wizard's call was a little elf who never had told a falsehood, or concealed aught that he knew. Of him Malagis asked many questions about the Princess Angelica and her brother Argalia. And this is what the elf whispered in the ear of the cunning wizard,—

"Angelica and Argalia are truly the children of mighty Galafron, king of Cathay. But they come to France on no peaceful errand. Their object is to destroy the bravest and the best of the Christian knights, and in the end to overthrow the whole of Christendom. Do you ask how a beautiful young lady, and a knight single-handed and alone, can hope to do so great mischief? It is all very simple. I will tell you. Prince Argalia carries an enchanted lance,—a beam which is sure to unhorse whomsoever it touches, and which has never been known to fail. His shield is equally wonderful; for every weapon that comes toward it turns aside in its course, and refuses to touch it. And he rides a horse which is as fleet as the hurricane: not even the famed Bayard can outstrip him. The stoutest warrior can scarcely hope to contend successfully with such a foe. But what I have told you is not all. Even should Argalia be defeated in the joust, it is not likely that the victor can ever gain the prize which has been promised; for the princess carries with her a magic ring the like of which is not known in your books. When any danger threatens her, she places this ring in her mouth, and all at once she vanishes from mortal sight; and she is carried with the speed of thought to whatever place she wishes to go."

When Malagis had learned all that was to be known about Angelica and her brother, he closed his book, and sent his fairy visitors away. And he sat for a long time alone in his chamber, planning what he should do. At first he thought of warning the king of the danger which threatened. But he knew that Charlemagne had little faith in magic, and that he would only laugh at his story: so, upon second thought, he made up his mind to keep the whole matter a secret, and to undertake alone the task of saving France from the cunning infidels. When every one in the palace was asleep, and all was silent and dark, the little man wrapped his long cloak around him, and stole quietly out of his chamber. Under his arm he carried his book of enchantments, and in his hand he held his wizard's wand, while beneath his cloak he carried a short sword. Straight to the Stair of Merlin he went, where he knew he would find the Princess of Cathay and her noble brother. He had no trouble in finding the place, even in the dark; for he had often been there, in times now long past, to talk with Merlin, the wise wizard of Britain, from whom he had learned all his lore.

In the midst of the meadow adjoining the Stair of Merlin stood a rich pavilion. It was covered with double blue satin, and rich cloths from India, upon which were embroidered many strange devices in silver and gold. And above it floated four and twenty banners bearing the arms and mottoes of the princes of Cathay. At the door of this pavilion two swarthy giants stood, with huge clubs in their hands, and cimeters at their sides. Fiercely they glared at Malagis as he came toward them; and, had he not glared back with something of the same fierceness, there is no knowing what mischief they might have done him. But they quailed beneath the glances of the little old wizard; and, when they saw the book which he carried under his arm, they began to tremble, for ignorance is always thus fearful in the presence of knowledge. Yet, when Malagis would have entered the tent, the giants raised their great bludgeons; and, although they dared not look him in the face, they stood ready to strike him down. Then the wizard waved his wand in the air, and opened his book, and began to read. And forthwith the giants dropped their clubs to the ground, and began to yawn. And, as he kept on reading, their eyes grew heavy, so that they could no longer keep them open. And soon they were fast asleep, and recked not who came in, or who passed out. Then Malagis walked boldly into the inner court of the pavilion. Inside of the door he found the other two giants seated on a bench; but they also were fast asleep, and the wizard passed by them unchallenged. In one part of the pavilion, which was hung with rich cloth-of-gold, and furnished most gorgeously, after the manner of the Far East, the charming Angelica was reclining on her couch; and near her sat her maidens and attendants, all wrapped in the deepest slumber. When Malagis gazed upon the sweet face of the Pagan princess, he thought that in the whole world there was not any vision half so lovely. He wondered if the angels were as beautiful, and he was half tempted to fall down and worship. Never before had wizard been so bewitched. He had come to the pavilion determined to kill both the princess and the prince, and thus save Charlemagne and his peers from the great peril which threatened them. But in the presence of the peerless beauty he forgot all his learning and all his wizard's skill and all his loyalty to the king. His book slipped out of his hands, and fell with a rustling crash upon the ground. The spell was broken, and the noise awakened the princess and her maidens. They sprang to their feet, and screamed with affright. Argalia, who was sleeping in another room, was aroused, and with drawn sword hastened to the rescue. The giants, too, rushed in with their huge bludgeons raised in air. But, when they saw only the trembling wizard standing in the middle of the room, they dropped their weapons, scorning to strike a foe so weak and pitiable. Sorry, indeed, was the plight of the wan-faced old man, shorn now of all his power, and forgetful of his magic lore. He fell helpless at the feet of the charming princess.

"Spare him," said Angelica to her brother, who had again raised his sword. "There is no honor in crushing a worm so poor and harmless. But let us turn his own enchantments against him, and send him to our good father Galafron in Cathay, that our folk may know what kind of knights these Christians are who would slay us while we sleep."

Then she took up the wand which had fallen from the wizard's hand, and with it she drew a circle upon the ground, calling three times upon the name of Mahmet. And she opened the book of enchantments, and read from it. And the pavilion was filled with a pale blue smoke; and forked lightnings flashed through the darkness, and the winds moaned, and the thunder rolled. And a score of strange creatures—hobgoblins and elves and winged afrits—came and stood around the magic circle.

Then, at a word from Angelica, they took up the trembling Malagis, and bore him away. And they carried him over fields and wooded plains, and across broad rivers and the snowy mountains and the billowy seas and many strange countries, until at last they reached the land of the rising sun, and gave him over to Galafron, king of Cathay. The king gazed with contempt upon the wan and shrivelled features of the fallen wizard, and he wondered if all the knights in Christendom were like this one. Malagis in vain prayed for mercy. Galafron could not understand a word that he said, nor was he in a mood to show kindness to one who had basely sought to take the life of his daughter Angelica. And he ordered that the old man should be imprisoned in a hollow rock beneath the sea, where he should never more behold the light of the sun, or hear the glad sounds of day.

Early the next morning the knights who had offered to joust with Prince Argalia rode out together to the Stair of Merlin. They found the Pagan mounted upon his wonderful charger, and ready for the fray. And a great company of lords and ladies and squires and serving-men had assembled there, eager to view the combat. And so noble was the bearing of the Prince of Cathay, that, had he been a Christian knight, he would have had the sympathy of all the lookers-on.

As the lots had decided, the first to enter the lists was Astolpho of England. The trumpets sounded for the onset, and the two combatants rushed toward each other with the speed of the wind. As everybody had expected, Astolpho was hurled headlong from his saddle, and lay entangled in his heavy armor, helpless in the dust. Argalia gallantly dismounted, and assisted him to rise. He kindly arranged his helmet, which had fallen from his head, and then, according to the terms which had been agreed upon, led him to the pavilion, where he was to remain a prisoner.

There was a general murmur among the lookers-on; but whether it was a murmur of regret for the not unlooked-for mischance of the poet knight, or of admiration for the skill and courtesy of the Pagan prince, I cannot say.

And now all was hushed in anxious expectation and dread, as the fierce Ferrau rode out and took his place in the lists. A very giant in size, boastful of speech, rude and uncouth in manners, he seemed no fair match for the light-built and courteous knight of Cathay. He was clad in a complete suit of black armor, and above his helmet's crest there waved a raven's plume. He was mounted on a charger black as night, the trappings of which were of black velvet embellished with gold embroidery and a figure of the new moon embracing the morning star. Not a single well-wisher had the fierce Moor in all that company of lookers-on.

When every thing was in readiness, the trumpets again sounded the signal for the onset. The two Pagans gave rein to their well-trained steeds, and dashed across the turf. Their lances crashed against the opposing shields, and every one expected that Argalia would be unhorsed. What, then, was the astonishment and delight of all, when they saw him ride proudly onward, while the fierce Ferrau was hurled from the saddle, and rolled ingloriously upon the ground! A great shout went up from the multitude of lookers-on,—a shout of joy, because they supposed that rude brute force had for once been vanquished by skill: for no one knew that the lance which Argalia bore was an enchanted one; and the rude Ferrau, although a guest at the court of Charlemagne, was no favorite. Again and again the air was rent with cheers for the valiant Prince of Cathay; while Argalia, never forgetful of the courtesy due to a fallen foe, turned and rode back in order to help Ferrau to his feet. But the fierce Moor, stung to madness by his unlooked-for overthrow, and goaded into still greater wrath by the cheers which were heard on every side, had already risen. He drew his sword from its scabbard, and dared the Cathayan knight to continue the fight on foot. The guards now stepped before him, and reminded him of the terms that had been agreed upon with Charlemagne.

"What are Charlemagne's agreements to me?" he cried angrily. "He is no king of mine: I owe him no allegiance."

Fiercely, madly, he attacked the knight of Cathay. Very skilfully did Argalia defend himself; but neither his skill nor his enchanted shield availed much against the furious strokes of his giant foe. The contest was a short one. Argalia was disarmed, and thrown to the earth. Ferrau knelt upon his breast, and, drawing his dagger, held it to the throat of the vanquished knight.

"On one condition only shalt thou have thy life," he growled savagely. "Promise me, on thy faith as a Mahometan, that thy sister Angelica shall be my wife, and that all her dowry shall be mine!"

Had Argalia been a Christian knight, he would have scorned to have asked for his life on any terms, much more would he have disdained to bargain for it thus. But he was only a Pagan; and, although he was very courteous and noble, he lacked some of those higher qualities of mind and heart which distinguished the true Christian knight; and so, after a little parley, he agreed to the terms offered by Ferrau. And amid groans, and cries of "Shame! shame!" from the lookers-on, he was allowed to rise to his feet.

But Angelica liked not the thought of being made the wife of a man so fierce and brutish as Ferrau. She had had no voice in the agreement with the Moor, and she made up her mind not to be bound by it. In spite of the guards, she sprang over the barriers, and hurried to her brother's side.

"Never will your sister be the bride of a knight so unworthy and so base!" she cried. Then in a low whisper she said, "Meet me in the wood of Ardennes."

She took the magic ring from her finger, and put it between her cherry lips. Quick as thought she vanished from sight. Only a thin, white cloud, beautiful as a midsummer night's dream, and not a whit more lasting, arose in the air, and floated away on the breeze toward the forest of Ardennes. When the Moor saw, that, after all, he had been outwitted, and that the peerless Angelica had escaped beyond his reach, his wrath knew no bounds. With uplifted sword he rushed a second time toward the knight of Cathay, intending to strike him dead. But Argalia was too quick for him. He had already mounted his swift-footed steed, and at a word he was flying with the speed of a hurricane across field and wood, and over hill and dale, toward the trysting-place named by Angelica.

Everybody was astonished at the strange ending of the jousts, and there was not a little disappointment and confusion. The fierce Moor gave spurs to his night-black steed, and followed in the wake of the flying Argalia. Roland, knowing that should the prince be overtaken he would fare but ill at the hands of his wrathful enemy, mounted his own favorite horse Brigliadoro, and rode swiftly after them. Then Reinold, burning with impatience to view once more the heavenly beauty of Angelica, gave rein to Bayard, and soon outstripped and passed both Roland and Ferrau. A strange, exciting race was that from the Stair of Merlin to the wood of Ardennes.

ADVENTURE XIV

IN THE WOOD OF ARDENNES

In the wood of Ardennes, far from the common haunts of men, there was a meadow, shut in on all sides by tall trees and a thick growth of underwood. There the ground was covered with a rich carpet of the tenderest green grass, speckled with daisies and buttercups, and broidered with wild roses and lilies-of-the-valley; and the air was sweet with the fragrance of the spring-blossoms, and musical with the joyous notes of the song birds. It was a place fitted for rest and pleasant thought, where the harsh sounds of warlike strife and busy labor could never intrude.

On one side of this meadow, half hidden in a grove of drooping willows, was a fountain, walled in with pure white marble and once very beautiful, but now sadly neglected and falling into decay. Men say that the wise wizard Merlin built this fountain in the days of good King Arthur, hoping that Tristram and the fair Isolde would drink of its waters; for whosoever tasted of them was filled at once with a strange feeling of hate toward the one whom he had loved before, and he loathed the things which formerly had seemed most fair to him. Not far from this spot was another fountain, built, it was said, in the golden times, when the gods walked and talked with men. The pool into which its waters fell was of wonderful depth, and yet so clear that the smallest pebble could be plainly seen at the bottom. Men said that the wood nymphs used often to come here to bathe, and that the naiäds delighted to sit on its banks, and admire their own beauty reflected from below. And some wise wizard of old had given to the waters of this spring qualities as strange as those which distinguished the fountain of Merlin; for whosoever drank of them was forthwith filled with the maddest love and admiration for the first human being whom he chanced thereafter to meet.

To this happy meadow Angelica came, after flying unseen from the tournament at Merlin's Stair; and here she waited the coming of her brother Argalia. All day long she busied herself, plucking the flowers in the meadow, or listening to the melody of the birds, or watching the plashing of the water in the fountains; and she wondered why Argalia so long delayed his coming. Alas! her princely brother would never meet her at trysting-place again. As I have told you, he had fled from the tilting place with the speed of the wind, intending to meet his sister in the wood of Ardennes, and with her to go back without delay to their old home in Cathay. But the midday sun shone hot and fierce upon his head, and, thinking that no one would be able to overtake him, he stopped in the shadow of a spreading oak to rest. The shade was so cool and tempting, and the twitter of the song birds was so pleasing, and the bees hummed so drowsily among the leaves, that he was persuaded to dismount. He tethered his steed to an overhanging bough: he took off his helmet, and loosened his war coat, and, stretching himself carelessly upon the grass, was soon fast asleep.

While Argalia thus slept in the shade of the oak, Reinold of Montalban, mounted on the fleet-footed Bayard, passed by. And, although he saw the knight of Cathay slumbering soundly, he cared not to waken him, but hastened onward, intent on catching one more glimpse of the charming Angelica. Soon afterward the fierce Ferrau, fuming with fury, and full of foul thoughts, rode up. He spied the sleeping prince under the tree: his eyes gleamed with a wicked light, and his face grew dark as any thunder cloud. No true knight would have harmed a sleeping foe: he would have awakened him, and given him time to arm himself. But the Pagan cared naught for knightly honor. Without dismounting from his steed, he raised his gleaming sword above the uncovered head of Argalia; and, when the weapon fell, the gallant Prince of Cathay slept the sleep that knows not waking. Ferrau returned his blade to its scabbard, and was about to ride on again, when he saw the helmet of Argalia lying upon the grass where that hapless knight had thrown it. It was a casque of great beauty and rare workmanship, bound round with brass, and inlaid with gold and many a rich gem stone. The Moor turned it over, and lifted it on the point of his lance. The jewels gleamed in the sunlight, and shone with a beauty which was very tempting to him. Save the helmet of Roland, which he coveted above every thing else in the world, Ferrau had never seen aught that pleased him so well. He unlaced his own black-painted casque, and tried the jewelled helmet on his head. It was a perfect fit, and he did not remove it. He threw the other, with the raven plume still waving from its crest, upon the ground by the side of the murdered prince; and then, setting spurs to his steed, he galloped hastily onward toward the wood of Ardennes.

Very soon afterward Roland, having followed as fast as Brigliadoro would carry him, came up, and saw the ill-fated

Argalia stretched upon the grass, and the well-known helmet and raven plume of Ferrau lying by his side.

"Ah, me!" said he. "What felony is this? This deed was never done in fair fight. Beastly treachery has done it. And thou, gallant Prince of Cathay, even though thou wert a Pagan, thou shalt not be unavenged."

Without pausing another moment, he gave rein to Brigliadoro, and galloped swiftly in pursuit of the base-hearted Moor.

In the mean while Angelica had become tired of wandering about the meadow in search of flowers. She had grown tired of the birds' songs, and tired of admiring herself in the clear mirror of the pool: so she drank a deep draught of water from the fountain of the nymphs and lay down upon a bed of roses and soft moss to sleep. While she slept, Reinold of Montalban rode into the meadow. He was very weary and very thirsty; and he stopped at the fountain of Merlin, and refreshed himself from its clear waters, little thinking what strange quality they possessed. Then, leading Bayard by the reins, he walked across the meadow toward the other fountain. There he saw the Princess of Cathay fast asleep among the roses. But in his eyes she was no longer beautiful. No toothless crone would have seemed so hideously ugly. He could not bear to look at her. With the deepest disgust he turned away, and remounted his good steed; and then, as fast as the fleet-footed Bayard could carry him, he hastened out of the wood of Ardennes, and back to the court of the king.

Scarcely had the hero of Montalban turned his horse's head, when Angelica awoke. She saw him riding away from her, and she thought him the handsomest knight she had ever seen. She called to him; but the sound of her voice only deepened the disgust which he felt and he rode all the more rapidly away. Soon afterward she was startled by a noise on the other side of the meadow. She heard the sound of angry words, and then the rattle and clash of arms, as if two knights were engaged in deadly combat. Thinking that one of them might be her brother, she ran to that part of the glade whence the sounds came. There she saw Roland and Ferrau, with lances in rest, in the very act of riding against each other. But great was her dismay and horror when she saw above the black armor of Ferrau the jewelled helmet of Argalia. Well did she understand the meaning of it all; well did she know that her brother would never come to meet her in the old trysting-place in the wood of Ardennes. Terrified and in great distress, she put her magic ring again between her lips, and quick as thought she was back in her father's palace in the sunrise land of Cathay.

Roland had overtaken Ferrau upon the very border of the forest meadow; and he had at once charged the Moor with cowardly and unknightly behavior in slaying Argalia while he slept.

"The Prince of Cathay was no Christian," said he; "yet he was a true knight, courteous and bold. Turn now, and defend thyself, or take the punishment due to a thief and a murderer!"

The two warriors rushed toward each other with the fury of tigers and the force of two mountain whirlwinds. The lances of both were shivered in pieces, and so great was the shock, that both reeled in their saddles. Roland was the first to recover himself. Quickly he dismounted from his steed, and drew his good sword Durandal.

"Come on, thou stranger to every knightly virtue!" he

cried,—"come on, and thou shalt taste the edge of Durandal, the terror of all wrong-doers."

But Ferrau had suddenly remembered that his liege lord, Marsilius of Spain, was in need of his help. He turned not back, nor looked around, nor seemed to hear the taunting challenge which Roland hurled after him. He set spurs to his night-black steed, and galloped away to the southward. Roland mounted Brigliadoro, and gave chase. But the Moor's black horse was the swifter of the two, and he and his rider were soon lost to sight. Then the hero changed his course, and slowly and thoughtfully rode back toward Paris.

ADVENTURE XV

ROLAND'S QUEST IN THE FAR EAST

THE spring months passed away, and summer opened, inviting heroes forth to manly action, and pious men to pilgrimages. Yet Roland tarried idly at the king's court. Very irksome, though, was this life of idleness and inaction to our hero; and when he looked upon the beaming blade of Durandal, or visited Brigliadoro stamping impatiently in his stall, he longed more than ever to ride out again on errands of knightly valor. But Charlemagne liked not to part even for a day with his favorite nephew. Week after week, under one pretence and another, he persuaded the hero to stay with him at court. And although there were jousts and tournaments and hunting-parties, and much feasting and merriment, and daily lessons in the school of good Alcuin, yet the days seemed to lag, and every thing to run slow, for the lack of more stirring action. By and by the king noticed the growing unrest which filled the mind of Roland, and he said,—

"Dear nephew, this idleness seems little to become one of thy restless nature. Methinks it wears upon thee."

"It does, indeed," answered Roland. "I should be only too glad were some war to break out, or were I sent on some errand of danger, that I might prove my title to knighthood."

"There is not much likelihood of war," said Charlemagne. "But, if there is any deed of knight-errantry thou wouldst fain undertake, thou shalt have leave to do what thou wilt."

Roland could not conceal his pleasure.

"In the fairy gardens of Falerina, in the Far East," said he, "I am told that the arms of the Trojan Hector await the coming of a hero to claim them. I have already the sword, the flaming Durandal, and I would fain have the complete armor. With your leave I will ride forth at once in quest of that fairyland; and, if I win not for myself the arms of the godlike hero, I will thereafter rest content with what I have."

When it became known that Roland was about to ride out as a knight-errant, and when it was told what the object of his quest was to be, all the folk in the king's court tried to dissuade him from the undertaking. No one knew just where the fairyland of Falerina was, for there were no maps or guide-books in those days; but every one knew that there were great difficulties and dangers to be met and overcome before reaching it. There were mountains and seas to be crossed, and forests to be traversed, and monsters to be slain, and wild beasts to be avoided or killed, and a thousand unknown and impossible adventures to be undertaken, before any one could hope to reach that far-away, cloud-covered land. And, if he should be so fortunate as to get there, there were still the weird enchantments of the witches and the fairies to be guarded against, requiring the knowledge of a sorcerer, as well as the strength and skill of a warrior. But Roland was not afraid of dangers and difficulties; and, the more his friends tried to dissuade him on this account, the more determined he was to undertake the quest. Then certain slanderers about the court, among whom was Ganelon of Mayence, whispered that it was the beautiful face of Angelica, rather than the matchless arms of Hector, which was luring Roland to the Far East;

and they said that his quest would more likely be in the sunrise land of Cathay than in the fairy gardens of Falerina.

To both the warnings of his friends and the evil speaking of his foes, our hero turned a deaf ear. He ordered Brigliadoro to be saddled; he bade his mother and the gentle Alda and his brother knights good-by; and then, clad in complete armor, with Durandal at his side, he rode away. For many days he travelled straight toward the rising sun, veering now and then to the southward. And he left behind him the broad lands of France, and the fair plains of Lombardy, and the heaven-towering Alps, and the great sea. And in every village or country where he came he was welcomed and kindly entertained as a Christian knight without fear and without reproach. And, when he inquired the way to the Fairyland of Falerina, men pointed toward the east, and shook their heads, and warned him to give up the quest ere it was too late. But he, in no wise disheartened, pressed onward, ever the more intent as the dangers and difficulties seemed greater and nearer.

One day he came to a bridge which spanned a silent, slow-flowing river, and whose farther end was hidden in a dark mist. On the bridge a pretty maiden stood to take toll of all that passed that way. Roland asked her the way to Fairyland.

"It is not far from here," said she; "but the way is beset with many perils. If you will drink this cup of water which I have dipped from the river beneath us, your eyesight will become clearer, and you will be able to see through the mists which hang over Fairyland and hide it from mortal sight."

But the maiden spoke of the Fairyland of Forgetfulness, and not of the gardens of Falerina. Roland thoughtlessly took the cup which she offered him, and drank the water which it held. In a moment he forgot all his past life, all his ambitions and his hopes: he forgot even his friends and himself and the quest upon which he was riding. He remembered nothing whatever. He only knew that beside him was a beautiful maiden, and that beyond the bridge whereon he stood was a fair country full of pleasant sights and sounds, of singing birds, and softly murmuring waterfalls, and gay flowers, and luscious fruits. Farther away he saw a tall castle, with towers and turrets pointing to the sky, and broad battlements, and a high wall surrounded by a deep, wide moat. And, having drunk of the waters of Forgetfulness, he no longer had any will of his own. He suffered the maiden to take him by the hand and to lead him into the halls of the castle. And there, with many other knights who had been entrapped in the same way, he passed days and weeks of pleasurable forgetfulness, content with that which each moment brought him, and having no remembrance of the past, and no thought nor care for the future.

No one knows how long Roland would have staid a prisoner in the castle of Forgetfulness, had it not been for Angelica, the Princess of Cathay. I will tell you how it happened that she came to set him free.

When Angelica returned to her own home, after the death of her brother Argalia, she found that a fierce Tartar chief named Agrican had long been waging war with her father, King Galafron, and had forced him to shut himself up in the walled town of Albracca. Week after week the Tartars besieged Albracca, striving in every way to pass the well-defended walls. But Galafron and his folk held out bravely; and, while they kept their foes a safe distance from their gates, they sent fleet messengers to Sacripant, king of Circassia, praying him to lend them some aid. Sacripant, who had long courted the favor of the Princess Angelica, came with an army of ten thousand men, and gave battle to Agrican outside of the city walls. Fierce was the fight, and great was the loss of life on either side. At last the Circassians cut their way through the ranks of the beleaguering Tartars, and reached the gates, which were opened to receive them. But so closely pressed were they, that, ere the heavy barriers could be closed again, a great part of the Tartar horde, with chief Agrican at their head, had crowded through into the city. Then was there terror and great distress in Albracca, and fierce fighting in every street. Of the ten thousand gallant Circassians whom Sacripant had led to the affray, not half a thousand remained alive. And, in the end, King Galafron, with the remnant of those who had escaped the storm-like fury of the Tartars, was obliged to retire into the citadel, a strong-built castle standing high on a rock in the middle of the town. But the castle was not very well supplied with arms, nor was it victualled for a long siege; and the hearts of all sank within them as they thought of the day when starvation would oblige them to open the gates to their fierce, unfeeling foes. It was then that Angelica bethought her of her magic ring.

"Do not yet give up all hope," she said. "Hold the citadel only seven days longer, and I will bring you help. In the castle of Forgetfulness, which lies on the borders of Fairyland, there are many brave knights imprisoned,—the noblest and the most daring in all the world. I will hie me thither, and awaken them, and call them to our aid."

Then she put the magic ring between her lips, and flew

unseen over the heads of the Tartar horde, and over the pleasant valleys and the wooded hills of Cathay, and stopped not until she came to the land of the fairies and the bridge which spans the River of Forgetfulness. The maiden who stood there to take the toll offered her the cup of water; but she dashed it to the ground, and went boldly onward to the castle. She passed through the wide-open gates unchallenged; for, in the dwelling where Forgetfulness reigns, there is no need of warder or of watchman. She entered the great banquet hall, where the guests and prisoners were at meat. There at the table sat Roland, and Reinold of Montalban, and many another fearless knight, eating and drinking and making merry, and not once thinking of their knightly vows, or caring to know each other. She stood in the doorway, her book of enchantments in one hand, and a trumpet in the other. She sang a song sweeter than a siren's voice, and so loud and clear that it was echoed in every nook and chamber of the sleepy old castle. The knights, intent only on the pleasure of the passing moment, scarcely raised their eyes to look at her. They kept on feasting and laughing, and merrily joking, as men are wont to do who never think of the morrow. Then she raised the bugle-trumpet to her lips, and blew a shrill, deep battle call. At the first blast the knights sprang to their feet, and gazed about in mingled astonishment and shame. At the second, all the memories of the past, all their hopes, all their ambition, came into their minds again. With one accord they rushed in hot haste from the banquet-table; they hastened to the armory and to the stables. Never before had there been in that place such a buckling-on of armor, such a mounting of war steeds, such looks and words of brave determination and hope. Old Oblivion, the lord of the castle, who was alike deaf to every call of duty, and blind to every noble impulse, shut himself up in the lowest depths of his dungeon-tower, fearful lest the stirring sounds of Angelica's bugle might arouse in him some slumbering thoughts of the great world outside.

It was not long until the awakened knights were fully equipped with their arms and armor, and mounted on their war steeds, ready to follow Angelica wherever she might lead, or to undertake any adventure she might direct. And they rode back over the now dry River of Forgetfulness, and out of the world of Fairyland and enchantments, into the nobler world of reality, of action, and of worthy effort.

On the third day they reached the country of Cathay, and saw the ruin and the ravages that the fierce Tartars had made. The harvests had been overrun, the vineyards had been trampled down, the villages had been burned, and, where there had been plenty and happiness, now naught was seen but smoking heaps and a desolate desert-waste. The country folk of Cathay had hidden themselves from their pitiless foes in the mountain fastnesses and in the thick woods. But, when they heard that many of the most noted warriors of the Far West were riding to the succor of their king at Albracca, they came out of their hiding-places, and hailed them as the saviors of their country. And every day, as Roland and his comrades drew nearer to the beleaguered city, great numbers of Cathayan warriors who had escaped from the Tartars, and who had been scattered abroad through the land, came and joined their standard. And when, at last, the tall towers of Albracca rose before them, Roland found himself at the head of an army of forty thousand fighting men. Great was the astonishment and dismay of the Tartars when this host burst unexpectedly upon them. Fearful indeed was the din of battle that ensued. The beleaguered Galafron, at the head of a handful of troops, sallied out from the citadel, and joined the army of rescuers. And, always in the thickest of that fearful fight, there Roland was seen, the flash of his angry eye and the glitter of the wondrous sword Durandal carrying terror into the ranks of the panic-stricken Tartars.

In vain did Chief Agrican strive to rally his men. All was fear and confusion; and most of his followers had at the first onset taken to shameful flight, followed by the victorious Cathayans. He saw, that so long as his foes were cheered on by Roland, who was a veritable host within himself, there was little hope for the Tartars, and he formed a cunning plan to draw him away from the field. He placed his lance in rest, and rode forward, as if he would make an attack upon Roland. Then suddenly, as though in fright, he fled. Roland followed in swift pursuit. The Tartar chief, as if he thought his life in deadly peril, galloped away as fast as his steed would carry him, and paused not until he reached an open glade in a forest, far beyond the sound of the battle's strife. Here he dismounted, to drink of the water which gurgled up clear and pure in a marble fountain which King Galafron had built and made sacred to the nymphs of the wood. Scarcely had he wet his lips, when Roland rode up close behind him.

"Ah, sir chief!" cried he, "how is it that the brave flee thus from peril?"

The Tartar leaped quickly into his saddle, and faced his enemy.

"Sir knight, whoever you may be," said he, "I am fain to

look upon you as the bravest warrior I have ever met. I have seen your daring; and, foe though you be, I cannot help admiring you. For your own sake I would rather not touch you, for it would grieve me much to see the death of so brave a man. Ride, therefore, back to your fellows, and goad me not to your destruction."

Roland was pleased with this gallant speech of the Pagan, and he answered mildly, "Pity it is that a warrior so courteous as thou, and withal so brave, should be an unbeliever. Let me urge thee to turn Christian, and to go back in quietness to thy own land. By doing so, thou mayst save both thy body and thy soul."

The Tartar's cheek grew white with rage. "Even though thou wert Roland of France, or any other knight as valiant, thou shouldst rue those taunting words! Draw now thy sword, and save thyself if thou canst!"

Fiercely, then, did the two knights join in fight, and the woods around them rang with the clashing of their good blades. But so well were they matched, and so skilfully was every thrust parried, that neither warrior was able to touch the other, or to gain aught of advantage over him. By and by the sun went down, and the stars came out, and the moon arose; and still the fight seemed no whit nearer its end. The Tartar was the first to ask a truce until morning. They tied their horses to the overhanging branches of an elm, and lay down upon the grass to rest,—Roland near the fountain, and Agrican by the trunk of a pine. The sky was clear and the stars shone bright, and the two knights talked with each other as two friends would talk. Roland pointed to the stars above them, and in earnest tones spoke of the goodness and wisdom and power of Him who had made them. The Tartar was not used to speeches of this kind, nor did he relish the way in which Roland sought to tell him of matters belonging to the Christian faith. At last, growing weary, and filled with disgust, he said,—

"You may be a very brave knight, but you are certainly very ill bred to make me listen to things which are so distasteful to me. If you will not let me sleep, you might at least talk of fair ladies, and daring deeds, and feats of arms,—things much better fitted for the understanding of a knight. But tell me, are you not that Roland of France whose name and deeds are in every one's mouth?"

"I am Roland of France," was the answer.

"And why are you here, so far from home, fighting for one who is no more a Christian than I?" asked Agrican.

"I am fighting for the rights of the Princess Angelica," answered Roland. "Every Christian knight has a liege lady whom he is bound at all times to defend."

The Tartar arose, leaped upon his horse, and drew his sword. Roland, much against his will, again mounted Brigliadoro, and made ready to defend himself. Old stories tell us, that the two warriors fought most furiously until the sun arose, and that Roland's shield was cut in twain, and his armor battered and scarred, and every joint in his body shaken and bruised, so terrible was the onset of the enraged Agrican. And they say that at last, in sheer desperation, and as his only hope, Roland gave his foe a stroke with the sword Durandal, that laid him low at his feet. Quickly then he dismounted from Brigliadoro. Tears of true, heartfelt sorrow, streamed from his eyes as he raised the dying chief tenderly in his arms, and laid him on the marble rim of the fountain.

"Pagan and foe, though thou wert," murmured Roland, "yet thou wert a man, and a most worthy knight!"

And there on the rim of the fountain he left him, clad in his full suit of armor, with his sword in his hand, and his kingly crown on his head.

ADVENTURE XVI

HOW REINOLD FARED TO CATHAY

You are curious to know how it happened that Reinold of Montalban had been entrapped in the castle of Forgetfulness to be liberated just in time to carry aid to the distressed Albraccans? I will tell you.

When the Princess Angelica returned to her father's dwelling, after that fateful day in the wood of Ardennes, she could not forget the noble form and bearing of the hero of Montalban, as he had appeared to her when she last saw him by the fountain of Merlin. So she ordered that Malagis the wizard should be freed from his dungeon beneath the sea, and brought into her presence. The little old man, very glad to see the light of day once more, bowed reverently to the princess, and humbly waited for her to speak.

"Knowest thou the French knight who is called Reinold of Montalban?" asked she.

"I do, most worthy lady," was the wizard's answer. "He is my cousin and my dearest friend."

"Listen, then," said the princess. "If thou wilt promise to bring this noble knight, by fair means or by foul, to Cathay, thou shalt have thy freedom, thy book, and thy wizard's ring."

The old man bowed low, and promised. He would have hazarded his soul for those things. He took his book and his ring, and without a day's delay hastened to return to France.

"Where hast thou been, wise cousin?" asked Reinold, as the dwarf bowed himself into his chamber.

"Only across the sea," was the answer.

"And what didst thou find across the sea?"

"A very great treasure, but it is guarded by a dragon so fierce and wakeful that I dared not go near it. Men say that this treasure has lain there for ages, waiting the coming of a hero brave enough to face the dragon, and strong enough to slay him. Methought that my cousin, Reinold of Montalban, might be that hero."

Very cunning were the wizard's words, and it was not hard for him to persuade Reinold to go in quest of the treasure. A ship with sails all set, impatient for the wind, awaited the knight as he rode down to the seashore. He stepped aboard, leading the horse Bayard behind him. A light breeze sprang up: the sails filled, and the ship sped gayly on its way across the sea. There was no one on board save Reinold and his steed; but the wizard had assured him that the ship needed neither pilot nor oarsman, and that it would sail straight to the shore where the treasure lay under the watchful eyes of the dragon. Two days the little vessel sped over the waves like a thing of life; nor did Reinold once doubt that the end of the voyage would be as the wizard had said. On the third day he came to a long, low shore and a goodly island, which seemed to be one large garden adorned and beautified with every thing that is pleasant to the sight. Close by the shore was a wondrous castle, the fairest that Reinold had ever seen. It was built of marble so white and clear that the walls seemed like great mirrors in which were painted the garden, the sea, and the sky. As the boat touched the shore, three ladies, handsome as fairies, came out of the castle, and greeted the knight.

"Welcome, brave hero!" said they. "Welcome to Joyous

Castle! Welcome in the name of our queen, Angelica of Cathay!"

Reinold heard the name of the fair princess with loathing. He remembered her only as she had seemed to him after he had drunk from the mystic waters of Merlin's fountain. He thought of an old witch, haggard and toothless and crippled, blear-eyed and gray, mumbling her weird spells, and muttering curses. Such to him was Angelica of Cathay. How he hated and loathed her! He turned him about in the ship, and would not look at the fairy palace and the gardens, which were said to be hers. The breeze again filled the sails, and the little bark left the shore, and the marble towers of Joyous Castle were soon out of sight. And a great storm arose on the sea, and the waves ran mountain high, and the ship was at the mercy of the winds. A dark night came on, and Reinold was in fearful peril, but he stood calmly at the helm, and cared not at all for the danger. In the morning the vessel ran upon a wild, rock-bound shore, and was dashed in pieces by the waves; but the hero and his horse escaped with great difficulty by swimming to the land.

The country in which Reinold now found himself was covered with a dark forest, where the owls hooted dismally, and the wolves howled, and the goblins of the wood held high carnival. As he made his way through the dense underbrush, and among the dead and decaying trees, he espied a low-built, gloomy castle standing in the middle of a marsh. He rode up to the gate, and called out loudly to the warder to open and let him in. For a time there was no answer; and, indeed, no sign or sound of life did he hear. Then, suddenly, there was a rattling of chains and a ringing of iron bars; and the gate flew open, and four giants rushed out upon the knight. Before he could draw his sword, or in the least defend himself, he was dragged from his horse, and bound with iron chains, and carried into the courtyard.

"Why this rudeness to a stranger and a knight?" he asked as soon as he was given time to speak.

The giants answered him not a word, but left him lying helpless and alone on the stone floor. After a while, an old woman came in to jeer and laugh at his mishaps.

"A fine morsel thou wilt be for the dragon," said she. "It is not often that he has a real Christian knight for his dinner, and thou wilt indeed make him gentle and gladsome."

Reinold asked the woman what she meant, and was told that on the morrow he was to be given to a terrible dragon who had overrun and ravaged all that country, and who could be appeased only by human blood.

"I fear him not," said the knight, "if they will but unbind me, and give me my good Flamberge."

All night long Reinold lay bound in the cold and desolate courtyard, while Bayard galloped hither and thither in the forest, seeking vainly for his master. Early in the morning the four giants came again; and, after unbinding Reinold, they threw him, with his arms and armor, into a deep-walled pit where the dragon was wont to come for his daily meals. The knight, glad to find that his limbs were free, and that his good sword Flamberge was in his hand, waited fearlessly for the coming of the monster. Not long, however, had he to wait. The horrid beast, his teeth gnashing with rage, and his nostrils flaming with poisonous fumes, rushed into the area, expecting to find, as usual, an easy prey. But Reinold attacked him bravely with his good sword, and made him pause in his hasty onset. Fierce and terrible was the fight that followed. The sharp claws of the beast tore off the knight's armor piece by piece. His head was laid bare; his hauberk and breastplate were broken; the strokes of his sword fell harmless on the iron scales which protected the creature's sides. Hard would it have gone with the knight, had not good fortune favored him. Six feet above his head a beam projected into the pit. He felt his strength failing him; the great jaws of the beast were about to close upon him. He called up all his energy, and with one mighty effort leaped upon the beam. He was safe. The dragon raged and fumed and threatened, but could not reach him. Yet how, after all, would the good knight escape? The walls rose, high and smooth, still many feet above him. There was no way to get out of the pit, save by passing the dread monster below.

While the knight sat half-despairing on the friendly beam, he heard a whirring of wings above him; and a fairy, which he at first mistook for a bird, alighted by his side.

"Most worthy knight," said she, "fortune comes always to the help of the brave. Now here are a ball of wax and a strong net, which you may use as your good sense may direct. But you must never forget that this aid has been sent you by the Princess Angelica of Cathay."

With these words the fairy flew away, and was seen no more. But Reinold wondered whether she were not really the princess herself in disguise. It was easy for him to understand what to do with the presents she had brought. He threw the cake of wax to the raging dragon below. Eagerly the beast seized it between his jaws, and, lo! as Reinold had foreseen, his teeth were glued fast together. Then, as the creature madly sought to remove the wax with his claws, it was easy for the knight to cast the net over him, and draw it tightly about his limbs and body. Helpless now, the great beast rolled upon the ground, an easy victim to Reinold's trenchant blade.

It was no hard matter for Reinold to find his way out of the pit, and into the wood again. There the good horse Bayard waited for him, and greeted his coming with a shrill neigh of pleasure. He looked around for the gloomy castle where he had spent so many miserable hours, but it was nowhere to be seen. He rubbed his eyes, and fancied, that, after all, he might have been only dreaming; for his armor was whole as ever, and his good blade Flamberge was clear and bright, and no whit tarnished with foul dragon's blood. He mounted his steed, and rode slowly and thoughtfully out of the forest. But, just beyond, he came to the River of Forgetfulness and the bridge which spans it; and there, like Roland, he drank of the cup which the maiden offered him, and was led helplessly away to the care-forgetting castle of Old Oblivion.

ADVENTURE XVII

IN THE GARDENS OF FALERINA

HAVING defeated the Tartars before Albracca, and driven them, as they supposed, forever from Cathay, the French knights began to bethink them again of their own country, and of the duties which they owed to their liege lord, King Charlemagne. Reinold, burning with anger and shame because of the deception which had brought him hither, turned away at once, and, deaf to every entreaty of the grateful Cathayans, hastened his journey back to France. But Roland was not yet willing to give up the adventure which he had undertaken; and he resolved to make one further trial to find the gardens of Falerina, and to win the arms of the godlike Hector of Troy. So he bade farewell to Angelica and to her father, King Galafron, and set out on his quest for the land of the fairies; and the grateful people of Albracca showered blessings upon his head as he passed out of their gates. And many of the noblest lords and ladies of the realm rode with him to the utmost bounds of their kingdom, where they parted from him with many heartfelt thanks and many a tearful godspeed.

"He is a Christian," said they as they rode back to their homes, "and yet he is the noblest of men."

And Roland rode alone through many strange lands inhabited by strange Pagan people, who looked upon him with wonderment as he passed. And so noble was his countenance, so proud was his form, and so brilliant was the armor in which he was clad, that the ignorant folk often mistook him for a god; but he pitied their lack of knowledge and their error, and told them what little he knew of Christ and of the holy saints. And when he asked them to show him the way to Fairyland, they could only shake their heads, and point toward the setting sun.

One day, after having crossed a barren hill country, where not any thing was to be seen save huge bowlders and lava-beds and yawning chasms, he came into a wood so dark and dank and lonesome, that he felt that this indeed must be the borderland between the world of reality and the world of the fairies. Owls hooted in the dead treetops; gray wolves howled in the thickets; bats and vampires flew through the air; hideous creatures skulked among the trees. Had such a thing as fear known lodgement in Roland's breast, he would have turned back, and given up forever his quest for Fairyland. But by and by the wood became less dense, the trees and grass grew as in a park, and the sun, which had been hidden behind a cloud, now shone brightly through the leaves. Birds flitted and sang among the branches; and the lonesomeness and horrors of the deeper forest gave place to light and hope.

As Roland rode leisurely along through this wood, he was suddenly aroused by hearing cries, as of some one in distress. Looking around, he saw that they were uttered by a fair lady, bound hand and foot to a tree, and guarded by an armed knight.

"How, now!" cried Roland, riding nearer. "What is the meaning of this? How dare you, who seem to be a knight, thus maltreat the helpless and the beautiful?"

The knight explained that the lady whom he held as his prisoner was dishonest, untruthful, and treacherous to her best friends, and that she was only being punished for her misdemeanors as she deserved.

"Her very name is Deceit," he said; "and, if she were once liberated, there would be no end to the mischief she would cause."

But the lady, tears streaming from her eyes, denied these charges, and begged Roland to set her free. And our hero, whose ears were always open to the pleadings of those in distress, without further parley placed his lance in rest, and challenged the knight to a trial of arms.

"If after what I have told you," said the knight, "you wish to befriend such a creature as she, I have not a word further to say." And, with a motion of disgust, he turned, and rode quickly away.

Roland very gallantly released the lady from the cords which bound her; and, as it was still a long way out of the wood, he helped her to a seat behind him, and together the two rode onward toward the west. The lady told him that they were now entering the enchanted regions of Fairyland, and that he must be very cautious in whatever he undertook to do. As she was talking they reached the edge of the wood, where they met another young lady, a beautiful damsel, riding on a white palfrey gayly attired in trappings of crimson velvet, with silver bells hanging from the reins.

"Ah, sir knight!" said she, courtesying very humbly, "it is indeed lucky that I met you on this spot. Had you gone ten yards farther, you would have been in plain sight of the gardens of Falerina, and you would have been slain by the watchful dragon who sits before the gate. If you would succeed in your venture, listen to me. Stay where you are until morning: stir not a foot farther, or you will be lost. Just at sunrise every day, the gates are thrown wide open for a time;

and then, and only then, if you are wise, you can enter the fairy gardens. But beware of the dragon!"

Then she gave him a little book in which was a map of the enchanted garden and a picture of Falerina's palace, and directions how to reach it, and how to enter it. And she told Roland that the fairy queen had been a long time shut up in one of the chambers of her palace, trying to forge a magic sword that should be proof against all kinds of witchery, and sharp enough to slay even those whose lives were protected by the unseen powers.

"For," said the damsel, "she has read in the book of Fate that a hero will come out of the West, and that he will trample down her fair garden, and take from her all her witch power."

"And is the sword yet finished?" asked Roland.

"I think it is," answered the damsel. "And, if you can once seize upon it, you will be safe from all the magic snares that are set for you. Yet many men have tried to enter these wonderful gardens, and every one has failed."

While they were yet talking, the sun had gone down; and Roland, thinking it better to take the advice of the damsel, and not attempt to go farther that night, dismounted from Brigliadoro, and lay down under the friendly shelter of a cedar tree to rest. He had no sooner fallen asleep than the woman whom he had rescued in the forest, and who was really as false-hearted and base as the strange knight had represented her to be, mounted his war steed, and rode away, carrying the sword Durandal with her.

When Roland awoke in the morning, and saw how he had been deceived and robbed, he was both angered and disheartened. He felt that the dangerous adventure which he had undertaken might, after all, prove to be a failure. Yet his knightly vows would not allow him to give up a quest which he had once begun, and he resolved to go forward as he had at first intended. The sky began to redden in the east: the sun would soon rise, and the gates of the garden would be thrown open. If he would enter those enchanted grounds, if he would prove himself worthy to wear the armor of the godlike Hector, he must be ready to act without delay. He tore off the stout branch of an elm to serve him instead of a sword, and went boldly onward in the way which the damsel on the palfrey had pointed out. A very few steps brought him to the top of the hill whence he could look down into the valley beyond. There a wonderful sight met his view. Not half a league away was the entrance to the long-sought-for gardens, closed now by strong iron gates hanging between columns of brass. In front of the gates the sleepless dragon paced to and fro, while high above them soared a mountain eagle. The wall was built of white marble, and was very high; but Roland, from his place on the hill, could see the trees and the fountains and the silvery lake beyond, and farther away he could discern the glass towers and turrets of Falerina's castle, shining like silver in the early morning light.

Roland held the green elm branch before him so as to hide himself from the ever-watchful eyes of the dragon, and went slowly forward toward the gates. The sun, now beginning to rise, gilded the treetops and the far-off mountain crags and the tall turrets of the fairy castle, with a golden light. The watchman on the tower blew a long, silvery call upon his bugle-horn, which was echoed and re-echoed from hill to valley, and from river to lake, until it was heard all over that Fairyland.

"Awake, awake!" he cried. "The daystar comes; the king of life blesses us again. Open wide the gates and let floods of light pour in upon us!"

The great iron gates swung round on their hinges: a passage-way was opened, wide enough for a score of knights to ride through abreast; and from the fairy gardens within there came the sound of music sweeter than any Roland had ever before heard. But he had no time to listen to these enchanting sounds; for he knew that the gates would soon close, and that the present golden opportunity would never return. The dragon stood now directly in the gateway, its eyes flashing fire, its nostrils smoking with sulphur fumes, its hooked claws digging into the soft earth, its clammy wings beating the air. To a man of less heroic mettle than Roland the sight of the beast would have caused unspeakable terror. But Roland faltered not. He strode straight onward, holding his shield before his face, that he might not breathe the poisonous breath of the monster. In his right hand he held the gnarly elm branch, which he had hastily stripped of its green leaves. Very near he drew to the hideous beast; he felt its hot breath; its fangs were almost upon him. He leaped forward. With a quick movement he thrust the branching boughs between the gaping jaws of the creature with such force that they stuck fast. The dragon stopped. Its mouth was propped wide open by the ugly elm branch. In vain it clutched at it with its crooked claws, and sought to free itself. Roland paused not a moment. He leaped clear over the back of the monster. Swiftly he ran toward the gates. He reached them, and passed through, just as they creaked on their hinges and closed with a mighty crash behind him. His foe, the dragon, had gotten free from the elm branch, but too late to do him any harm; for the massive gates were between them.

Roland looked around him. On his right was a fair fountain, pouring water by a hundred silver jets into a little lake whose surface was dotted with water-lilies, among which swam dozens of noble white swans. Out of the lake a little river flowed, meandering through meadows bright with roses and violets, and flowers of every name and hue. In the middle of the stream stood a marble image,—an image of a river nymph, such as in the golden days haunted fountain and waterfall and every flowing stream. Above the brows of the image an inscription was written in Greek: "SEEKEST THOU THE ENCHANTED PALACE? FOLLOW THE RIVER." The knight, never doubting, did as the inscription directed. The stream flowed through scenes more delightful than any he had ever dreamed of. So sweet was the music with which the air was filled, so pleasant were the perfumes, so beautiful were the birds, the flowers, the waterfalls, the grottos, and the garden-walks, that, if Roland had not borne well in mind his knightly vows, he would have been sorely tempted to live amid these joys forever.

After a long walk, which, however, seemed to him only too short, he reached the fairy palace of Falerina. It was a gorgeous and most beautiful structure, built within and without of glass and precious stones, and adorned with every thing that is pleasing to the senses. The doors were wide open, and bevies of fairies were passing in and out, singing gayly, and making the palace resound with the music of their sweet voices. They cast inquiring glances at the strange knight as they passed; but, as they had never known an enemy in Fairyland, they thought him only some stranger whom the queen had invited to her court. Seeing that every one moved freely from one chamber to another in that vast palace, without hinderance and without ceremony, Roland walked boldly in. For some time he strolled carelessly about, listening to the music, and watching the nimble dancers in the great halls, or admiring the many wonderful things with which the palace was stored. At last, in a lower chamber which opened into the garden, he found Falerina, the fairy queen. She was sitting alone, as was her wont in the earlier hours of the day, while her attendants amused themselves in the garden. Before her, leaning against the wall, was the magic sword, the blade which had cost her so many weeks of anxious labor. She had but lately finished it and tested it, and now she was quietly admiring her own good looks as they were reflected from its bright silvery sides. And very beautiful indeed was she,—so beautiful, that Roland paused in reverent admiration. She was dressed in rich white robes from every fold of which rare jewels gleamed; and upon her head was a golden crown, flashing with diamonds. She seemed something more divine than a mere fairy, and akin to the Peris of whom Roland had heard the Saracens speak.

The hero paused but a moment. Before the fairy could hinder, or call for help, he seized the magic sword, and raised it threateningly above her head.

"Yield, and I will spare thee!" he cried.

The queen, never having known such thing as fear, sat still, and said not a word.

"Show me the Trojan Hector's arms," said he, "and thou shalt live."

"Surely," then answered the queen, "thou art a brave warrior thus to threaten me in my own dwelling. Methinks thou art Knight Roland from the West."

"Roland is my name," said he. "And I have come in quest of Hector's arms. Tell me where I shall find them."

"I shall tell thee nothing," answered the fairy, folding her arms.

When Roland found that neither threats nor prayers would persuade her to tell him the secret, he carried her gently into the garden, and, with cords which Malagis the wizard had given him, he bound her, hand and foot, to a beech tree, so that no fairy could ever unbind her. Then he went out of the palace to follow his quest as best he might, well knowing now that no witchery of the fairy queen could harm him. As he was again following the course of the winding river through meadows and groves and many a scene of delight, he bethought him of the book which the damsel on the white palfrey had given him. He opened it, and looked at the map. There was nothing said about the place where Hector's arms were hidden. But he saw that on the south there was a gate which was always open. Between the gate and the palace was a large lake; and in the lake, the book said, there was a siren, whose song charmed all passers-by, and had caused the death of many a brave knight.

As he was now not very far from the lake, Roland resolved that he would rid himself of another danger by seeking the siren, and silencing her voice. As he strolled across the meadows, he gathered great numbers of daisies and violets, bluebells and buttercups, and filled his helmet and his ears with them. Then he stopped, and listened if he could hear the birds sing. He could see their mouths open, their throats swell, and their plumage ruffle; but he could not hear the slightest sound.

He felt now that he was proof against the enchanting song of the siren, for music never lured a deaf man to his destruction. He went boldly forward to the lake, and wandered leisurely along the shore, admiring its mirror-like surface and the clearness and great depth of the water. Suddenly, near the centre of the pool a ripple appeared; and then a strange creature, somewhat like a bird, and somewhat like a fish, arose above the surface, and began to sing. The siren was not at all beautiful; but her song was so sweet, that all the birds were silenced, and came flying down in great flocks by the shore to listen. The cattle and the wood-beasts hastened in troops and crowds to the waterside, where they stood fixed and entranced by the soft, melodious strains. The leaves of the trees quivered in sympathy with the sounds, and even the rocks seemed to hearken and to smile. Roland alone was unmoved, because he heard nothing. Yet as the siren still sat in the water, and kept on singing, he made a pretence of yielding to the charms of her bewitching song. He fell down among the flowers by the lakeside, and closed his eyes as if in a trance. The siren ended her song. The birds and the beasts went slowly back to their places, and all was quiet about the lake. Roland lay very still. The siren swam close to the shore, thinking to seize him, as she had seized many another brave knight, and drag him down into her dismal den at the bottom of the lake; but Roland arose suddenly, and grasped her long neck. Fearful were the struggles of the creature, and loud were the songs that she sung; for she hoped even yet to bewitch the knight with the strange power of music. But the hero raised the magic sword of Falerina above her, and with one stroke severed her hideous head.

IN THE GARDENS OF FALERINA

Freed now from this last source of danger, Roland started out again in search of the arms of Hector. He followed every garden walk to its end; he sought in every grove and every grotto: yet he could nowhere find the wished-for prize. He asked the fairies whom he sometimes met; but they seemed downhearted and sad, and shook their heads, saying that they had never heard of Hector, nor of his arms. But an old man, who had lived in Fairyland for a great many years, told him that the object of his search had long ago been carried into another garden, and that he could not hope to find it without undergoing many hardships and meeting many dangers of which he now knew nothing.

Toward evening Roland found his way back again to the enchanted palace of the queen, but all was changed. The fairies whom he had seen there in the earlier part of the day had fled, leaving the splendid mansion silent and desolate. The music had ceased; shadows had taken the place of sunshine; the flowers had closed their petals; the birds had flown away. As the knight walked across the deserted courtyard, the only sound that he heard was the echo of his own footsteps on the hard pavement. The silence was more dreadful to him than any danger that had ever threatened him. The hapless fairy queen was still bound fast to the beech tree where he had left her, but she was no longer happy and defiant. Bitterly she wept, and earnestly did she beg him to set her free. He asked her again where the arms of the Trojan hero were hidden.

"By my troth," said she, "I know not. They were long ago given into the keeping of my sister, Morgan the Fay. If you would win them, you must make your way to her castle, and prove by your prowess that you are worthy of the prize. Then, when Fortune is ready to award her gifts, be sure that you let not the golden opportunity slip by unimproved."

The hero loosed the fairy queen from the magic cords which bound her. He called around her the frightened attendants, and assured them that he had no wish to harm either them or their queen. Then he bade the fair Falerina good-by, and went forth from her gardens in search of the far-famed dwelling of Morgan the Fay.

ADVENTURE XVIII

MORGAN THE FAY

THE castle of Morgan the Fay stood in a pleasant valley between two forest-crowned mountains. It was built of the finest white marble, as pure as alabaster, and as clear as ice. The high walls which hemmed it in on every side were of granite; and the deep moat was full of water and spanned by a single bridge. A mighty giant, clad in steel armor, and wielding a huge club, kept the bridge, and allowed no one to pass over it unchallenged. And this giant had never yet been foiled or beaten in battle; for, whatever might be the strength or the prowess of his foe, his own strength was greater. Hence no living knight had ever entered this fairy castle save as the prisoner of its grim warder.

Now, when Roland, eagerly pursuing his quest, approached this bridge, the giant, as was his wont, challenged him to a combat. The knight was nowise loath to measure arms with a churl whose only virtue was his strength. He drew the sword which Queen Falerina with such infinite pains had wrought, and met the giant on his own ground. The boasted armor of the bridge warder was no proof against the biting strokes of the magic blade. He would have been killed upon the spot, had he not saved himself by a cunning stratagem. Watching his chances, he seized the knight in his arms, and leaped with him into the moat. He could live in water as well as in air, and he hoped by this means to drown the foe whom he could not overcome by force of arms. But so well did Roland still ply his sword, although half choked with the cold water, that the giant was glad to let go his hold. The knight rose to the surface, and climbed upon the bridge. The gates were wide open, and he walked boldly through.

He found himself, to his astonishment, in a broad field, where the ground was covered with diamonds and pearls, rubies and emeralds, and every other sort of gem-stone, as thickly as the spring meadows are covered with sprouting grass. But he stopped not to gather or to admire. He hastened across the field, and came into a garden which was far more beautiful than that which belonged to Falerina. Every thing tempted him to stop, and to pursue no farther his uncertain quest. The shady walks, the flowery borders, the cool bowers, the plashing waterfalls, the rippling stream, the singing birds, the sunshine, and the breeze,—all seemed to say, "Stay! here is happiness enough." But the hero allowed none of these things to tempt him. He kept always in mind that part of his knightly vows which forbade him to give up any quest that he had once undertaken until he had followed it out to the end.

In the middle of the garden there was a beautiful fountain, and near it was a bower of surpassing loveliness. Around the bower a score of fairies danced, keeping time with the most bewitching strains of music. As Roland came near to this spot, the timid creatures ceased their merriment, and fled in great affright. He peeped into the bower, and beheld a being more beautiful than his dreams had ever pictured. It was Morgan the Fay, fast asleep on a bed of roses. Very small was she,—as, indeed, were all the folk in this garden,—and so wondrously fair that the knight stood long still, as if entranced. And in fact it was only by bearing always in mind his duty as a knight, that he resisted the temptation to give up all his ambitious hopes, and, forgetting the busy world of men, to swear fealty to the fairy queen. Long he might have stood thus gazing, and wavering between duty and inclination, had he not heard a voice cry out, "Seize the beauty by the forelock while yet the golden moment lasts!"

Then Roland noticed for the first time that the back part of the fay's head was quite bare and smooth, while above her forehead there was a rich growth of long golden hair. It was thus that men in the earlier days pictured the head of old Father Time. The knight was surprised at hearing the voice, and he thought not once of obeying its strange command. He looked up. A wondrous sight met his eyes. Halfway between earth and sky, hanging in mid-air, he saw, as he thought, a great and busy city. There he beheld tall towers and crystal palaces, and churches with their spires pointing heavenward, and bustling market-places, and long lines of streets crowded with hurrying men and women, and cool, shaded avenues where knights and ladies walked, and all that makes up the glory, the beauty, and the misery of a well-peopled burgh. For a time he forgot where he was, and all about the errand which had taken him there; and he imagined himself to be no longer a knight-errant courting danger, and bound on deeds of love and daring, but a busy merchant in that air-built city, intent upon showing his wares, and eagerly counting his gains. While he still gazed, the vision slowly faded away. Churches and palaces and market-places and busy streets melted into thin airy clouds, and then were seen no more. Then Roland, as if awakened from a trance, remembered himself again, and the quest upon which he was bound. He looked into the bower where Morgan the Fay had been sleeping, but she was not there. She had arisen, and with the lightness of a leaf driven about by the fickle autumn wind she was dancing before the fountain. And as she danced, she sang,—

"Seek'st thou gifts from Morgan le Fay?
Seize her forelock whilst thou may,
Let not dreams thy purpose stay:
She'll not come another day.
Fortune's a fickle fairy.

Once, and only once, men say,
To every one she shows the way
To gain the good for which we pray.
While the sun shines, make the hay.
Fortune's a fickle fairy."

Roland hesitated. Had he been attacked by giants, or set upon by fierce beasts, or had the doughtiest hero in all the world challenged him to a duel, or had he been called upon to perform any deed of strength or daring, he would not have paused to think, or to calculate his chances. But to seize Morgan the Fay, this fairy Fortune, while she danced in whirling mazes before him,—he wondered how it could be done. While yet he waited and doubted, the fay suddenly bounded away, and fled from him with the fleetness of a deer hunted by hounds. He followed as fast as his feet would carry him, resolved now that nothing should hinder him from attaining that fortune whose favors are but seldom withheld from the brave. But the fairy, although at times almost within his grasp, was not easily caught. She led him a long chase through gardens and fields, and among thickets of underbrush and briers, and over many a barren, stony waste; and at last she flew over the top of a snow-crowned mountain, and the disappointed knight never saw her again. Then a storm of rain and hail burst from the clouds above; and the lightnings flashed, and the thunder rolled, and all the demons of the air seemed to be abroad. And a gaunt and pale-faced witch came out of a cavern on the mountain-side with a scourge of leather thongs in her hand, and she drove the hero down the slope, and back again into the valley, lashing him at every step furiously and without pity.

"Who are you?" asked he, meekly receiving his punishment. "Who are you who dare thus to scourge a peer of France?"

"My name is Repentance," answered the hag. "It is my duty to punish every one, who through hesitation or neglect fails to seize the fairy fortune at that one golden moment which is allotted him. Go thou, now, back to France. Thy quest is vain. The prize which thou sought has been won by another."

When Roland came down again into the valley, he looked to see the snow-white castle of Morgan the Fay, and he thought to find himself still in the gardens of Fairyland. But it was not so. Castles and towers, rivers and fountains, flowers and birds, dragons and giants, and all that had helped to make up those wondrous scenes, had vanished like the mirage with which he had been so enraptured. Splendid dreams had given place to sober reality. The hero saw before him the desert plains and the rocky mountains of Persia; and a voice whispered to him that fame and fortune were to be attained, not through the pursuit of fairy phantoms and vain chimeras, but by honest, worthy deeds, and noble efforts for the bettering of humanity. In his hasty pursuit of the fairy he had lost the magic sword that he had taken from Falerina. He was now without arms, and he had no horse. He was a stranger, alone in a strange land; and many a weary league and many unknown dangers lay between him and sweet France.

As he stood at the foot of the mountain, pondering upon this strange ending of his visionary quest, an old man drew near, riding upon a mule and leading a war-steed fully caparisoned, with saddle and bridle and trappings of velvet and gold. Across the saddle bows lay a sword, sheathed in its scabbard, but whose hilt fairly shone with its wealth of priceless gems. The horse was his own lost Brigliadoro, and the sword was Durandal.

"Sir knight," said the old man very courteously, "allow me to be your squire. I bring you your horse and sword. Mount, I pray you, and let us hasten back to France and to Charlemagne, who is in need of your help."

"But the arms of Hector are not yet mine," answered Roland; "and I doubt if I may honorably return without them."

"You can scarcely do otherwise," answered the squire; "for while you waited and dreamed, and hesitated to seize the fairy by the forelock, another knight, a Tartar prince, went boldly in, and seized the prize and bore it away. And he is even now well on his way toward France; for he has vowed that he will win from you the sword Durandal, and thus make all of Hector's matchless arms his own."

Then Roland mounted Brigliadoro, and, followed by the good squire, rode bravely back toward France. But he coveted no longer the arms of Trojan Hector, and felt only happy in the possession of his own.

ADVENTURE XIX

HOW OGIER REFUSED A KINGDOM

Long had been Roland's fruitless quest for the arms of Trojan Hector; and many were his adventures, as, wiser but no richer, he fared homeward again. Time would fail me to tell of the strange lands that he traversed, of the seas that he crossed, of the monsters that he slew, and of his many knightly feats of arms. And, when it was known that he had come back to France without the prize for which he had been seeking, many unkind words were whispered among the peers.

"A true knight," said old Ganelon, "never gives up an undertaking once begun. Any but a coward would rather die than say, 'I have failed.'"

Others whispered, that it was not the arms of Hector at all, that Roland had been in quest of, but rather the love of Angelica, the Princess of Cathay.

"And now, since she has slighted him, and cast him off," said some, "he comes back again to lord it over his betters, as of yore. Yet it is said that he did many valiant deeds in the Far East."

"So much valor," said others, "would have been better spent in the service of the king."

Charlemagne had been beset with enemies on every side. The Moors of Spain had broken over the mountain wall of the Pyrenees, and had again overrun Gascony, and carried fire and sword into the fairest portions of Southern France. The Saxons, ever restless and ill at ease, had again taken up arms against the empire. The wild Hungarians had been making inroads into the eastern provinces; and the Lombards were ready at any time to rise in rebellion. Very gladly, therefore, did the king welcome his valiant nephew back to France, for he needed the help of his strong arm.

One day early in spring there came to Charlemagne's court a number of Danish knights bearing a message from their king, the false-hearted Godfrey of Denmark. They brought from Godfrey a great store of rich presents for Charlemagne, and treasure more than enough to make amends for the tribute which had so long been neglected and left unpaid. And the Danish king prayed Charlemagne that he would pardon his former misconduct, and receive him once more into humble and faithful vassalage; for pirates and strange sea-kings from the Far North had come down upon the coast of Denmark, and were robbing and burning, and carrying terror into the very heart of the country, and Godfrey hoped that Charlemagne would aid him in driving out the invaders. Charlemagne, although not always quick to forgive, was quite ready at this trying time to make friends with the Dane. And he kindly entertained the messengers, and sent them back on the morrow, with assurances that he would pardon the offences of King Godfrey, and send him the wished-for aid. Then he called Ogier the Dane into his presence.

"Ogier," said he, "your father, the king of Denmark, is sorely pressed by his enemies, and needs our help. No one knows better than yourself how he has neglected and cast you off among strangers. And yet it is our wish that you lead a company of warriors to his aid."

"It is well," answered Ogier. "Naught save death can ever excuse a son from helping his father."

HOW OGIER REFUSED A KINGDOM

A thousand knights, the bravest in all France, at once enlisted under Ogier's banner; and without a day's delay they began their march toward Denmark. With Ogier, and next to him in command, was Roland; and the very presence of the two heroes inspired the whole of the little army with high-hearted enthusiasm and courage. Their march was rapid, and not long were they in reaching the land of the Danes. But the foe whom they sought had fled; for, when the rude sea-kings heard of the coming of the steel-clad warriors of the South, they hastily embarked in their ships again, and sailed across the sea to other shores. They lived by pillage and robbery, and they were fearful of risking a battle with an enemy so renowned and powerful.

Ogier with his little army now rode on toward his father's castle. But, as they drew near, they saw the towers draped in black, and heard the bells tolling a solemn knell. A black banner, on which the arms of King Godfrey were rudely painted, floated above the gate. And a company of knights, all clad in mourning, came out to meet and welcome the heroes.

"What mean all these signs of sorrow?" asked Ogier. "We have come to you expecting to be greeted with cheers and songs and glad thanksgiving, and we find naught but weeping and doleful signs of death. Has any thing happened amiss to my father the king?"

"Alas!" said the sorrowing knights, "he is dead."

Then Ogier, unable to answer by reason of his great grief, covered up his face, and wept. And Roland and the Danish knights led him into the castle and into the chapel, where the body of King Godfrey lay. The hero knelt beside his father's bier, and bathed the face of the dead with his tears. Touching indeed was it to behold this warrior melted with sorrow in the presence of death. For although he had been maltreated and despised, and cast out among strangers, he had never forgotten that a son's first duty is to honor his father. Long he knelt on the floor of the little chapel, while the monks who watched beside the corpse chanted their prayers, and told their beads; and the tapers on the altar burned low; and the daylight gave place to darkness. Then he arose, and was about to leave the room, when the priest who had been his father's confessor touched him on the shoulder.

"Ogier," said he, "allow me to be the first to greet you as king of Denmark. The last words of your father were, 'Let Ogier be king.' "

Ogier stood for a moment in silent thought. He hesitated as to what his duty might be. Ought he, by taking that which was clearly his own, to deprive his younger brother of the crown which he had been taught to expect? Suddenly a heavenly light burst upon him and filled the room with its soft radiance; and a voice like that of an angel said,—

"Ogier, take not this crown. Leave it to Guyon thy young brother. It is enough for thee to bear the title of 'The Dane.' Fame waits for thee elsewhere, and greater kingdoms than that of Denmark may be thine."

It was the voice of Morgan the Fay, the fairy guardian of his life. But Ogier thought that it was an angel from heaven who had spoken; and he humbly crossed himself, and bowed in submission to the command. He sought without delay the step-mother who had so cruelly wronged him.

"Mother," said he, "all that which thou hast so long desired has come to pass."

And he embraced his young brother Guyon, and hailed him king. And he said, "I am a peer of France, a knight of the household of Charlemagne. I seek no higher honors."

And heralds were sent into every city and burgh proclaiming Guyon as the lawful king of all Denmark. And Guyon solemnly promised to hold his kingdom in fief and vassalage from Charlemagne.

ADVENTURE XX

HOW ROLAND SLEW A SEA MONSTER

When, at length, the days of mourning for Duke Godfrey were passed, Ogier and the knights who were with him turned their faces southward, and rode back again to France. But Roland parted from their company, and went another way, for Charlemagne had intrusted him with a message to Oberto, the king of Ireland; and to that country he directed his course. At the nearest port on the coast a little ship awaited him; and in this he embarked, and sailed across the western sea.

For many days the vessel ploughed the waters, and the sky was clear, and the wind was fair, and the voyage was a happy one. And those on board beguiled the hours with pleasant talk and with many wonderful tales of the sea. The captain was a browned and weather-beaten Norseman, who had sailed the waters for more than twoscore years, and who knew every strait and shallow and every point of land, from Gothland to the Pillars of Hercules. And he delighted to tell of the many scenes of danger through which he had passed, and of the feats of daring which he had seen on land and sea, and of the strange beings which people the deep. One day he talked about the mermaids and the men of the sea; and he told of the great Midgard snake whom the Northmen believe to lie hidden in the deepest ocean; and he related the story of Old Ægir the Ocean King, and of his nine daughters, the white-veiled Waves. And when he had finished, Roland said that what he had told reminded him of certain stories which he had heard in the South, —stories of the old Pagan times, when the gods were thought to live on earth, and to take some sort of interest in the doings of men. And he spoke of Poseidon, whom the Greeks called the ruler of the sea; and of old Nereus and his fifty daughters, the silver-footed sea nymphs. And this led him to relate the beautiful fable of Andromeda, and her rescue by Perseus from the sea monster whom Poseidon had sent to devour her.

"But the gods are all dead now," said he, "and neither Ægir nor Poseidon rules the sea."

Then an old Irish harper who happened to be on shipboard spoke, and said, "Sir knight, if all reports be true, some of the sea deities still live, and are known in regions where the Christian religion has not yet been preached. Indeed, I have heard that in the Island of Ebuda, a day's sail west of Ireland, old Proteus, the servant of Poseidon, is even now imitating the deeds of his ancient master."

Then the company insisted that the harper should tell them all that he knew about this matter, and he did as they desired him.

"In the golden age," said he, "it was the task of Proteus to keep the seals and sea calves for his master Poseidon, to lead them into the pleasantest waters and to the freshest pastures, and to see that no one wilfully harmed them. When the times changed, and his old master was dethroned and no longer needed his services, he still kept on herding and caring for the seals and sea calves; for the power of habit was so strong that he could not tear himself away from his old haunts, nor change his occupation. And as he was usually very peaceable, and thought to be quite harmless, very little attention was paid to him; and he was allowed to live on, and ply his vocation, long after all the other sea deities were deposed and forgotten. One day, as he was driving about in his swan chariot, and looking after his herds, he came to this Island of Ebuda of which I have just spoken. It chanced, that, as he drove close by the shore, the golden-haired daughter of the King of Ebuda stood on the beach. She was more passing fair than ever were the sea nymphs of old, or the mermaids, or the white-veiled daughters of Ægir. And the heart of the ancient Proteus was moved with love for the maiden, and he forthwith besought the king that he would give her to him in marriage. But the father of the maiden scorned his suit. Should he, the king of Ebuda, wed his only daughter to the last of a dying race,—to the last and the least worthy of the sea gods? Let him go back to his seals and sea-calves, and never again think of making himself the peer of human beings.

"Then the love of old Proteus was changed to hate, and he vowed that he would not rest nor slumber until he had avenged the slight that had thus been put upon him. And he sent great troops of sea-calves to ravage the coasts of Ebuda; and after them he caused a huge and shapeless monster, called an orc, to come, and overrun the whole island. Never was there greater distress and terror. The frightened people fled from their farms and villages, and sought safety in the walled towns; and, between famine and the ravages of the sea monsters, it seemed as if the entire nation would be destroyed. Now, it appears that there was in Ebuda some kind of an oracle, in whose decisions the people placed great trust. And the king prayed the oracle that he might know how to appease the anger of old Proteus, and turn his fearful wrath away. And the oracle answered, and said that this could be done only by offering a daily sacrifice to Proteus to be devoured by the monster orc.

" 'What shall that sacrifice be?' asked the king.

" 'The fairest maiden that can be found either in Ebuda or in the neighboring isles,' was the answer.

" 'And how long shall this fearful payment of tribute continue?' asked the king.

"And the oracle answered, 'Until a hero shall come to Ebuda's shores brave enough and strong enough to slay the orc. Then, and not till then, will Proteus withdraw the curse which he has laid upon you, and leave your people in peace.'

"And it was done as the oracle had bidden. Each day a damsel, the fairest that could be found, was offered to the orc; and the creature ceased his ravages, and allowed the people to return to their homes and farms. And each day, as a new victim was led to the horrible sacrifice, the people prayed for the coming of the hero who should save their loved ones from this dreadful doom. But he came not.

"And it is said that still in the Island of Ebuda this cruel usage is continued, and that the Pagan folk who live in that land no longer look upon this sacrifice with horror and aversion, but that, grown barbarous and unfeeling, they send their ships to the neighboring coasts, and bring home scores of fair captives to be offered to the bloodthirsty orc. Many a noble Irish maiden, I know, has been stolen from our shores, and sacrificed thus horribly by the Ebudans."

"Where sayest thou this savage Island of Ebuda lies?" asked Roland.

"In the great western ocean," answered the harper. "It lies many leagues west of green Erin."

"Turn, then, thy course, good sea captain," said Roland to the master of the ship. "Steer straight for that island kingdom. If such barbarous custom still continues there, it shall not be much longer."

But the winds, as if in league with the wrathful Proteus, hesitated to hasten the vessel on its way; and as the eagerness of the knight waxed stronger, so was the progress of the ship delayed. Sometimes the breeze died away, and there was a calm; the sails hung loose and useless upon the masts, and, had not the seamen plied their oars, the vessel would have stood still. Sometimes a west wind sprang up, and blew strong against them, and they were forced to tack about, and veer far from their intended course. And so it befell that many days passed by, ere, at length, they came in sight of the wooded shores of Ebuda, and the captain pointed out the high rock where the fair victims were daily left as food for the ravenous orc.

When they drew near the place, Roland ordered the ship's boat to be lowered; and in it he placed the largest anchor and the strongest cable that could be found. Then he sat down in the boat; and alone and unarmed, save that he carried the trusty Durandal, he rowed toward the rock. It was about the hour of sunrise,—the time when the monster, they said, was wont to come for his daily meal. As the hero rowed close to the shore, he fancied that he heard faint moans, and feeble cries of distress. He looked around, and saw a maiden chained to the rock with iron links, her feet wetted by the rising tide, and her face hidden beneath the long tresses of golden hair that fell about her neck and shoulders. His heart melted with pity, and the sight nerved his arm for the strange contest which was

The voyage in quest of the Orc.

near. He was about to speak to the maiden, when a sudden sound was heard,—a roaring like that of a strong wind among the forest trees, or of the waves rolling madly into some ocean cave. He heard the loud shouts of his companions on shipboard: the breakers began to rise around his little boat. The monster was at hand, huge as a rock-built castle, dark and terrible as a thunder-cloud, fearless as the waves themselves.

Quickly Roland went to meet the beast; he stood up in the boat with the anchor in his hand; quietly he awaited the onset. The orc saw him, and opened his jaws to swallow both him and the boat. The red eyes of the creature glared like baleful bonfires in the morning light; his huge tail lashed the waters into a foam. It was a fearful moment, but Roland faltered not. He raised the heavy anchor still higher; and then, with the strength of a knight well trained in the use of every weapon, he hurled it into the monster's wide-open mouth. And there it remained, propping the huge jaws apart, and so firmly fixed that the orc could by no means remove it. At nearly the same moment Roland drew his sword, the mighty Durandal; and, calling up all his strength, he struck the monster a blow which almost severed his head from his body. Then guarding the rope to which the anchor was fastened, he seized the oars, and rowed swiftly to the shore. He leaped upon the beach; and, encouraged by the shouts and cheers of his friends on board the ship, he dragged the now dead monster to the land.

And now he bethought him of the captive maiden chained to the rock, and half fallen into a swoon, scarcely knowing that she had been saved from the terrible death that had threatened her. With a single stroke of Durandal, the hero severed the iron links; and then he took her gently by the hand, and led her away from that dreadful rock, and seated her in a pleasant, sunny place high on the shore. With kind and cheerful words he sought to arouse her drooping spirits; for she seemed dazed and bewildered, as if waking from a dream, and unable for a time to remember where she was. He asked her her name, and inquired how she, so unlike the dwellers in Ebuda, had been cast on this barbarous shore and offered in sacrifice to the bloodthirsty orc. She told him that her name was Olympia, and that, in her own home beyond the seas, she was a princess, loved and honored by hosts of subjects. And then she related, how, one day while walking alone on the seashore, she had been seized by pirates from Ebuda, and, with other fair captives, had been brought to this savage shore, and reserved as a peace-offering to the monster whom the Ebudans foolishly believed to have been sent by old Proteus.

Scarcely had the princess ended her story when a new and unexpected danger threatened our hero. The folk of Ebuda had heard of the strange combat between the knight and the orc, and now in great numbers they came trooping to the shore. They stood upon the cliffs above, and along the beach, and some came down even to the water's edge, to see the dead monster and the hero who had slain him. But, although they had been freed from the terror of their lives, they were not pleased; neither felt they in the least thankful to their deliverer.

"Alas!" cried they, "this man has slain the servant of old Proteus, and now it will go hard with us who were charged with his keeping. For will not the sea god curse us again, and send his herds of sea calves to lay waste our shores? Better it is to endure a single evil than to risk the coming of a multitude of others. The poor orc was not as bad as he might have been;

and, now he is dead, there is no telling what may befall us."

"That is true," answered others; "and the only safe way for us to do is to turn away the wrath of old Proteus by punishing the man who has lifted up his sacrilegious hand against the orc. Let us pitch this busy meddler, whoever he may be, into the sea, that he may give his own account to the outraged sea god whom we serve."

Then a great clamor and shouting arose; and those who stood highest upon the cliffs began hurling stones and darts at Roland; and those who were nearest rushed toward him with drawn swords. There is no telling what would have been the end of this affray, had not a company of armed knights rushed unexpectedly upon the scene. They were men of Ireland, who with their king, Oberto, had come with a fleet of ships to punish the savage islanders for their piracies upon the Irish shores. So great was the surprise of the Ebudans that they turned at once, and fled in wild dismay from the shore; nor did they stop in their flight until they were safely shut up within their city walls.

The meeting between Roland and King Oberto was a happy one; for they had been pages together at the court of Charlemagne, and they recognized each other as old and tried friends. And when the Irish king saw the dead orc, and heard Roland's story of the combat which had taken place, he resolved that he would return at once to his own land and leave the Ebudans in peace. And when all had gone aboard their ships again, the sails were spread, and the fleet sped gayly back toward Ireland. And Roland and the Princess Olympia were guests on board the king's own vessel. And old stories tell us that Oberto afterwards wedded Olympia, making her the

Queen of Ireland; and that for many years they lived most happily together, loved and honored by all their subjects. As for Roland, he tarried not long at the Irish court; but, having delivered the message which he bore from Charlemagne, he took ship again and hastened back to France.

ADVENTURE XXI

HOW ROLAND FELL INTO PRISON

It was indeed high time that Roland should hasten his return to France; for Charlemagne, hard pressed by foes on every side, was in sore need of help. From every Saracen land, fierce hordes of Pagans came pouring into France, and threatening to overrun the whole of Christendom. Sacripant, the Circassian king, with ten thousand picked warriors from Persia and India, had landed on the southern coast, vowing that he would not return to his own country until he had overcome Charlemagne in battle and made France his own. Marsilius of Spain had again crossed the Pyrenees with his Moorish chivalry, and had hastened to join his forces with those of Sacripant. Agramont, the king of Africa, with a great fleet of ships, was coming over the sea; and Rodomont, the most renowned of all the Algerian chiefs, had landed near Marseilles. Unless help should come soon, it seemed as if all France would fall into the hands of the Pagans. Charlemagne hastily gathered his hosts together, and marched to meet the foe. With him were many of his bravest knights,—Duke Namon, and Ganelon, and Oliver, and Ogier the Dane, and Richard of Normandy. But Reinold of Montalban was in England, and Roland had not yet returned from his embassy to the Irish king.

Christians and Saracens met face to face in a wooded valley between two mountains, and both sides began to make ready for battle; but the unbelievers outnumbered the Christians two to one.

"If Roland were only here," said the French among themselves, "all would go well with us. His presence would be worth more than a thousand men."

Just as the fray was about to begin, a fair lady was brought as a prisoner before King Charlemagne. It was Angelica, the Princess of Cathay. What mishap had again forced her to leave her native land, and placed her at this moment in the power of the Christian king? Some said that she was a witch, and that she had come hither to ply her magic arts for the destruction of the Christian host? Others whispered that she had followed Roland from the Far East, and that she bore in her heart great love for that matchless hero. But the truth of the matter is, that a scheming thief had stolen her magic ring, and carried it to Africa or to Spain; and it was in search of this wonderful talisman that she had come again to the West. The king commanded that the maiden should be closely guarded until after the battle; and he said that then he would find out the measure of her faults, and decide what punishment should be hers.

The battle began. Many were the deeds of valor on both sides, and never before had the peers of France fought so bravely. But to the Saracens the victory seemed, from the beginning, to be assured. Oliver was unhorsed; Ogier was sorely beset by numbers of Moorish knights; Duke Namon was taken prisoner. Ganelon, the traitor and coward, giving up all for lost, turned, and fled ingloriously from the field. The king himself was wounded, and with great difficulty saved himself from capture. The Pagans were everywhere the masters.

"If Roland or Reinold had been here, it would not have

been so," sadly said the defeated knights as they unwillingly withdrew from the fight.

When the squires who had been left behind to guard the Princess Angelica learned that the day was lost, they mounted their horses, and fled in great disorder from the scene of battle. The maiden, finding herself free, also mounted a palfrey, and rode aimlessly away.

As Angelica wandered onward through the wood, trembling at every sound, and fearing to be overtaken by either Christian or Moor, she came at length to the bank of a deep and rapid-flowing river. Anxiously she rode up and down, seeking to find some shallow ford, or other means of crossing. While doing this, she was startled by seeing in the middle of the stream a tall knight, dark-browed and fierce, wading about as if in search of something lost in the water. The knight's head was bare, and she rightly guessed that it was his helmet which he sought in the rushing river. She had seen that cruel, brutish face once before. What if he should see her, and make her his prisoner? She stopped not a moment, but turned her palfrey about, and again sought safety in the leafy shadows of the wood.

It was the Moorish prince Ferrau, whom Angelica had seen wading in the stream. He had paused in his fierce pursuit of the vanquished Christians to quench his thirst from the river. As he bent over, his helmet—the very one that he had stolen from the murdered Argalia of Cathay—slipped from his head, and fell into the water. Vainly did he seek for it. Vainly did he wade up and down, and dive beneath the surface, groping with hands and feet upon the slippery bottom. From an overhanging tree he broke a forked branch, and with it raked and dredged with fruitless care the river from shore to shore. No helmet could he find. He was about to give up the search, when a strange figure seemed to rise up in the water before him. The fierce Moor had never known such thing as fear. In the dreadful din of battle, with death before him and threatening foes on every side, he had never shrunk from danger. But now, at sight of that mysterious figure, he trembled in every limb, and the hair on his uncovered head stood out like the bristles of a porcupine. Never was knight so utterly horrified. It was a dim white figure that rose up silently before the Moor, like the light mist which sometimes hangs over river and meadow in the early morning twilight. But its shape was that of a man,—of a warrior in white armor, his head uncovered, his face beaming in the uncertain light of evening, his right arm uplifted as if to threaten or to warn. To Ferrau this ghostly shape was none other than the spirit of Argalia, the Prince of Cathay, whom he had foully slain in the wood of Ardennes. He tried to fly from the spot; but his feet were rooted to the ground, and the cold waters of the river seemed to hem him in, and hold him there. Then he saw that the figure held in its left hand the helmet which he had been seeking,—Argalia's helmet,—dripping with water, and glittering brightly in the light of the rising moon.

"Foul traitor!" said the ghost, "this helmet is none of thine, and nevermore shall it incase thy brutish head. If helmet thou wouldst have, go win it! Win Reinold's, or the matchless Roland's. Argalia will have his own."

Then the figure slowly melted away in the moonlight. And Ferrau found himself standing on the shore, his teeth chattering from terror, and his limbs numb with cold. It might have been merely a horrid dream,—this vision of the slain Argalia,—yet the fierce Ferrau did not think so. He verily believed that he had seen a ghost. And as he mounted his steed, and rode away from the scene of his fright, he vowed that nevermore should helmet touch his head until he had won, by fair means or by foul, the matchless casque of Roland.

In the mean while Roland, returning from Ireland, was riding leisurely toward Paris. He had not yet heard of the Saracen invasion, and he knew not how greatly his presence was needed in the South. But messengers from Charlemagne met him on the road, and told him how the Saracens had landed on the southern coasts, and how, in the late battle, the French had been sorely defeated. "My warriors are altogether disheartened," was the word they brought from Charlemagne. "They will not fight unless Roland leads them against the foe."

So Roland hurried forward with all haste to join the king. He stopped but an hour at Paris to see his mother, the Princess Bertha, and then, without further delay, he gave spur to Brigliadoro, and rode straight onward toward the Pyrenees. Not once during the day did he leave his saddle; and at night, whether he reposed in the castle of some friendly baron, or whether he lay down to sleep in some lonely wood, he never removed his armor. And the good people along his route came out and blessed him. "Now will the arms of Charlemagne prevail," said they; "for Roland rides to the rescue." And many who through fear had fled from their homes took fresh heart when they saw the gallant hero; and they turned back again, resolved to fight bravely for their country so long as their lives were spared.

One day, as Roland was crossing a plain at the foot of a range of mountains, an unexpected sight met his view. High up on the top of a steep mountain crag, seemingly among the clouds, he saw a beautiful and strangely built castle. The battlements and towers gleamed in the sunlight like burnished steel, and it seemed hardly possible that any creature without wings could scale the steep heights upon which the airy fortress was built. As our hero paused, and admired the strange structure, and wondered by what pathway it might be reached, he fancied that he heard a cry of distress near at hand. He spurred his horse forward toward the place whence the sound came, and was surprised to see an armed knight riding leisurely across the plain in the direction of the castle. Before him, lying across the pommel of the saddle, the knight held a captive maiden, who struggled and wept, and called out loudly for help. The cries of helpless innocence never fell in vain on Roland's ears; and, no matter whether they came from the lips of a princess or those of a peasant, he was equally quick and ready to rush to the rescue. He gave spurs to Brigliadoro, and galloped nearer. The maiden was very beautiful; and the rich clothing and the jewels which she wore showed that she was a lady of no mean birth. He fancied that she looked strangely like Angelica, the Princess of Cathay. He called to the felon knight who carried her, and bade him stop. But the more he called, the faster did the stranger urge onward his steed. Swiftly across the plain flew Brigliadoro in pursuit; but the knight held on his way, and was not to be overtaken.

Up the steep mountain side, along pathways narrow and rough, pursued and pursuer climbed; and, ere he was aware,

Roland found himself inside the narrow courtyard of the castle. The place was one of rare richness and beauty, and more like the palaces of the Far East than the warlike fortresses of the Goths and Franks. The walls were built of granite, the yard was paved with marble, the great gate was of gold, and the doors were of steel inlaid with ivory: the towers and battlements were plated with polished steel. A very magician's castle it was, perched on the topmost crag of the mountain, and almost seeming to hang suspended in the air. At the door of the great hall, the knight dismounted; and, leaving Brigliadoro behind, he stalked boldly into the inmost palace, still intent on finding the felon knight, and setting his fair captive free. Through hallway and chamber and spacious kitchen he passed, calling loudly, but receiving no answer save the hollow echoes of his own voice. Then to the upper rooms he climbed, and to every chamber and balcony he went.

Rich and fair were all the appointments in this stronghold. The ceilings were high and bright; the walls were hung with richest curtains, and adorned with finest tapestry; the floors were hidden beneath soft carpets such as were known only in Persia and in the remotest lands of the Saracens; the beds were of the softest down, and curtained with cloth-of-gold and the rarest blue silk. Yet Roland stopped not to admire this richness and beauty. He climbed to the tops of the towers, he went down into the cellars, and even into the dungeons beneath the prison tower; but not a human being did he see or hear. He wondered why a palace so richly furnished should be empty of inhabitants. It angered him to think that those who lived in the castle were doubtless skulking slily in some secret hiding-place, and watching every movement that he made. He called out again, more loudly than before; he challenged, he threatened: yet no one answered.

At last, finding that the search was a vain one, he went again into the courtyard, and remounted Brigliadoro. He would give up this useless quest, and hasten to continue his journey. What was his surprise and anger to find the great gates closed and barred! Furiously he shook them, calling to the porter to unfasten them and let him go. Still not a man could he see or hear. Finally he again dismounted, and went by another way into the palace. He fancied that he heard the sound of voices. He looked into the banquet room, and there, seated at the table, were a score of armed knights, loudly talking while they feasted. He found upon inquiry that they, like himself, had been entrapped in this strange place; and none of them knew who was lord of the castle, or where he had hidden himself. Yet all had some charge of villany to prefer against their unknown host. One complained that he had stolen his steed; another, that he had treacherously taken his arms; another, that he had imprisoned a near and dear friend, or carried away his lady-love. All were raging with anger and disappointment; and all were equally resolved to punish the offender most unmercifully, should they ever be able to find him.

Among these knights were some of the bravest Saracen chiefs,—fierce Ferrau the Spanish Moor, Sacripant the Circassian king, Gradasso the king of Sericane, and a noble Moorish youth named Roger. But such was the witchery of the magician who had entrapped them in this cage, that these warriors did not know each other, nor did they care to know. They only thought of the vile deception which had led them there, and joined in forming plans to escape. Then, when their anger began to cool, they wisely concluded to make the best of their strange imprisonment, hoping that it would not last long. They amused themselves at quiet games in the hall; they listened to sweet strains of music played by unseen hands; they engaged in manly feats of arms in the narrow courtyard; they sat at table in the banquet hall, and feasted on choice viands brought to them by speechless attendants. Yet they never laid off their armor, nor put aside their arms. And their steeds stood always in the stables, saddled and bridled, and ready, on a moment's notice, to be mounted and ridden away.

Day after day passed by, and, for aught they knew, weeks and months, and the captive knights found no means by which they could break away from their enchanted prison. Nor could they have escaped at all, had not help come to them from without. And now, that we may learn how this help was brought, we must leave them for a while, and visit other scenes, and become acquainted with personages whom we have not yet met.

ADVENTURE XXII

BRADAMANT THE WARRIOR MAIDEN

THE Princess Angelica, frightened at sight of the fierce Moor wading in the river and searching for his lost helmet, fled through the forest as fast as her poor palfrey could carry her. Ah, how she wished now for the magic ring which had so often befriended and saved her! With its aid she might have bidden defiance to danger, and flown safely and quickly back to Cathay. But, having it not, she was fain perforce to fare like other folk, and plod painfully and slowly, on foot or on horseback, from one place to another. Yet whither now should she go? That was a question which she could not answer. It seemed to her that all men were her foes, and her chief thought was to keep safely out of sight of every one. For a day and a night, and half the following day, she wandered through dark and dreary woods, or across barren and lonely moorlands, shrinking from every sound, and affrighted even by the rustling of the leaves.

At about noon on the second day, the princess found herself so wearied with her long flight, and so overcome by the heat, that she could go no farther. She was close to a thicket of flowering hawthorns and wild-rose bushes, overshadowed by tall oak trees. So cool and secluded was the place, that it seemed to invite her to stop and rest. Down from the saddle she sprang among the untrodden flowers; and she gently removed the bridle from her faithful palfrey's head, and turned him loose to graze along the river's bank. Then, within the thicket, she found a pleasant bower, where the leaves and twigs were so interlaced that the light of day could scarcely struggle through; and there, on a bed of moss and flowers, the over-wearied maiden sank down and sought repose. On either side of the thicket a brooklet strayed, singing a pleasant lullaby as it murmured over the pebbles; and the gentle zephyr stole through the leaves and branches, and lovingly kissed the maiden's cheek, and told her of happier and more peaceful climes. Scarcely had she touched her woodland couch, when her eyes closed in slumber; and she forgot her terror and her flight and her great weariness, and dreamed only of her palace home in the sunrise land of Cathay.

How long the princess slept, I cannot tell. But when she awoke, she fancied that she heard the tramp of a horse not far from her resting place. It was not the light tread of her palfrey, but sounded more like the heavy step of a war steed. She arose softly, and peeped out through the leaves and branches. An armed knight sat by the river's bank, while his steed stood cropping the grass close by. In doleful mood seemed this knight; his head was resting upon his hand; his eyes were downcast and sad. Long time sat he there, silent and thoughtful; and then he began to bewail some cruel mishap that had overtaken him.

"Ah, me!" cried he. "How false and cruel is fortune! What avails the victory that we have won, when the hopes which were nearest my heart have come to naught? Better would it have been, had I died on the field of battle."

Angelica, in her safe hiding-place, heard the knight's piteous plaint. She fancied that she knew that voice: she had certainly heard it before. She longed to see the face of the speaker. A dry twig snapped under her feet: the knight, in alarm, sprang up and looked around. It was indeed he: it was Sacripant the Circassian king, her father's friend and her own. It was for her sake that he had come from the Far East, and joined himself to the foes of France and Christendom; and it was for her sake that he had fought so valiantly in the late battle. For he hoped, that, by thus proving his valor as a warrior, the heart of the maiden would be kindly inclined toward him. But now, after the battle had been fought and won, he could hear no tidings of Angelica, and it had been whispered that she had returned alone to Cathay. And the sorrowful king moaned, and beat his breast, and bewailed that he had ever been born.

The princess heard the words of the dolorous knight, and was not slow to learn the cause of his grief. But her heart was still her own, and she felt neither love nor pity for him. Yet she was sadly in need of a friend; and she knew that Sacripant, with all his faults, would prove kind and true. She resolved, therefore, to make herself known to him. So, softly as the summer's breeze in the meadows, she stepped from her hiding-place; and, radiant with mingled smiles and tears, she glided to the place where he sat.

"God bless you!" said she, laying her white hand on his shoulder; "and may he put all troublesome thoughts out of your mind."

Never was brave knight so wonder-stricken. He could scarcely believe that it was indeed Angelica who stood thus unexpectedly before him: he thought that it was her spirit, or that some cunning wizard was deceiving him. But when she spoke to him again, and called him by name, his doubts vanished, and he welcomed her most joyfully. Then the two sat down together on the grassy bank, and talked of plans for the future; and they resolved that they would forever quit the land of France, where both had met with only disappointments, and together hasten back to Cathay.

While they were yet talking, a noise was heard in the wood close by,—the sound of tramping feet and clanging armor. Sacripant, not knowing whether it was a friend or a foe, at once donned his helmet, mounted his steed, and placed his lance in rest. A single knight, clad in steel, came threading his way through the wood. He wore over his armor a snow-white mantle bordered with ermine; above his helmet there waved a large white plume; and the steed which he rode was the color of milk. His shield, too, was white, and on it were emblazoned the arms of Montalban. When Sacripant saw that it was a Christian who approached, he challenged him at once to engage in deadly combat. The stranger was no whit alarmed by the overbearing mood and tone of the Circassian. He said not a word in answer, but quietly laid his lance in rest, and made ready for the onset. Both knights struck spurs at the same moment, and, with the fury of untamed lions, rushed toward each other. The lances of both were broken in twain; and, as each struck the other, the earth seemed to tremble beneath them, and the woods and hills rang with the sound. The Circassian's horse fell dead upon the ground; and the White Knight's steed was brought to its knees. Sacripant was so entangled in the trappings of his horse, and so weighted down with his armor, that it was some time before he could gain his feet. But the stranger, deeming that he had done enough for his own honor's sake, touched his horse gently with the spur, and rode carelessly away. Not a word did he say, nor did he glance once back to the place where the discomfited Pagan lay.

With troubled face, and many half-smothered curses, the Circassian arose from the ground. He cared not so much for the bruises which he had gotten by the fall, as for the disgrace of being thus unhorsed in the presence of the princess. But Angelica, as if scarcely noticing his mishap, consoled and cheered him with kind, courageous words.

"Surely, sir knight," said she, "it was not your fault that you tumbled upon the grass, but rather that of the awkward beast who lies dead at your feet. Come, my lord, cheer up, and let us out of the wood, and away to dear Cathay!"

While she was speaking, a messenger mounted on a fleet horse, and bearing pouch and horn, rode toward them. Both man and beast were covered with dust, and seemed weary with long travel.

"Kind sir," said the messenger to the Circassian, "have you lately seen a warrior pass this way, bearing a white shield, and riding a milk-white steed?"

"Indeed," said Sacripant, "I have seen him to my sorrow. It was such a knight who but a few minutes ago threw me headlong into the grass, and then went proudly on his way. Tell me his name, I pray thee, that I may remember him another day."

"Willingly will I tell you," answered the rider; "for you will be proud to know that you have been defeated by no common warrior. The knight with the white shield is none other than Bradamant the warrior maiden, the fair sister of Reinold of Montalban." And with these words and a laugh of derision, the man put spurs to his jaded horse, and hastened on his way, leaving the Circassian chief but little pleased with his news. Angry, ashamed, and disheartened, Sacripant mounted the palfrey of Angelica; and, taking that princess up behind him, the two rode silently away through the wood.

The White Knight, who, as we have learned, was Bradamant the warrior maiden, kept steadily on her way until she came to a road which wound round the base of a steep mountain. Here was a very pleasant place, overshadowed with oaks and twining vines, and looking out upon the quiet green orchards and vineyards in the valley below. A fountain of water, clear and cold, gushed out from among the rocks; and Bradamant dismounted to drink. But, just as she was raising her helmet, she saw a stranger sitting in the shade close by. He seemed to be a knight, young, sad-eyed, and melancholy; and the shallow smile which played about his lips betrayed his kinship to the house of Ganelon of Mayence. His horse was tethered, not far away, to the low-hanging branches of a beech; and his shield and helmet were cast carelessly upon the ground at his feet. Curious to know the cause of the stranger's sadness, Bradamant kindly asked him what mishap had brought those tears into his eyes, that look of woe into his face.

"Fair sir," said the sorrowful knight, "my name is Pinabel. I loved a maiden fairer than dream can picture, gentler than words can describe. And she, I am sure, thought well of me. One day, as we sauntered happily along the banks of the Rhone, a strange shadow crossed our path. We looked up; and to our great amazement we saw a winged horse—yes, a winged horse—circling like an eagle high in the air above us.

Round and round he soared, now rising among the clouds, now sinking to a level with the treetops, and seeming merely to amuse himself. Then all at once, like a falcon let loose from the wrist, or an arrow shot from the bow, he darted down upon us. Before I could cry out, or hinder, he had seized the maiden in his talons, and was bearing her away to his mountain eyry. Vain was it to try to save her. He carried her over the dark and barren valleys, and the rough hill-country of the Pyrenees. There, in the midst of the caverned mountains, is a fair and wondrous castle planted on the top of a craggy rock, and shining in the sunlight like a beacon fire. Men say that it was built by a mountain sprite, and that a Moorish magician keeps it, and that the winged horse is but a servant who does his bidding. All round are horrid cliffs, and giddy precipices, and dark gorges, and roaring torrents; nor can one find the least sign or trace of a pathway to this robber's nest. It was thither that the winged steed carried the hapless maiden."

"But followed you not the monster to his den?" asked Bradamant.

"I did," answered Pinabel. "But of what avail is it to contend with a sorcerer? Six days I rode around the mountain, eying the prison towers, to which no wingless creature ever climbed, and daring their wizard lord to meet me in combat on the plain. But the robber staid close in his mountain keep, and sallied not forth at my call. Then there came one day into the valley two noble knights, who, like me, had been bereft of that which they held most dear. One was Gradasso, the Pagan king of Sericane; and the other looked strangely like Roger, the pride of the Moorish court. Boldly they rode across the plain, and halted not until they reached the foot of the tall cliffs. Then Gradasso blew his bugle until the whole valley rang, and the rocks and crags seemed to tremble with the sound. And soon afterward I saw the winged horse, with the wizard on his back, leap from the steel-bright tower above. Upward, at first, he sprang, and higher and higher he soared, until he seemed a mere speck in the sky. Then, like a well-trained falcon, he shot straight down upon his prey. I heard a swooping, whizzing sound in the air above me. I closed my eyes, and fell to the earth; for I dared not look upon so fearful a combat. When at length all was quiet again, I raised my eyes, and saw the wizard seated on his steed, and holding a prisoner in either hand, calmly returning to his castle home."

Bradamant listened with great interest to Pinabel's story, and she besought him to lead her to the place where this wonderful castle stood. She would give battle to the wizard, she said; she would free the prisoners whom he held in durance there; she would restore to Pinabel the maiden whom he had lost. The sad-eyed knight readily agreed to lead her to the place,—it could be reached in three or four days,—but he felt not at all hopeful of the result.

"If you wish to risk these dangers," said he, "it matters nothing to me. You will challenge the cunning wizard; he will swoop down upon you ere you can raise a finger; he will take you under his arm, and carry you gently to his prison house. Yet I am ready to do your bidding."

Then the knight mounted his steed, and the two rode onward together. But the traitorous Pinabel had noted the arms of Montalban emblazoned on the white shield of Bradamant, and he began to plan in his mind how he might betray and kill her. For many a league they rode, over rocky hills, and through wooded valleys until the sun went down, and darkness began to settle around them.

"It would be well," said Pinabel, "to seek some place of shelter from the night, and the storm which I see is brewing. I know of a farmer's cot, just over the ridge of this mountain, where I have often rested, and found a hearty welcome. Let us ride to it by the nearest way."

So saying, he left the beaten road, and spurred his horse up the rough side of the mountain. He hoped to lose the White Knight in the thick wood which crowned its top, or lead her unawares over the side of some high precipice. But Bradamant kept close behind him, and foiled all his wicked plans; for, to tell the truth, she had little faith in this sad-eyed kinsman of Ganelon.

Just after passing the crest of the mountain, the two knights were surprised at seeing a light streaming up as it were from the ground. On drawing nearer, they found that it came from the bottom of a well-like cavern,—a great cleft in the rock,—whose steep, smooth sides descended sheer twenty yards and more. Pinabel was the first to dismount and look over the edge of the chasm.

"Ah, me!" cried he as if in great surprise. "What villany is this I see?"

The warrior maiden, eager to know the meaning of his words, leaped from her horse and ran to look down into the cavern. But she saw nothing save the smooth walls of polished rock, and a narrow door at the bottom, through which streamed a flood of light as from a torch. She asked Pinabel what he had seen.

"I saw," said he, "a most beautiful damsel, clad in the garb of a princess, trying in vain to scale those slippery walls. And while I looked, a fierce ruffian, who seemed to be her jailer, seized her rudely, and dragged her back through the narrow door into the inner cave."

"If I had any means of reaching her, I would save her," said Bradamant earnestly. "Ah! what would I not give for a rope, a ladder, some way of getting down to the bottom of this well!"

She glanced around her. An elm tree, tall and straight, grew on the brink of the cave. It would be but an easy matter to make a ladder, she thought. So with her sword she cut down the longest, straightest branch, and shaped and trimmed it to suit her wishes. Yet, when she thrust this rudely-made ladder into the cave, she found that it lacked several feet of reaching the bottom.

"Do you hold on to the upper end," said she to Pinabel, "and I will climb down. I may at least get low enough to peep through the door, and see what is going on in the inner cave."

The treacherous fellow seemed very willing to do her bidding; but she had not climbed far when he suddenly let go of the branch, and plunged the helpless Bradamant down to the bottom of the great well. Had not the stout elm branch broken her fall, the warrior maiden would have been killed outright. As it was, she lay for some time, stunned and helpless, upon the hard stone floor; while the wretched Pinabel, chuckling with delight, mounted his steed and rode away.

"Only too gladly," said he to himself, "would I hurl Reinold and all his kin of Montalban down into the same deep grave."

When Bradamant recovered her senses and arose, she saw that the door which led into the inner cave was still open; and the bright light which she had seen from above now shone full into her face. Without fear or hesitation, she passed boldly through the narrow entrance-way, and came soon into a large, well-lighted chamber. This place seemed to be an underground temple, roomy and square, with vaulted roof upheld by fluted columns of marble and alabaster. In front of the central altar was a large lamp, whose clear-burning flame lighted up all the space around, and shone through the passageway and the door into the well-like entrance beyond. The warrior maiden, in thankfulness for her delivery from death, and touched by the softening influences of the place, knelt before the altar and prayed. But, ere the prayer was finished, a secret wicket in the wall opened silently, and a weird woman, barefooted, and with dishevelled hair, entered the room.

"Ah, Bradamant," said she, "you have come at last! Long have we waited for you, yet we knew that you would not fail us."

"Where am I?" asked Bradamant, rising. "And who are you, who seem to know me so well?"

"My name is Melissa," answered the woman. "Men sometimes call me Melissa the witch. The temple in which you are was built by Merlin, the great wizard in the days of King Arthur. You have heard how he was outwitted by the Lady of the Lake, and how he laid himself down in a cavern cell, and could never rise again? This is the cavern. And in the innermost chamber he still lies, not dead, but sleeping; and his voice still foretells the doom of those who come to consult him. Wouldst thou see the place where lies this ancient seer? Come with me."

Then the weird woman led Bradamant through a long, dark passageway, to the chamber in which the sage Merlin reposed. The bed, or tomb, in which he lay, was built of marble and red jasper and many precious stones, and shone like a sunbeam in the darkness. And the room was paved with rich gems; the ceiling was covered with gold; the walls were hung with the rarest tapestry. Bradamant trembled with awe as she gazed around upon this strange scene. She wondered why it was that the Fates, against whose decrees no man may struggle, had brought her hither. She wondered if it were true that Merlin still lived, and if he would vouchsafe to tell what fortunes were held in store for her. She was about to speak, when a voice solemn and grand was heard, coming as it were from the tomb.

"Brave warrior maiden," said the voice, "may all thy dearest wishes have fulfilment!"

And long the wizard talked with her, urging her not to give up the undertaking she had begun. And he promised her that in the end she should be the most favored of women, the mother of kings and heroes as noble as those of ancient Rome.

Then Melissa led the warrior maiden back into the chapel; and the two sat down, and talked long hours together concerning the deeds of the past and the things which were still to betide. And the weird woman said, "If thou art still intent on the quest of the winged horse and his master, and the steel-bright mountain fortress where they dwell, it were well that thou shouldst know their history." And then she told this story to Bradamant.

The Story

In the first place, you must know that old Atlantes, the wizard who built the fortress of which we are speaking, is one of the most knowing of sorcerers, and that he has a nephew named Roger, who is the bravest and noblest of the Moorish princes. Years ago, when Roger was but a child, the old wizard opened the book of fate, and read, much to his sorrow, that the boy was destined in early manhood to leave his home and his kindred, and the friends who had cherished him, and ally himself with their Christian foes. Then Atlantes began to plan how he might fight against the Fates. And by his magic arts he built in a day and a night that mountain stronghold; and he adorned it with every thing that is pleasant or beautiful, and placed in it every thing that would amuse the young prince whose prison home it was to be. And he brought wise men from foreign lands to teach the boy, and minstrels from north and south to while away the tedious hours with music. And, as Roger grew into young manhood, the bravest knights and the fairest ladies were enticed into the castle, and there imprisoned to keep him company. "His life," said the old wizard, "shall be as pleasant and as gay as it is possible for the life of a prisoner to be. But, whatever the Fates may say, he shall not leave his kin, nor shall he become a Christian."

At about this time Agramant, the king of Africa, began to think of invading France. Very bitter did he feel toward Charlemagne for wrongs which his people had suffered; very greatly did he covet the vine-clad hills of Gascony. He called his wise men around him, and they discussed their plans together.

"There is but one way by which you can succeed against the French," said the oldest of his counsellors. "You must enlist under your banner young Roger, the Prince of Morocco. He will prove a host within himself; and, without his help, you will fail."

"But how are we to get him?" asked Agramant. "You know how zealously his old uncle guards him in his steel-clad castle among the Pyrenees. No one can go in or out of that castle; and the wizard, with his winged horse and his magic, is as much to be feared as an army of Christians. Indeed, it would be easier to conquer Charlemagne single-handed than to take Roger from his uncle."

"To do this," said the wise man, "you must oppose magic with magic."

"You speak in riddles," answered the king. "Explain yourself."

"You have heard of Angelica, the fair Princess of Cathay?" asked the wise man.

The king nodded.

"You have doubtless also heard that she wears a magic ring on her finger, and that this ring, placed between her lips, makes her invisible to the sight of men?"

The king nodded again.

"Well, then, you must get possession of that ring."

The king flew into a great passion. "You trifle with me!" he cried. "You set me a task,—yes, two of them. I ask you how I am to outwit and overcome Charlemagne. You answer by telling me to enlist Prince Roger in my army, and to get possession of Angelica's ring, either of which is harder than fighting all the kings in Christendom. Should I ask you how

I am to get the ring, you would answer by telling me to do some other task equally impossible."

"Not so, great king," was the humble answer. "You have here in your court the greatest thief in the world, the dwarf Brunello. It is well known that you would like to rid yourself of him, and that you would have done so long ago if he had not had a charmed life. Send him to Cathay, and offer him, in case he can steal the magic ring for you, the governorship of one of your outlying provinces. If he fail, you will have good riddance of him; for he can never come back. If he succeed, it will still be well; for, being made governor, he will steal from his subjects, and not from you."

The king was pleased with the wise man's advice, and he forthwith sent Brunello on his mission to Cathay. He promised him, that, if he came safely back with the ring, he should have the rich province of Tingitana for his own. Now, the dwarf was somewhat of a magician himself; and he had but little trouble in reaching Albracca, and stealing the ring from the finger of the princess while she slept. How he made his way back to the West it matters but little to us now. We are only concerned in knowing that at this very moment he is on his way to the Pyrenees with the magic ring on his finger, intent upon trying its powers against the wizard skill of Atlantes.

"And now," said Melissa to Bradamant, "if you would outwit Atlantes, and overthrow the magic castle wherein are imprisoned the bravest knights and the fairest ladies of France, you must get possession of Angelica's ring ere Brunello has tested its powers."

"How is that to be done?" asked Bradamant.

"To-morrow," answered the weird woman, "I will lead you out of this cavern, and show you the road which you shall take. Follow it until you reach the seashore and a little inn, where you will meet the dwarf Brunello. You will readily know him, for an uglier little being never called himself a man. Make some excuse to go with him on his way, but do not touch him until you are in sight of the high towers of the wizard's castle."

Much more did the gentle Melissa whisper in the warrior maiden's ear; and all night long they sat in that quiet cave temple, talking of the bright future, and the glorious possibilities which Merlin had promised to the true and great-hearted Bradamant. And at the earliest break of day the weird woman led her guest through a long, dark gallery, out of the cave temple, into a narrow glen deep hidden between two mountains.

All day they travelled on foot through narrow gorges, and by the side of roaring torrents, and beneath frowning precipices, until at eventide they came to the sea and a broad highway that followed the shore. Here Melissa bade the warrior maiden a hearty godspeed, and turned another way, intent on other duties. And Bradamant went fearlessly onward, until, late in the evening, she came to a little roadside inn. There she found the dwarf Brunello, a hideous little man, hunchbacked and misshapen, and uglier than pen can describe. She lost no time in making his acquaintance. But the wily thief, who supposed he was talking to one of Charlemagne's warriors, was on his guard, and answered her questions with many cunning falsehoods. He told her that he was a poor laborer driven by the ruthless Saracens from his home in Gascony; and that he was now on his way to Charlemagne to lend the king what little aid he could in driving the invaders from the land. Then he, in turn, questioned Bradamant concerning her name, her home, and her kinsfolk. But the warrior maiden met guile with guile, and answered him with many a feigned story; and her eyes glanced cautiously toward his hand to assure herself that the magic ring was there.

ADVENTURE XXIII

THE WINGED HORSE OF THE PYRENEES

Early the following morning Bradamant was awakened by hearing a great noise in the courtyard of the inn. She quickly donned her armor and ran to the window to see what was the cause of the disturbance. The host and all his family were gazing upward as if at some wonderful thing in the heavens. Every one about the house seemed greatly excited, and all were talking and shouting and gesticulating in the wildest manner possible. Even the dwarf Brunello was on the balcony, shading his eyes with his hand, and looking upward with an interest too strong to be hidden.

"What is it?" asked Bradamant.

"A winged horse," answered the dwarf.

"A winged horse! Where? Ah, yes, there he is!"

Bradamant saw the creature very plainly, sailing serenely through the air above them, and making his way toward the west. His wings were very broad, and, as the rays of the rising sun fell upon them, they seemed colored with every hue of the rainbow. Upon his back sat a knight clad in glittering armor, and holding an open book in his hand. And so rapid was the flight of the strange animal, that in a few moments he was lost to sight among the far-off clouds and mountain tops.

"A very strange creature that is," said the host, ever ready to amuse his guests. "It is what we call a hippogriff, and I have been told that there is not such another beast in the world. The man who rides him is a great wizard. He reads books, and dabbles with the metals, and gazes at the stars. His name is Atlantes; and they say, that, on the other side of the mountains, he has the most wondrous castle that ever was built. I have been told that it is made of steel, and that it crowns a crag so steep and high that no creature without wings can reach it."

"And does the wizard live there all alone?" asked Bradamant.

"Ah, no!" answered the host. "He has many fine guests, and others arrive every day. The noblest men and women of France are in attendance at his court."

"How can that be when the only road to the castle is through the air?"

"Oh! he has his own way of inviting his guests. Whenever he sees a knight more handsome or more noble than the common sort, he merely swoops down upon him with his hippogriff, picks him up, and carries him aloft to his mountain eyry. Many fair ladies and young damsels have been stolen from their homes, and doomed to imprisonment in the wizard's airy palace. And we can only guess whether they are happy or miserable there, for who once goes up to those shining halls can ne'er come down again."

"How I should like to try a passage at arms with old father Atlantes!" cried Bradamant. "I wonder if he would think me worth carrying up to his lofty den."

"It is very likely that he would have you there ere you could deal one stroke with sword or lance," answered the host, shaking his head.

"I have made up my mind to try the venture, at any rate,"

said the maiden. "Is there any one here who knows the way to the thief's retreat, and who will serve me as a guide?"

"May it please you, sir knight," spoke the dwarf very quickly, "I myself will show you the way. I have here a little book in which the road is set down and the whole country described. I shall only be too glad to serve you."

Bradamant thanked him very kindly, and the two began at once to make ready for the journey. As the White Knight had no steed of her own, she bargained with the host for a palfrey which he had to sell,—a light-footed creature, well suited to the road, but ill fitted for the combat. And, before the sun was very high, the knight and the dwarf bade their friends at the inn good-by, and set out on their dangerous venture. Bradamant, clad in her white armor, and bearing a long lance and the white emblazoned shield of Montalban, rode erect and proud as any peer of the realm; while the dwarf, with becoming humbleness, followed at some distance, riding upon a lowly mule. Through a deep valley they passed, and over rugged hills, and through untrodden woods, until they reached the foot of the snowy mountains. Then, with many a mishap and many a weary turn, they climbed the rocky slopes, and came to that place where one may look down and see on one side Spain, on the other the fair fields of France. Then, following a narrow path, they painfully wended their way down again, and came at last to a broad, low plain, and, glancing upward to the craggy slopes on the farther side of the valley, they saw the object of their search,—the wizard's air-built castle. The bright towers of steel could be plainly seen, glinting and glistening in the sunlight, but so high that the neighboring cliffs seemed left far below.

"Behold!" cried the dwarf, riding up close to the knight,—"behold the enchanter's dwelling, the prison house where many ladies and cavaliers pine their days away!"

Bradamant knew that the time had come for her to take the magic ring; but she scorned to harm a creature of so base a sort as the dwarf,—weak, unarmed, and unskilled in self-defence as he was. So, while he gazed in rapt wonder at the high-built towers, she suddenly seized his hands, and slipped the precious ring from his finger. Then she lifted him from his mule, and with strong cords bound him to a neighboring tree. The poor dwarf, with tears and groans and piteous cries, begged her to set him free. But she knew the cunning thief too well, and staid not to listen to his pleas. Leisurely adown the hillside she rode, until she reached the treeless meadow close under the castle; then pausing, she raised her bugle to her lips, and blew a shrill blast, the sound of which was echoed from cliff to cliff, and from valley to valley, until both earth and sky seemed to ring. And, ere the sound had died away, the winged courser, with his master on his back, leaped from the shining towers above, and soared leisurely up into the mid-air. Then slowly he began to settle toward the earth, circling down, nearer and nearer to the fearless warrior maiden. But Bradamant noticed that the wizard carried neither lance, nor sword, nor other weapon, but that on his left arm he bore a small round shield covered all over with crimson silk, and in his right hand was the open book from which he seemed to be always reading.

As the wizard with his winged steed charged down upon our heroine, she aimed blow after blow with her lance at the silk-covered shield which he held before him; but every stroke glanced harmlessly aside. At last, growing tired of this kind of fray, she dismounted from her palfrey, and drew her sword. The wizard, feeling now that he had amused himself long enough, began to lift the silken cover from his shield. Bradamant had learned from the weird woman Melissa what sort of shield this was. The magic light which shone from its polished sides had the power to blind, disarm, and overthrow all who looked upon it; and it was by means of this shield, and not through any strength or skill of his own, that the wizard won all his victories. Yet such was the virtue of Angelica's magic ring, that it rendered its wearer proof against all enchantments of this kind.

With the ring tightly clasped in her left hand, and her sword in her right, Bradamant went boldly forward to meet her foe; but, as she saw the shining shield laid bare, she closed her eyes, as if overcome by its glare, and fell to the ground. The wizard, well pleased, made his steed alight; and, covering the shield again with the crimson cloth, he hung it upon the pommel of his saddle, and dismounted. With a strong cord in his hand he went leisurely forward to bind his prisoner. He had captured scores of valiant knights in this way, and no thought of any mishap had ever entered his mind. So you may imagine his astonishment, when Bradamant, who had only been feigning, rose quickly, and seized him, and bound him fast with his own strong cord. The first thought of the warrior maiden was to slay the wicked wizard; but when she saw that he was a very old man, with sorrowing, wrinkled face, and snow-white hair, she pitied his age and his grief, and would not harm him.

"Ah, brave knight!" said the helpless old man, "you have conquered me, and all my magic has come to naught. Slay me, I pray thee, for life is no longer worth the living."

"Tell me, first," said Bradamant, "why you carry on this

cruel and unknightly warfare against your fellowmen. Why have you built those prison towers?"

"It was all for young Roger's sake," answered the wizard. "He is the noblest and fairest of men, and the only being on earth that I love. I built the castle for him. I stored it with every comfort, and I brought to it every pleasure that the four quarters of the globe could afford. I have sought out the most worthy knights and the handsomest ladies in Christendom and in Paynimry for his companions. I have kept them in prison, it is true; but it is a prison more delightful than many a palace."

"Ah, sir wizard!" said Bradamant, "you should know that a prison, however gilded and painted, is a prison still. Liberty is the sweetest of enjoyments. So come with me at once, and open your gates, and set your prisoners free."

Old Atlantes, writhing and groaning in helpless distress, obeyed. He led the way to the narrow cleft and the steep, hidden path, up which Roland, as I have related, had ridden blindly into prison. They climbed the rugged precipice, and stood at the golden gate of the castle. Here they paused. From the threshold, whereon were graven wondrous signs and many a magic rune, the wizard lifted a broad flat stone. In a little chamber underneath the sill were ranged all kinds of crucibles and pots and strangely shaped lamps, wherein burned secret fires such as only sorcerers know how to kindle.

"Oh, sad, sad day!" sighed the old man, groaning and trembling in deep distress. "Sad day that sees the end of my dearest hopes! But then it becomes not poor mortals to struggle against the decrees of Fate."

Then he took the magic vessels, and one by one he hurled

them over the precipice into the depths below. As the last one fell, and was shattered on the rocks, a wondrous thing took place. The fairy castle, with its steel-bright walls, and its tall towers, and its broad battlements, and pleasant halls, and narrow courtyard, and golden gate, faded away into nothingness; and in its place was a bleak and cheerless mountain cave, through which the cold winds whistled and shrieked, and in which there was neither light, nor comfort, nor aught that could give pleasure or enjoyment. And out through the rocky cave mouth where erst had stood the golden gate, there passed in long procession the prisoners who had been entrapped in the wizard's toils. First came the knights, each clad in full armor, and riding his own war-steed; and as they went out they gazed around in utter amazement, not knowing where they were, nor remembering aught of that which had happened to them. There were all the noblest chiefs of Paynimry,—Roger the Moorish prince, for whose sake all this witchery had been planned; and Sacripant the king of Circassia; and Ferrau the dark-browed Moor, wearing no helmet; and Gradasso of Sericane. There, too, were Roland, and Astolpho of England, and a great host of noblemen and warriors of lesser note. Then came the ladies and the fair young damsels, all mounted on prancing palfreys, and in their wonder scarcely knowing whether to rejoice at this unexpected turn of fortune, or to look upon it as the beginning of new and unknown evils. And last of all came Angelica, the matchless Princess of Cathay, who, like the others, had been entrapped into the wizard's prison-house. And as the sad, glad, bewildered company wound round the rugged hill in their slow and difficult descent to the plain, Bradamant thought that never in the world had there been seen a nobler and more varied array of valor and of beauty. She looked around to speak to the old wizard; but he had skulked away, grieved, ashamed, and disappointed, to hide himself from the eyes of mankind. And, when the last of that strange procession had passed, Bradamant herself followed them to the plain below; and there, without a word, they parted, each choosing his own way.

ADVENTURE XXIV

HOW ROLAND LOST HIS HELMET

ROLAND did not know how long he had been confined in the wizard's castle. It might have been a few days, it might have been many months. The whole affair was to him but a dim remembrance, a vague and shadowy dream. When he found himself free to go where he pleased, he turned his horse's head toward the east, and hurried forward, hoping within a short time to join the hosts of Charlemagne. He had not gone far, however, when he was overtaken by two knights, who, like himself, had just escaped from the prison-towers of Atlantes, and were on their way back to the scene of war. They were Sacripant the Circassian king, and Ferrau the dark-browed Moor. But the eyes of the three knights had been so blinded by the wizard's enchantments, that they did not know each other.

"Who are you?" cried Ferrau, riding furiously down upon Roland. "Turn back, or take another road!"

Roland grew very angry at the words and the tone of the Moor; and, turning himself about, he answered, "Thou beastly fellow, were it not that thy head is bare, I would soon teach thee who has the best right to this road. Turn back thyself, or else ride on in peace."

"Trouble not thyself on account of my bare head," said Ferrau. "I am well able to take care of it, as I will show thee if thou move not out of my way!"

"Friend," said Roland to Sacripant, who had just ridden up, "I pray thee lend this fellow thy helmet. I would fain teach him something of knightly courtesy."

"Dost thou take me for a fool?" asked Sacripant. "Whose head would then be bare? Lend him thine own helmet, or hush this pother."

Then Ferrau, fairly boiling with rage, cried out, "Fools are ye both! As if I might not help myself to a helmet if I wished. But I have sworn to go bareheaded until I win the matchless casque of Roland. No other helmet shall ever touch my head."

"I warrant," said our hero, smiling, "that, wert thou to meet the knight of whom thou speakest, thy very knees would quake with fear, and thou wouldst not only forego the helmet, but wouldst gladly buy thy life with thy other arms."

Then Ferrau began to boast that he had often before had Roland on the hip, and that it would be mere child's play to win the helmet from that much over-rated hero.

"Thou brutish braggart," cried Roland, no longer able to hold himself, "know that I am he of whom thou speakest! Now see if thou hast the might to take the helmet from me." And with these words he lifted the fair casque from his head, and hung it upon a branch of a spreading beech, and at the same time he drew the dread blade Durandal, and called upon Ferrau to defend himself.

Long and fiercely did the two heroes fight. Their swords flashed hither and thither like the lightning's play. Their shields were bruised and dinted in many a place, and yet neither seemed to get the better of the other. Sacripant, who was now more eager than ever to return to his own country, stopped not to see the issue of the combat, but rode onward, little caring which of the knights should be the victor.

Now, it happened that the Princess Angelica had taken the same road; and as she came near to the scene of combat, and heard the clashing of the swords, and the ringing of the shields, she felt curious to know who it was that fought thus furiously. The thick undergrowth of shrubs and the leafy branches of the great beech hid her from the sight of the busy combatants; and, without any fear of being seen, she paused, and watched the conflict with great interest. She saw the glittering helmet hanging from the bough above her, and she understood at once what the fighting was about. She did not want the fierce Moor to win that casque: he should not have it, even though he should be the victor. So, while the two knights were blinded by their angry strife, she quietly took the helmet down, turned her palfrey about, and galloped away toward Marseilles.

It was long ere either of the knights noticed the loss of the prize. Ferrau was the first to turn his eyes toward the spot where it had hung.

"Ah, silly blockheads we are!" he cried, "to fight thus blindly, while the knave who rode hither with us carries the rich prize away."

When Roland saw that the casque was really gone, he agreed with Ferrau in thinking that it had been stolen by Sacripant; and the two who had just been the bitterest of foes, now ceased their fighting, and spurred onward in pursuit of the supposed thief. By and by they came to a place where the road forked, and here they were at a loss to know what to do; for they saw the prints of horses' hoofs going either way. At length Roland took the road which turned to the right, hoping to overtake the thief in the valley below, while Ferrau kept the path which led nearer the slope of the mountain. All day long did Roland urge his steed forward; but no traces did he find of the Circassian chief, nor did he for many a month recover the gleaming helmet that he so highly prized.

As Ferrau rode leisurely along the pathway which he had chosen, he came to a pleasant grove, where a spring of water gurgled up among rocks and flowers. He stopped a moment to enjoy the pleasant shade; and, as his eyes glanced upward, he was amazed to see the coveted helmet hanging on a branch above the spring. With a hoarse cry of delight he sprang forward, and seized it in his hands; and, as he did so, he caught a glimpse of the fair princess fleeing, like a frightened deer, through the forest. Well pleased was the fierce Ferrau. The matchless helmet of Roland was at last his own. What cared he now for the success of the Pagan arms in France. He turned his horse about, and with his swarthy head incased in the long-wished-for casque, he rode back leisurely toward Spain.

ADVENTURE XXV

THE BATTLE

HARD pressed was Charlemagne by his Pagan foes. Great, indeed, was the peril of the French. The enemy, under Marsilius and Agramant of Africa, hemmed them in on every side: they shut them up within the city walls, and battered at the city gates. All France was in distress: all Christendom seemed in danger. Where now were the heroes upon whose valor and strength the hosts of Charlemagne were wont to rely? The faithful Roland was a helpless prisoner still in the mountain keep of old Atlantes. Oliver was sick from a grievous wound, and unable to leave his chamber. Ogier the Dane had fallen into disgrace, and dared not come into the presence of the king. Reinold of Montalban still tarried in Britain. Of all the mighty peers of the realm, Duke Namon alone was with the king; yet age had dimmed the old counsellor's eye, and unnerved his hand, and he was no longer a hero in battle as he had been in the earlier days.

And every day the French host looked with eagerness and hope for the coming of Roland or Reinold; but no tidings were heard of them. And some went boldly to the king, and prayed him to pardon Ogier his offences, and call him to their aid. But the king would not. And, to make the matter worse, fresh hordes of Saracens came daily to strengthen the besiegers. Rodomont, the lion-hearted king of Algiers, and Dardinel, the gentlest born of all the Moorish heroes, crossed the sea, and joined their forces to those of Marsilius and Agramant; and the Saracen lines pressed closer and still more closely upon the outposts of the French.

Just at the time when all hope seemed lost, a herald made his way into the city, bearing glad news. Had Roland come at last? No; but Reinold, with eight thousand Scotch and English fighting-men, horse and foot, was but a day's journey away. Hope sprang anew in the hearts of the besieged, and their drooping spirits rallied. The next night, by means of bridge and boats, Reinold and his little army silently crossed the river, and early in the morning they attacked the besieging Moors. Reinold, on his famed horse Bayard, led the charge, leaving his brave Scots fully a bow-shot length behind. At very sight of the well-known hero, the Moorish lines began to waver; the lances quivered in the hands of the Pagan knights; their feet trembled in the stirrups; they were ready to retreat. Never had warrior been seen who rode with a prouder grace, or fought with greater skill. Well worthy was Reinold to be called a son of Mars. Many were the valiant feats of arms that he performed that day, and many were the foes who fell before him. At last, having splintered his good lance, he drew his sword Flamberge, and rode like a destroying hurricane into the Pagan ranks. Right and left the Saracens parted before him. Their arms seemed made of brittle glass, so easily were they shattered by the descending blade. Their bucklers of oak and tanned hides, their quilted vests and twisted turbans, seemed but as thinnest drapery under the lightning-strokes of Flamberge. And the swarm of Pagans who flocked to the field fell in his way like the yellow corn before the sickle of the reaper.

The battle thickened. The Moorish hosts for miles around

seemed aroused, and rushing to the combat. The trumpets bellowed forth their deep, sonorous battle-call. The drums beat to arms. On every side were heard the twang of the bow, the whiz of the sling, the crash of lances, dire shrieks, and dismal groans, and loud laments, and all the terrible din of battle. From the more distant parts of the field fresh recruits came and filled up the gaps which Reinold and his Scotchmen had made; and it seemed as though the number of the foe grew greater rather than less. The meadows which but yesterday had been so green and fair were red now with human blood; and where the violets and buttercups had bloomed before, now heaps of slain men and slaughtered steeds were seen.

While this fearful battle was raging outside of the walls, Rodomont, the fierce Algerian chief, rode around to the other side of the city. Single-handed he broke through the unguarded gates. From one street to another, like a raging lion, he roamed. On every hand he slew, he burned: he spared no one. Charlemagne, who was intent on aiding Reinold in front, knew nothing of this foe who had come in from the rear. Two thousand Englishmen had cut their way through the Moorish lines, and the gates were opened to receive and welcome them. The king was about to order a sally to be made; his warriors were in line, waiting his word of command, when suddenly a squire, all pale with dread, and panting for breath, rushed into his presence.

"Alas, alas!" he cried, scarcely able to say more, "the foe is within the walls! Turn, look around, and see the red flames and the curling smoke, and hear the cries of the terror-stricken townsfolk!"

Charlemagne waited not a moment. With his bravest

knights he turned, and hastened to meet and drive back this unexpected foe. But he found ruin and desolation everywhere. The palaces were burned; the churches were in flames; women and children were hurrying to and fro, seeking places of safety. The king, supposing that a large force of the Moors had broken through the walls, rallied his men around him, and made his way toward the citadel; for he gave up all else as lost, and thought to make a last stand in that strongly walled fortress. But Rodomont, drunk with blood and victory, and despising all mankind, with a sword in one hand and a torch in the other, was already there. He had followed the terror-stricken people to the very gates of the castle; and these he was shaking and smiting, as if he would force an entrance. From the roof above him the warders threw down every sort of missile they could lay hold of, hoping to crush their terrible foe. But Rodomont, fearless and unharmed, and like a demon glittering bright in his armor, still hewed furiously at the gate. At this moment the king and his knights hove upon the scene. Great was their surprise to learn that all this panic and destruction had been the work of a single man. All together they dashed upon the Pagan. Eight lances struck at once against the armor of Rodomont, but all glanced off harmless. The Algerian chief bore a charmed life, and easier would it be to pierce an anvil with a needle than to have smitten him with any weapon. At the call of Charlemagne other knights rushed upon the Pagan. They barricaded all outlets, and sought to take him prisoner. But Rodomont walked straight through their midst, and seemed not to think that any danger threatened him. With long steps and slow, he made his way toward the river; but he was hindered and galled on every side by a mob of knights and daring men-at-arms. Now and then he turned upon his foes, and fought them like a lion at bay. At length he reached the river-bank, and cast himself, all armed as he was, into the foaming water. Across the stream, without any seeming effort, he swam, as if borne up by corks and wafted by the wind. He climbed upon the farther shore, and, without looking back at his baffled foes, strode leisurely away.

Meanwhile the battle outside of the walls continued with ever-increasing fury. The carnage lulled not, nor slackened, but wilder grew, and worse. Many times the Moors began to waver; and they would have given way before the terrible onsets of Reinold and his Scotchmen, had they not been rallied by their gallant young chief, King Dardinel. This chief bore a shield upon which were red and white quarterings, the same as those emblazoned on Roland's arms; and very rare was his skill in combat, and very great his valor. And when Reinold saw that the fate of the battle depended upon him, he cried out, "This is an evil plant, which it were well to uproot ere it becomes too great and strong." Then, spurring his horse toward the young chieftain, he called out, "Poor child, whose buckler is that thou bearest? It is a dangerous thing for one like thee to carry. Come, show us how thou canst defend the chosen colors of our own chief Roland! Doubtless thou hast gotten them by fraud, and thou shalt lose them by force."

Dardinel was not at all dismayed by the threatening tone and manners of the Montalban hero. "More honor than dishonor shall be mine from these quarterings of red and white," he answered. "You shall see, that, though I am a child, I know well how to defend that which I bear. I trust in God, and I shall not disgrace my father's teaching."

When he had spoken, the boy raised his sword, and rushed manfully to the conflict. But his weapon fell harmlessly upon Reinold's helmet; and before he could turn about or defend himself, that knight dealt him so furious a blow in the breast, that he reeled in his saddle, and fell lifeless to the ground. As the violet uprooted by the plough lies fading in the scorching sunshine, or as the poppy droops its head and in its beauty dies, so perished this young flower of Moorish chivalry. And with him died the hopes of all his followers.

The Saracens, dismayed and beaten, now began a wild retreat, and had not Marsilius of Spain wisely led them into a fortified camp which he had made ready, some miles away, few, if any of them, would ever have escaped from France. That night the French host encamped upon the battlefield; and watchfires high and bright were built all around that bloody plain. And the remnant of the Moors lay uneasily behind their hastily built earthworks, and planned how they might steal away and escape under the friendly mantle of darkness.

ADVENTURE XXVI

MEDORO THE MOOR

In the Moorish camp were two young knights named Medoro and Cloridan, the bosom friends of the ill-fated Dardinel. Cloridan, the elder, was tall and slim and supple as the twig of hickory or of elm; and he loved the greenwood and the chase much better than the clashing of arms and the horrid scenes of war. Medoro was very fair, like a Saxon rather than a Moor; and his long golden hair fell in ringlets about his shoulders; while his jet black eyes snapped and sparkled like diamonds set in alabaster. Never has painter pictured an angel more beautiful than he.

On that sad night which followed the day of battle, the two young men, with others of the Moorish host, stood guard before the camp; and every word they spoke was of their lost lord Dardinel, whom they bewailed and mourned through the earlier watches of the night.

"Ah, Cloridan," Medoro said, "what grief it is to me that he whom we loved so well should lie unburied upon the plain, the food of the raven and the wolf! Gladly would I give up my own life to save his body from this last, most dread disgrace."

And then the two recounted together the noble deeds of the young chief, and talked long of his manly virtues and of the rare graces of his mind and heart. And at length Medoro, carried away by his feelings, cried out, "Cloridan, he shall not lie thus ingloriously upon the field of battle! I will go now, and find him where he fell, and give him a burial worthy of one so noble hearted. Do you stay here; and, if I come not to you again, you may say that I have died for the master whom we loved so well."

Cloridan was amazed to find in his comrade so much love and loyal devotion; and he would fain have dissuaded him from a venture so rash and full of danger. But Medoro was not to be moved from his purpose; rather would he die than forego that which he had resolved upon. So Cloridan, finding him deaf to all entreaties, persuaded him no more, but grasped his hand, and said, "Thou shalt not go alone, Medoro. I will be thy companion, and share with thee the danger and the glory. Rather would I die with thee in arms than that thou shouldst perish in this venture, and I be left to grieve for thee."

Then the youthful pair stole silently away from their post, and in the darkness of the night made their way to Charlemagne's camp. All there was still. The watchfires had burned low; and only an uncertain light was shed among the tents by the few red heaps of coals and the flickering flame of some half-extinguished torches. The sentinels, exhausted with the toil and the turmoil of the day, slept at their posts. In their tents, and around the smouldering watchfires, the soldiers lay asleep among their arms. About the field, with stealthy steps, wandered the two young Moors, eagerly seeking the place where their young master had fallen. Many were the strange sights which met their eyes as they carefully picked their way among the sleeping and the dead. Here, by the side of his tent, was the learned Alpheus, famed all the world over for his skill in magic and astrology. He had fallen asleep over his mystic charts and tables, while watching the stars and vainly trying to read his own doom. Near him lay a beastly drunkard, clasping an empty barrel in his arms, and dreaming of vine-clad hills and rivers flowing with wine. A little farther on sat a Greek and a Saxon, who had spent the larger part of the night over goblet and dice, and had at last fallen asleep in the midst of a game. Lightly trod the two Moors among the host of sleepers, and it is little wonder if they were tempted to avenge their friends by sheathing their bare blades in the bodies of their slumbering foes. By and by they halted in sight of Charlemagne's pavilion, where the barons and the noblest knights were tented; and they deemed it best to change their course, for it was not likely that all in that warlike company were carelessly sleeping. So they left the tents behind them, and groped their way across the field, where the thickest of the battle had been. Here they saw, lying side by side, or piled in horrid heaps, the dead and the dying, the king and his vassal, the lord and his tenant, the rider and his horse, friends, foes, broken lances, shields and helmets, and bows and falchions, and all the wrack and ruin that follow in the wake of pitiless war. And long did they seek among this dread confusion for the body of their loved Dardinel.

They were about giving up their search in despair, when suddenly the moon peeped out from behind a gloomy cloud, shedding a soft and ghostly radiance over the sad, silent scene. In front of them the young Moors saw the cold walls and high gray towers of the city, standing like great spectres in the pale light. Behind them were the white tents of their foes, in long lines, stretching many a rood on either side. The field of death upon which they stood seemed a thousand times more dread and lonely than when it was hidden beneath the cloak of darkness. Very near to them, on a spot where the moon seemed to shine the brightest, lay a warrior with his arms beside him. It was Dardinel: they knew him at once by his shield and its quarterings of white and red. Tenderly and reverently Medoro knelt beside the body of his young lord, and many tears he shed for the noble life so cruelly cut short. Then silently the youths lifted the king upon their shoulders, and with careful steps hurried from the field.

And now the dawn began to appear in the east, and the clouds which had seemed so dark became flecked with red and gold. The faithful young Moors were still far from their own camp; nor did they know that their friends had stolen away during the silent night-watches, and were now many leagues on the road toward Spain. Slowly and painfully they toiled forward with the burden on their shoulders, more fearful now of discovery than they had been while in the camp of their sleeping foes. Close by was a strip of thick woodland: if they could reach it, they would be safe. Suddenly a hundred horsemen who had been sent out to reconnoitre dashed into view. Before the young Moors could hide themselves, they were seen and pursued. The youths heard the ringing of armor and the clatter of horses' hoofs close behind them; yet such was their haste that they dared not look back.

"Let us save ourselves!" at length cried Cloridan. "It were folly for two lives to be lost for the sake of one who is already dead."

And he gently shifted his part of the burden from his shoulders, and ran as swiftly as he could to the friendly shelter of the grove. He doubted not but that Medoro was following close behind. But the poor boy would not desert his master, even to save his own life. Without saying a word, he took the whole of the burden upon his own shoulders, and slowly and painfully toiled onward. He reached the edge of the wood. Fiercely rode the horsemen down upon him, and thick flew the arrows about his head. He might yet have saved himself, had he been willing to leave the body of Dardinel. But he was sorely hindered and distressed. The place was strange to him, full of fallen trees and clumps of underbrush; and he was soon lost in its mazes. The horsemen, knowing the wood better than he, were not long in surrounding him. Cloridan, in his safe hiding-place, heard the loud cries of the pursuers, and then the voice of the boy Medoro defying them. It was not until then that he thought of his friend's danger.

"Ah!" cried he, "why was I so careless thus to think of my own safety only?—Medoro, I will save thee, or die with thee!"

He ran from his hiding-place back toward the more open ground. He saw Medoro, followed closely by a hundred rude soldiers, running hither and thither among the trees, but all the time clinging closely to the cherished body of young Dardinel. At last, wearied, and in despair, the youth laid his burden down upon the grass, and, like a wild beast at bay, stood over it and faced his foes. And now Cloridan, eager to save his friend, fitted the sharpest arrow to his bow, and from behind a leafy tree let it fly among the horsemen. So well aimed was the shaft, that it struck a Scotch knight fairly in the forehead, and stretched him helpless upon the ground. The rest of the band, surprised at this unlooked-for blow, turned to see from whence it came; and Cloridan, quickly launching a second arrow, laid another horseman low. Fiercely, then, the leader of the soldiers dashed toward Medoro; he seized him by his long golden curls; he dragged him roughly forward, and drew his sword to slay him. But when he saw the lad's angel face upturned toward him, he paused.

"Ah, kind knight," said Medoro, "I pray, for the sake of the God whom thou adorest, be not so passing cruel as to slay me ere I have buried my master. No other favor do I ask, nor do I wish to live longer than to see the kind earth cover his dear body."

The sweet, persuasive words of the boy would have moved the stoniest heart. The captain listened, and fain would have spared him and let him go; but a churlish fellow, rude and brutish, rode suddenly forward, and smote Medoro with his lance. The captain's heart was deeply stirred within him at sight of this base act, and, full of sorrow and wrath, he sprang toward the unfeeling wretch, intending to strike him down. But he, marking his danger, gave spurs to his steed, and fled.

When Cloridan saw Medoro fall bleeding to the ground, he could no longer hold himself, but, springing from his covert, he ran to meet his foes. He cast his bow aside; he brandished his sword above his head; he charged furiously among the horsemen. A dozen weapons pierced him at once: the leaves and flowers were tinged with his blood, and dying he fell by young Medoro's side.

"Come, my men," cried the captain, growing heart-sick at sight of this sad scene,—"come away! Let us have no more such work as this. It is not the part of true knights to slay young, unoffending boys."

And the whole company turned about, and followed their chief out of the wood and back to the camp of Charlemagne. And there, side by side, lay the two young Moors upon the blood-stained grass,—the one dead, the other sadly wounded, the life-blood streaming from his veins. And the loved prince for whom they had risked so much and lost all, lay in his steelly armor by them. And there Medoro would have died, had not help come soon and unexpectedly.

It so happened that a young maiden journeyed through the wood that day, and chance brought her near the spot where the three Moors lay. She was clad in the rustic garb of a peasant; yet she was very fair, and her noble face betrayed her kinship with noble men. It was Angelica, the Princess of Cathay. By some means—it matters not what—she had gotten her magic ring again; and now she was on her way back to her eastern home, fearing no danger, and scorning the thought that she had ever asked the aid of living knight. When she saw the young Moor lying, bleeding and uncared for, upon the ground, her heart was touched with a feeling of pity such as she had never known before. She knelt upon the grass beside him, and listened while he told the story of his sad adventure.

"Be of good cheer," she said when he had finished, "I will save you."

Then she called to mind the half-forgotten knowledge of physic and surgery which she had learned in Cathay, and she began to bind up his wounds. In a meadow which she had crossed that morning she had seen a plant of wondrous virtue, which she knew would stop the flow of blood and ease every pain, and she resolved to go back and get it. So, bidding Medoro wait patiently and hopefully till she came again, she hastily retraced her way, and stopped not until she had found and plucked up the precious weed. As she was running back again, she met a peasant riding through the wood.

"Ah, kind sir!" said she, "I pray you come with me. A gentle youth lies in the greenwood, wounded unto death. Come and help him, and the fairies shall bring you good luck and happiness all the days of your life."

The good swain, although loath at first, could not resist the maid's persuasive pleading, but rode back with her to the place where Medoro lay. They found the youth very faint from loss of blood, and nigh, indeed, to death's door. Quickly Angelica bruised the healing plant between two stones, and squeezed the juice upon the young man's wounds. Then soon Medoro began to revive. The blood stopped flowing; the color came again into his cheeks; he staggered to his feet; he was strong enough to sit on the peasant's horse. Yet he would not leave the place until his lord, King Dardinel, and his young friend Cloridan, were laid in the earth. In a grave which the peasant scooped out beneath the trees they laid the bodies of the two noble knights, and covered them with turf and soft moss and the grassy sod. And then Medoro gave himself up to his new-found friends, and was ready to go whithersoever they should lead him.

The countryman was moved alike by the rare beauty of the maiden and the noble bearing of the knight; and he urged them to go with him to his own home,—a pleasant farm-house in a green and flowery valley. And thither they went; the wounded youth riding the peasant's horse, while the maiden and the countryman walked on either side. Glad was the welcome with which the peasant's wife and children greeted them at the cottage. The best room was set apart for Medoro's use; and Angelica, not wishing to lay aside her humble disguise, became as one of the family, and cheerfully helped the good housewife in her daily round of duties. And many years afterward, when the two lived in a gorgeous palace, with every luxury at hand, they were fain to remember this time as the happiest period of their lives.

And there the princess and the noble young Moor lived many a week with the kind-hearted peasant folk; nor would Angelica leave her patient until his dangerous wound had healed. At first she had felt only a strange pity for him; but as day after day she gazed into the depths of his flashing eyes, and listened to the pleasant words which fell from his lips, a deeper and far different feeling possessed her. And, when he grew strong enough to walk about in the open air, the two spent whole days together in the greenwood, listening to the song birds, and gathering flowers and ferns, and talking of the great world of which they knew so little and yet so much. And sometimes, to amuse Angelica, Medoro would carve their names upon the rocks and trees. In divers ways, in ciphers quaintly interlaced, he graved the words, ANGELICA, MEDORO. And, ere the summer had fled, the princess and the knight were wedded in the peasant's humble dwelling, and two happy hearts beat henceforth as one.

And when at length the days began to grow shorter, and the autumn leaves to fall, Angelica bethought her of returning to Cathay, where she intended to share all her honors with Medoro. They had no money wherewith to pay their humble friends for their kindness, nor, indeed, did the good peasants wish any reward. But, as they were about to depart, Angelica took from her wrist a golden armlet rich with rarest gems, and bade her hostess keep it always in memory of them.

Then with many kind godspeeds, and many tears, the noble couple turned away from the cottage, and took the highroad that runs toward Spain. Together they climbed the rugged Pyrenees, and descended into the sunny plains beyond; and not many weeks later they came to Barcelona, where they made themselves known, and where they waited for a vessel to sail and bear them to their distant home.

ADVENTURE XXVII

A CONTEST FOR DURANDAL

Roland came to the scene of battle only a single day too late. The victory, as we have seen, had been won through Reinold's valor. The Pagan hosts, beaten and disheartened, were flying toward Spain. France was freed from her great peril. Roland felt mortified and ashamed, that, while others had been fighting for their country's honor, he had been delayed in the air-built castle of the magician Atlantes. Yet Charlemagne and his peers welcomed him as heartily as if he had come in the time of need; and a day was set apart for glad thanksgiving, not only for the great victory which they had gained over their foes, but also for the safe return of the hero whom they had mourned as lost. And it was long ere Marsilius, or Agramant, or any other Saracen chief, dared lead his hosts again into France.

After this, Roland did many noble deeds of arms for the honor of France and Christendom. I cannot stop to tell you now of his gallant feats at Rome when that city was besieged by Laban and Lukafere, the kings of Babylon; nor of his famous passage-at-arms with the Pagan Sir Ferumbras; nor how he fought and slew the giant Ferragus, a monster thirty feet high, and the terror of the Christian host; nor how he conquered Sir Otuel of Spain in fair fight, and forced him to submit to baptism. All these stories, and many more, you may read in the songs and poems of the old days of chivalry. While everywhere there were tyranny and wrong-doing, Roland, with his strong arm and manly voice, sought to defend the right and uphold justice. The vows which he had taken upon entering knighthood were ever in his mind; and he deemed that his life could not be spent more worthily than in the service of his country, his king, and his fellow-men.

Once on a time, as he was riding through a mountainous country near the sea, he found himself belated and overtaken by the darkness of night, while yet he was many miles from any dwelling. As he looked around to find some place of shelter, he was surprised to see a light streaming from a narrow cleft in the mountain side. Did it come from the cell of a hermit who had hidden himself in this lonesome place in order to escape from the bustle and bloodshed of those cruel times? Or did it betray the hiding-place of robbers,—of men whose hands were lifted against their fellow-men, and who cared nought for knighthood's vows or valorous deeds? Roland did not stop long to consider. Whatever kind of dwelling it might be from which this light came, he was determined to enter it and demand a night's lodging. In front of the entrance to the cave was a great thicket of thorns and bristly underwood,—so dense that any one passing that way in the daytime would not have noticed any break in the rock. It was not likely that a hermit would thus guard and conceal the entrance to his cell.

The knight tied Brigliadoro to the branch of an elm, and stealthily threaded his way through the thicket. It was not hard to find the narrow door of the cavern, for the bright light streaming through it showed him plainly the way to go. A short flight of narrow steps cut rudely in the stone led downward into a vaulted chamber, which seemed chiselled out of the solid rock. The smoke-begrimed ceiling was very high; and through an opening in the centre, which served at once as window and chimney, the twinkling stars looked down. Upon the floor beneath this opening a bright fire burned, casting a ruddy glow around the room, and lighting up the doorway, and sending its rays far out into the darkness beyond. Before this fire sat a damsel, very young and very fair, clad in a garb which Roland thought would have been better suited to a palace or a king's court than to this dismal place. Her great blue eyes were swollen with much weeping; yet she was so exceedingly fair, that her very presence seemed to drive all gloom from the cheerless place. Seated on the floor, not far away, was an old hag, withered and gray and toothless, who was mumbling and scolding and cursing, as if in a terrible rage about something. Roland, seeing that these two were the only persons in the room, advanced, and kindly saluted them. Both dame and damsel were greatly surprised at the sight of a knight in armor standing thus unexpectedly before them; but they arose quietly, and each, in her way, welcomed him to their cavern home. The old hag, like one who is afraid of the day, shrank from the hero's gaze, and cowering sought the deeper shadows of the room. But the maiden, with hope beaming in her fair countenance, looked up with tearful, pleading eyes, into his face. The knight knew at once how matters stood in that rude dwelling.

"Tell me," said he kindly to the maiden, "why thou art imprisoned in this cheerless place. Who is it that is so void of gentleness and manly feeling as to bury thee in this mountain dungeon?"

Then, with floods of tears rolling down her cheeks, the maiden told him her sad story. She told him that she was the only daughter of the old Saracen king of Gallicia, and that her name was Isabella; that she had been secretly betrothed to Zerbino, the son of Scotland's king; that, without the consent of her father, she had embarked on shipboard at Bayonne, intending to follow her lover to his own country; and that on the first night of the voyage a great storm had arisen, and had driven the vessel upon the shore, where it was wrecked among the high, pointed rocks.

"The captain saw well our danger," said she. "He lowered the galley's skiff, put me in it, and, with two of his men, embarked among the breakers. Landward over the raging surf we were driven; and, what was little short of a miracle, we safely lighted on a shelving beach. The shore was bleak and barren. No dwelling was in sight, nor any pathway, but only bare cliffs, and high, wood-crowned hills. Yet the first thing that I did was to fall upon my knees, and offer up thanks to kind Heaven for our deliverance. But, alas! I found that I had been snatched from the waves, only to fall into the hands of foes more pitiless than the sea and the storm. A band of pirates who infest these shores, and who had seen the wreck from the cliffs above, rushed down upon us ere we were aware. Vainly did the good captain and his men try to defend me. The robbers slew them on the beach, but they harmed me not. I was a rich prize, they said, and some time I should be sold for a high price to some wealthy Moorish prince. And they brought me to this cave, and gave me into the care of this old dame, who is my jailer. And here for weary months I have been imprisoned as in a living grave, scarce hoping ever to be free."

While yet the damsel was speaking, a company of men

came silently down the stairway, and stood in the cave. They were rude, brutish-looking fellows, some armed with hunting spears, and some with swords; and they paused in surprise at sight of the knight seated before the fire, and eagerly listening to the maiden's story.

"Ah, my good man!" cried the leader of the band, "thou hast come in the very nick of time. I have long wanted a good suit of armor; and that which thou wearest will certainly serve me well."

With a look of scorn upon his face, Roland turned, and faced the robber crew. "If you win these arms," said he to the leader, "you shall pay a dear price for them."

Then, disdaining to use his sword against foes so vile, he seized a burning brand, and hurled it fiercely among them; and, picking up a heavy table that stood close by, he dealt such lusty blows about him, that those of the robbers who were not entirely disabled were glad to save themselves by a disgraceful flight. He waited not to see whether they would return; but he took the maiden Isabella by the hand, and led her out of her prison.

"I have heard of the Scottish chief Zerbino," said he. "He follows now the banner of my cousin Reinold of Montalban; and there are but few braver knights than he. Come with me, and we will find him."

With this he mounted Brigliadoro and lifted the maiden to a place behind him. Then the two wended their way through the forest. As they rode along the silent paths, the stars moved slowly across the gray sky above them, and the moon journeyed far to the west, and sank in the ocean waves; and the red dawn began to appear in the east. And just as the sun arose they found themselves standing on the brow of a wooded hill, while in the valley below them was a small village, or cluster of peasants' houses; and farther away, on the brow of another hill, was an old, half-ruined castle.

There seemed to be a great excitement in the little village, if one might judge from the uproar which was heard. The dogs were barking; the men were shouting, the women scolding, the children crying; every one was running hither and thither, as if the world were coming to an end. On the farther edge of the village a small company of knights was seen slowly approaching, with long pennons floating above them.

"Wait here," said Roland to his fair charge, as he helped her to alight. "I will ride forward, and see what is going on."

Isabella concealed herself among the thick underwoods, while Roland gave spurs to Brigliadoro and was soon galloping through the single street of the village. It did not take him long to find out the cause of the commotion which he had observed. The knights with the pennons were the men of Count Anselm of Mayence, and they were leading a prisoner to execution. The people were wild with excitement, and kept shouting, "Death to the traitor! Off with him!"

Roland rode close up to the procession; and the country folk, being unused to a knight of so noble a mien, parted right and left before him, and allowed him to advance until he was very near to the prisoner. You may judge of his surprise when he saw that this man was none other than Zerbino, the Scottish cavalier in quest of whom he had so lately set out. The young man was fettered with ugly chains, and bound to the back of a draught horse; and he sat with drooping head and downcast eyes, scarcely noticing the jeers and threats of the rude rabble.

"What is the meaning of this?" cried Roland. "What has this man done?"

"He is a murderer," answered one of the guards. "Count Pinabel, son of our master, Anselm of Mayence, was found dead yesterday in the mountain glen; and this is the man who slew him."

"It is false!" said Zerbino, not raising his head.

"It is true!" said the man. "For he came last night to the village inn for lodging, and while he was there the body of poor Pinabel was carried in. No sooner had this man come near than the wounds of the slain knight began to bleed afresh. There is no surer proof of guilt than that."

"Ay," cried the rabble, "there is no surer proof!"

"Untie the man!" said Roland. And he swept his lance around him, and knocked a score of the rude fellows prone into the dust. "Untie him, and let him go!"

Zerbino raised his head, and turned to see his deliverer. The crowd of angry churls fell back, and began to disperse. The rude fellows were not more afraid of the knight's long lance and glittering sword than of his flashing eye and towering form. Within three minutes the road was cleared: guards, peasants, and all were flying across the fields, eager to escape the fury of the hero. Roland and Zerbino were left alone. It was but the work of a moment to sever the cords and break the chains with which the prisoner was bound. Then, full of thankfulness for his unexpected delivery from death, Zerbino went back to the inn where he had stopped, and donned the armor which had been taken from him. He found his steed still feeding in the stable; and, having mounted him, he rode out of the village proudly by Roland's side. You may judge of his surprise when he met the fair Isabella on the hilltop; and as for her—no happier maiden ever lived than she. And the three friends left the village behind them and turned their faces northward, intending to make their way by the shortest route to Paris.

They had not ridden far, however, when they were overtaken by a tall and powerful knight, clad in the richest armor they had ever seen, and bearing a shield on which were engraven the arms of Trojan Hector. It was none other than Mandricardo, the Tartar chief to whom Fortune had given the arms which Roland had at one time so greatly coveted. Long time had he sought Roland, for he wished to win from him the doughty blade Durandal. As he rode up, he scanned the two knights with curious, searching eyes; but most he gazed at Roland; for he knew by his bearing that he was no common knight. At last he spoke.

"Thou art the man I seek," said he. "For ten days I have followed thee. I have heard of thy deeds, and I have sought thee long,—first to see thee, and second to prove thy might."

"And how knowest thou that I am the man?" asked Roland.

"By thy port and thy haughty bearing," answered Mandricardo. "I would know thee as a hero among ten thousand."

"Thou, too, mayst be a valiant cavalier," said Roland; "for brave desire is not often lodged in weak minds. If thou wouldst fain see me, I will lay aside my helm that thou mayst look. Yet thou must know that a man's heart is not always seen in his face."

He lifted his helmet, and the Tartar looked long at his noble face.

"Thou hast gratified my first wish," then said Mandricardo. "The second still remains. Come on, let us prove whether thy valor is equal to thy good looks!"

Roland looked with surprise at the Tartar; for although he examined on both sides, and even in the pommel of his saddle, he could see about him neither sword nor mace.

"You have no sword," said he courteously. "How will you save yourself if your lance should fail?"

"Know thou," said the Tartar proudly, "that I am Mandricardo, and that I bear the arms which great Hector bore a thousand years ago. To them there is nothing lacking save the sword Durandal, which I am told one Roland of France carries. And I have vowed that never shall mace or falchion be wielded by my hand until I win that doughty blade, and avenge my father Agrican, whom that same Roland treacherously slew."

"Not so!" cried Roland, growing angry. "Thou liest! Never slew I any man treacherously. I am Roland, and this blade is Durandal, the sword thou seekest. Win it, and thou shalt have it. See, I hang it on this tree, and he who conquers in this combat shall have it."

So saying, he hung the sword on the limb of a sapling close to the highway; and the two knights, turning their horses, rode off the distance of a bow-shot from each other. Then, wheeling suddenly, they plied their spurs, and rushed together with a shock like that of an earthquake. The lances of both were shivered into a thousand pieces, only the staff-ends being left in their hands. With these club-like fragments they then engaged, beating each other most mercilessly over shoulders and head. Soon these weapons, too, were splintered, and the combatants were without arms. They would have fought with their fists; but wherefore, when he who strikes suffers more than he who is smitten? As a last resort, they grappled with each other; and the Tartar chief strained Roland to his bosom as if he would squeeze the breath from his body. In his earnest fury he thoughtlessly dropped the rein of his horse's bridle. Roland, sitting firm in his saddle, saw his opportunity, and quickly slipped the bridle from the horse's head. The steed, frightened, and feeling himself free, started off with a bound: little recking whether his road were smooth or rough, he galloped swiftly away over fields, and through the woodland, carrying his unwilling master with him.

Roland waited a long time for the Tartar's return, and finally bethought him that he would follow and overtake him. So he bade Zerbino and Isabella a heartfelt godspeed on their way to Paris, and set out in search of his enemy. For three days he sought him, but all in vain: he could find no traces of either the Tartar or his horse. On the fourth day he gave up the venture, and turned his face once more toward Paris and the court of Charlemagne, from which he had been long time absent.

ADVENTURE XXVIII

HOW ROLAND BECAME HIS OWN SHADOW

It chanced one day that Roland came to a pleasant woodland, which was bordered on one side by a meadow and on the other by a hoary mountain. Tall trees lifted their heads toward the sky, seeking the sunlight, and defying the storm; climbing vines formed many a pleasant arbor among the trunks and branches; and cool bowers invited the tired knight to take shelter within them from the hot beams of the midsummer sun. A mountain brook, whose banks were bordered with wildflowers of every hue, wound here and there among the trees, singing on its way to the grassy meadow beyond; and the air was filled with the smell of fragrant blossoms and the sound of drowsily humming bees. Our hero was weary with his long journey, and overcome with the excessive heat. For many days he had been on the road, scarcely stopping for a night's rest, or to partake of needed food. This grove seemed so cool and inviting, that he determined to dismount and sit for a while in the shade. There was a strange throbbing in his head; the blood in his veins seemed boiling hot; his pulse beat hard and fast. He had never felt so miserable. He loosened his helmet, and laid it upon the grass; he knelt down, and drank a long, refreshing draught from the flowing brook; and then he bathed his feverish temples in the cool liquid, and lay down among the flowers to rest. By and by he arose, but he felt not a whit better than before. He looked up at the great trees which lifted their heads so high above him: he admired their gnarled branches, and their smooth, sturdy trunks. On one of them he noticed some strange letters carved, and he wondered what they could mean. He went nearer, and saw that they formed the word "ANGELICA." He thought it strange that the name of the Cathayan princess should be engraved in this out-of-the-way place; and yet she herself might have carved it while resting here in the shade, just as he was doing. He walked a little farther into the grove, and saw the name again; but this time another—"MEDORO"—was written beneath it. Who was Medoro? He had never heard of such a person, but the name had a Moorish sound about it. Farther on, the trees seemed covered with these names written in every conceivable way,—in letters Arabic, Roman, and German. Even the rocks were scribbled over with chalk and charcoal, and always with the words "Angelica, Medoro." Filled with a nameless feeling of disgust, Roland turned away. He mounted his good Brigliadoro, and rode forward on his journey.

But he did not ride far. In the valley between the mountains he saw blue smoke rising from a shepherd's cottage; he heard the bleating of sheep and lambs, the lowing of cattle, and the glad voices of children. He thought that this would be a pleasant place to rest until the morrow, and he determined to stop. As he rode into the yard, the shepherd met him, and asked him to alight, for the sun was sinking, and night was at hand. A boy ran forward, and led Brigliadoro to the stables, while Roland and his kind host walked side by side into the house. All the good folk of the cottage were eager to serve the warrior. One took his shield, another his helmet, a third his cuirass, and a fourth his golden spurs. The shepherd himself, with becoming reverence, took care of the dread blade Durandal, all sheathed in its gemmed and golden scabbard; and the good wife busied herself in making ready the evening meal,—a meal such as should be worthy of so noble a guest.

As Roland, well pleased with his lodgings, looked about him, he was surprised to see that the walls and rafters of the humble dwelling were scribbled over with the same words that he had seen on the trees in the grove,—"ANGELICA, MEDORO." The shepherd noticed his wonderment, and, being a talkative fellow, was not long in telling him the whole story. He related how the young Moor had been sadly wounded, and how he had been nursed back to life by the fair and gentle Princess of Cathay; and how, at length, the handsome pair had been married, and had gone away to their home in the golden East.

"And if you don't believe it," said the swain, seeing a strange, wandering look in the warrior's face, "I will prove the truth of my story; for we have here the fair maiden's bracelet. She gave it to my wife as a keepsake."

And he brought from an inner room a golden armlet which Roland remembered as the same which he himself had given, long time before, to the handsome maiden of Cathay. He gazed at the pretty ornament a moment, and then silently gave it back to his host. His eyes seemed dazed; and there was a strange feeling about his brows and temples, such as he had never before known. His hostess pressed him to eat of the food which she placed before him,—fresh venison from the woodland, the whitest loaves made from the farmer's own wheat, wild honey from the wooded mountain slopes, and all the delicacies that the good woman knew. But he would taste nothing. Somehow, the words, "Angelica, Medoro," rang in his ears, and burned in letters of fire before his eyes, and so filled his mind that he could think of nothing else.

Some men say that our hero had been deeply and madly in love with the Princess of Cathay, and that all his distress at this time was caused by his feelings of disappointment.* But I cannot think so; for the fair and heroic Alda, the sister of Oliver, had long been betrothed to him, and waited now for him in Paris, and prayed for his happy return. More likely it was the tiresome journey over dusty roads and in the broiling sunshine, that set Roland's brain on fire, and made him forget himself so long.

The best bed in the only spare chamber was given to Roland, and there, through the long hours of the night, he tossed in pain; and whether he closed his eyes, or gazed about the room, those two fatal words, "Angelica, Medoro," were ever present to his sight. The morning came; and still the warrior lay upon his bed, but not in pain. His mind wandered far away to his mother the gentle Bertha, or to Alda his betrothed; or sometimes he thought himself in the din of battle, fighting manfully for the king and sweet France; or he dreamed that he was again in Fairyland, among the cooling waterfalls and shady groves, listening to the songs of the birds and the hum of the bees and the gay music of the fairies. Day after day he lay in the quiet, darkened chamber, carefully watched and tended by the good shepherd and his wife. And more than once did he step down very near to the dark door of death, but good nursing and ceaseless care saved him. Little by little, he grew stronger and stronger; yet he was not the same Roland. He did not know where he was: he fancied the humble room

*So says Ariosto in the Orlando Furioso.

wherein he lay to be a lofty chamber in some grand castle; and, instead of the good host and hostess, he saw by his bedside his brother knights and ready squires and pages in waiting. And when, one day, the kind housewife drew aside the curtains, and allowed him to look out over the meadows, and the fields of ripening corn, he thought himself again a barefoot boy, wandering among the byways of Sutri and longing for the time when he should be one of Charlemagne's peers. And the country folk could not understand why it was that, while his body grew hale and strong again, his mind still remained clouded.

"I am not the Roland whom you think me to be," he said. "That Roland is dead, and I am his shadow."

One day, after he had gotten strong enough to sit up, he amazed his host by calling for his armor.

"The king is in danger," he cried. "I must ride to the rescue."

He donned his coat of mail, and put on his greaves and his helmet. The shepherd's wife buckled on his golden spurs; and the shepherd brought him his shield and his good sword Durandal.

"Where now is my horse Brigliadoro?" he asked. "Without him, I shall fare but ill on the battlefield."

They had hoped, that, after his arms were girded on him, he would forget this last illusion; and they tried to persuade him that the king was in no need of help. But he would not listen. He must have his steed, and he must ride at once to Charlemagne. The peasant's son led the horse, all caparisoned in steel and gold, to the cottage door. The noble beast was impatient for a canter across the plains, or another encounter in the tourney or on the battlefield; and he neighed with pleasure at sight of his master. The knight mounted him, and rode down the hill-slope toward the wooded plain and the meadow. The way led him through the grove where he had stopped and rested on that afternoon when last he was himself. He saw the trees and the rocks still bearing the words, "Angelica, Medoro;" and a nameless fury filled his soul. He fancied now that he was in the thick of battle, and that giant foes beset him on every side. He drew his sword, and smote madly about him. Wherever he saw the hated names engraved, there he hacked and cut, until not a single letter remained. He alighted from his horse, and hewed down the underbrush, and filled the mountain brook with stones and turf. And after he had exhausted all his strength he seemed to grow calmer. He stopped, and stood a long time, as if in thought.

"I am not the Roland whom some take me to be," he said, speaking to himself. "I am only the shadow of that knight, and shadows need no arms." And then, moved by a sudden freak of madness, he threw his sword upon the ground: he rushed from one part of the wood to another, all the while loosening and tearing off his armor. In one place he left his shield, and in another his helmet; while farther away he doffed, one by one, his gauntlets and his greaves, his breastplate, and lastly his golden spurs. Then, with loud cries that were echoed among the mountains, and even carried back to the kind peasant's cottage, he strode aimlessly away, nobody knew whither. Well was it, that in those dark and troublous times people were wont to look with awe upon the madman, and regard him as one specially protected by Heaven; for, had it been otherwise, the sad shadow of Roland would have fared but badly, wandering alone through strange and unfriendly lands.

HOW ROLAND BECAME HIS OWN SHADOW

It happened, not long after this, that a knight and a lady rode by that way. The knight was Zerbino, the Scottish cavalier; and the lady was the fair Isabella. As they approached the woodland, they were surprised to find the golden spurs of Roland lying in the dust by the roadside. A little farther on, they saw other pieces of his armor, and lastly his shield and sword. And as they looked about them, wondering what all this meant, they espied the good steed Brigliadoro, calmly grazing in the meadow, his bridle reins hanging loose from the saddle-bow. They noticed that the trees around them had been strangely hacked and hewed, and that the grass and flowers had been rudely trampled down; but they could see no signs of bloodshed, nor of any conflict with arms. The longer they paused and studied about this matter, the more puzzled they became.

While yet they stood, uncertain what to do, the shepherd's son came down the road, on his way to the sheep pasture. He stopped, and told them the whole story of Roland's long illness, and of the strange madness which had seized upon him.

"Alas!" said Zerbino, "our brave friend is no longer himself. Yet, when his fury is all spent, his senses may return to him, and he will need his good arms. We will take care that they are not lost."

Then he carefully gathered up all the pieces of that matchless armor, and hung them on the branches of a pine-tree by the roadside. And beneath them he carved in the soft bark these words: "THESE ARE THE ARMS OF ROLAND." And he knew that no true knight who read this inscription would remove or disturb them. When he had done all that could be done for the honor of his noble friend, Zerbino remounted his steed; and, leading Brigliadoro behind them, he and the fair Isabella went on their way.

Scarcely were the Scottish knight and his companion well out of sight, when the sound of clattering hoofs and ringing armor was heard far down the road; and the shepherd's boy, who still lingered near the pine, admiring the richness and beauty of Roland's armor, saw a tall knight riding fast toward the spot. He was mounted on a white steed, and was clad in a coat-of-mail whose brightness rivalled that of the sun. On his arm he bore a shield of great splendor, and his crested helmet glistened with many a jewel. Yet he wore no sword at his side; and his lance, which was new, seemed a very inferior one. This knight was Mandricardo the Tartar chief. When he saw Roland's arms hanging upon the pine, he halted, and drew near to read the inscription. Twice he read it; and then, to make sure that there was no mistake, he scanned with great care every piece and part of the armor, but looked most at the sword Durandal.

"Ha!" cried he in great delight, "this is indeed the blade of Trojan Hector."

He drew it from its scabbard, and looked with pleased eyes upon its fire edge, and read the quaint inscription on its side. He admired its jewelled hilt, and tested its temper by bending its blade into a perfect circle, and by hewing the trees and rocks around him. Then he turned suddenly toward the trembling boy.

"How came this armor here?" he asked in tones of thunder.

The boy told him the story of Roland's madness, and how he had thrown his armor away and run roaring into the forest; and how Zerbino had picked up the pieces and hung them on the pine.

"I understand it all," said the Tartar. "The fellow is not mad: he is only feigning. He has left his armor here only because he knew that he was not strong enough to keep the sword Durandal. He is afraid to make trial of arms with me again, and he has taken this plan to present the sword to its rightful owner. I shall take it, but small thanks shall I render to him."

Then he unbuckled the scabbard and the jewelled belt, and fastened them to his own armor. After again glancing at the shining edge and the richly carved sides of Durandal, he quietly returned it to its sheath. "My long quest," he said, "has not been in vain. With Hector's arms complete, who now can contend with Mandricardo?" And, striking spurs into his horse's flanks, he turned and galloped back in the same direction whence he had come.

In the meanwhile whither wandered the shadow of the mighty Roland? Aimlessly, as one walking in his sleep, he roamed through the forests, and over fields and desert wastes. At night he slept in the open air, with no shelter but the blue vault of heaven. His only food was the wild fruits of the forest,—nuts and berries,—and, when these failed, the bark of trees. He shunned the dwellings and faces of men, and seemed to have forgotten his own manhood. A thousand times was his life in peril, and a thousand times did some mysterious power shield and save him. Sometimes, in his lonely wanderings, he encountered wolves and bears and other fierce beasts of the wood; but they harmed him not, for they knew that he was but the shadow of a man. Sometimes he was endangered by storms and floods, but the good fairies who guard the lives of heroes led him safely through them. And he wandered in the darkness of night among the mountain crags, and on the edge of steep cliffs, and amid pitfalls and bottomless gorges; but an unseen Power guided his footsteps, and no harm befell him. Then he went southward, and climbed the Pyrenees, and crossed over into the country of the Spanish Moors. And there a strange adventure happened to him.

Rodomont, the warrior king of Algiers, of whom I have elsewhere told you, had withdrawn into Spain, breathing words of bitterness and hate to all mankind. He had done many very wicked deeds and slain many innocent and hapless folk, and he was ever haunted by the remembrance of his wrong doings; and so he not only hated others, but himself also, and sought some means of escaping from his gloomy, guilty thoughts. So he caused to be built in a narrow mountain pass, a tall tower of solid mason work, in the centre of which he placed a little chapel and the tomb of some of his most noble victims. On three sides of the tower there ran a mountain stream, swift and deep, the water as cold as the ice-cliffs from which it was fed. Across this stream a wooden bridge was built, scarce two yards wide, and guarded by neither rail nor banister. Upon the tower a sentinel stood, to give notice when any strange knight should approach the bridge. Rodomont himself sat in a narrow chamber, like a giant in his cave, ready to ride out and meet any new-comer—not with warm words of welcome, but with couched lance and hoarse cries of defiance; for he had vowed that he would not rest until he should have the arms of a thousand knights wherewith to deck the strange tomb that he had built. And he obliged every one who came that way, either to fight him on the bridge, or to give up his arms to him as a trophy. From time to time, many knights had fallen into

The madness of Roland.

his trap. Some, from mere bravado and love of adventure, had come thither on purpose to meet him in combat on the bridge; but the greater number of his victims were innocent travellers, who had been belated in the mountains, and had ventured to seek shelter in his inhospitable tower. Some had been, at the first onset, knocked off the bridge, and drowned in the raging torrent below: others had been taken captive by the Algerian, their arms hung up as trophies, and they themselves thrown into a dungeon.

One day the sentinel called out, as usual, to his master, that some one was approaching the bridge. Rodomont quickly mounted his war steed, and, with lance in rest, galloped out to meet the intruder. But, when he saw what kind of man it was who stood on the other end of the bridge, he paused. Who would have dreamed that it was Roland? His clothing was mere tatters and rags; his feet were bare; his long hair fell in tangled masses upon his shoulders. He glanced uneasily at the raging waters beneath him, and then at the high tower beyond; then his eyes rested upon the mailed warrior who confronted him at the other end of the bridge, and some of the old fire which had so often amazed his foes in battle seemed to flash from beneath his shaggy brows.

"Go back!" cried Rodomont. "Keep off the bridge! It was not built for such as thou."

Roland heard the words, and dimly understood their meaning. He was not wont to obey commands, nor could he ever brook an insult. Instead of doing as the Algerian bade him, he walked boldly upon the bridge. The angry Rodomont at once dismounted, threw his lance to the ground, and went forward on foot to meet him.

"Turn back, and save thyself!" he cried. "Thou art not worthy to be touched with lance or sword; but, if thou come another step, I will throw thee into the torrent below us."

Roland said not a word, but strode fiercely onward. The two met at the middle of the bridge. They grappled each other. But the struggle was a short one. Roland lifted the Algerian giant in his arms as if he had been a child, and held him dangling over the side of the bridge; then, with all his strength, he flung him down into the roaring waters below. But the madman had not wit enough to free himself altogether from the grasp of his enemy; and losing his balance, he, too, fell into the stream. The waves dashed high about them; but the water was deep, and both escaped being dashed upon the rocks. Roland swam at once to the shore, and climbed out of the gorge, and went on his way, aimlessly and thoughtlessly as before, toward the south. And Rodomont, after being drifted far down the stream, was cast upon a sand bank, whence, with the greatest hardship, he at length succeeded in reaching the shore.

It so happened, that while Roland and the Algerian chief were struggling on the bridge, a maiden of France, named Flordelis, was passing by. She had been brought up at Charlemagne's court, and had known Roland all her life. So, when she saw him in his pitiable plight, wrestling with the fierce Rodomont, she knew, notwithstanding his rags and his unkempt hair, that he was none other than the hero whom all Christendom mourned as dead. She watched the issue of the fight with the greatest anxiety; and when he had fallen into the stream, and clambered to the shore again, she tried to approach him and speak with him. But he fled so fast through the mountain pass, that he far outstripped the palfrey which she rode, and was soon out of sight. For three days she sought him among the mountains and the valleys; but all that she could hear or learn of him was that some Moorish peasants had seen him, making his way with long and hasty strides toward the south. And so she gave up the search, and rode back to France, to tell Charlemagne and his peers, that Roland, the noblest warrior of them all, was still alive.

ADVENTURE XXIX

A FLIGHT TO THE LAND OF PRESTER JOHN

King Charlemagne sat in his council-hall, and the noblest peers of the realm stood before him.

"Who now, for the love of our dear nephew," said he, "will seek for him, and bring him back, that we may see him happily restored to his right mind?"

And Duke Namon answered, "My lord, such wonder was never known, that a madman should recover his senses. And, however much we have loved him, the Roland whom we once knew is now no more. Only a shadow remains where there was a man before."

And Reinold of Montalban said, "There are other knights in your service as loyal, as brave, and as true as ever our cousin Roland was. Trust them to uphold your power, and defend your kingdom."

And Ganelon, the old traitor, smiled, and said, "Methinks that this Roland is now well out of our way, and that we shall nevermore hear it said, 'Behold the king's nephew,—the knight without fear and without reproach!' "

But Oliver said, "My lord, I will follow my brother to the ends of the earth, rather than not find him. I will bring him back to France, to his home and his kindred and those who love him, that through their care and kindness he may be healed."

And Astolpho, the poet knight, said, "I also will go in search of the lost hero; for although I have neither the strength nor the skill of a warrior, yet who knows but that my fancy in its highest flights may discover the lost senses of Roland, and bring them back to their owner?"

Then Oliver and Astolpho mounted their steeds and rode away; and they pledged themselves that they would never come back to France, nor undertake any other adventure, until they should find Roland, and see him whole again in mind and worthy to be called the peerless knight.

Now, it chanced that Astolpho owned a wonderful winged horse,—the same creature that had once belonged to Atlantes, the Moorish wizard. Astolpho had long kept this steed, with care and secrecy, in his own castle among the mountain peaks, where the wild eagles soared, and the air was fresh and pure, and the busy hum of the laboring world was seldom heard. Sometimes, merely to amuse himself, the knight had mounted his winged courser and taken short flights into fairyland, or soared aloft toward the sun. And he had often thought, that when Charlemagne's wars were over, and he was no longer needed either at court or in the field, he would take a longer flight and stop not until he had reached the farthest boundaries of the earth. So, now, he hastened back to his mountain castle, resolved to make use of the winged steed in his search for the lost hero.

At Astolpho's command the wondrous horse was led out of the marble halls, where he had been stabled, and accoutred for a flight longer than any he had ever yet taken. It was early morning. The sun was rising dripping from the waters of the great midland sea. The crags and peaks shone like burnished silver against the dark-blue sky. The crimson clouds turned golden, and then melted away into nothingness. The mountain eagles flew down from their rock-built eyries, and screamed around the hero and his steed, and then soared high toward heaven, as if daring him to a loftier flight. Astolpho vaulted into the saddle. The noble steed spread his wings, and leaped into the air. Upward and still upward he soared, until the green fields of France, and the rugged mountains and the snow-crowned peaks dwindled almost out of sight. The screaming eagles were left far behind, the great sun seemed not much higher. The whole earth was transformed into a scene of beauty such as the knight had seldom dreamed of. Sweet France lay directly beneath him, spread out like a map, its rivers and mountains and forests and fields dimly outlined in the hazy distance. To his right was fair Spain, bounded on three sides by the sea, and on the fourth by the great wall of the Pyrenees. In front of him was the midland sea, stretching away and away, as far as the eye could reach, until its shining waters seemed hidden behind the sun. And there he saw vine-clad Italy basking in the morning light; and farther away lay the isles of Greece, where the gods in the golden time taught men the sweet secrets of music and song.

And the winged steed sailed onward toward the rising sun, faster than falcon or swiftest bird that flies. Over the midland sea he flew, and over many strange countries, and amid many beautiful scenes. He came to the land where grow the date and the palm; he soared above the shaggy tops of the Atlas Mountains, and the Great Desert, which lies sultry and bare beyond; he winged his way over Nubia and the land of the Pyramids and the Nile. Yet Astolpho allowed not his steed to stop. He had heard of another land still farther, where he hoped to learn tidings of the sad-minded Roland. From

Egypt, his course now lay southward: he followed the great River Nile even to its mysterious head-spring, and over the boundless regions of Ethiopia he directed his flight. He came at length to the wondrous realm ruled by the mighty Prester John, and there his steed alighted.

The land in which Astolpho now found himself seemed to be a very paradise of delights. It was governed by an ancient Christian prince, whose birth and lineage were unknown, and whose dominion stretched eastward to India, and southward to the great sea. In that land every man was a hero,—not one who wins a name and fame through bloodshed or on the battle-field, but one whose heart is free from guile, whose brain is clear, whose every deed is noble. In that land there were temples and palaces and cities surpassing in riches and beauty any thing that Astolpho had ever before seen. There every kind of gem-stone was found,—emeralds, sapphires, carbuncles, onyxes, and beryls; and gold was more plentiful than iron. There, too, every strange and useful animal lived. It was the home of the elephant, the camel, the white and red lion, the white bear, the wild horse, the wild ox. There, also, roamed those wondrous creatures of which we read in the old myth-stories of Greece, such as centaurs and fauns and satyrs and pygmies and strange chimeras. And there dwelt the phœnix, that solitary bird, which, after living a thousand years, burns itself on its own funeral pile, and afterward rises with renewed youth from the ashes.

Near the place where Astolpho first alighted there was a garden, and in the garden was a fountain. On either side of the fountain sat two saintly men, who were dressed in long white robes, and whose hair and beard were whiter than the drifted snow. These men, as the knight approached, arose and saluted him.

"Art thou a Christian?" asked one.

"I am," answered Astolpho, making the sign of the cross.

"Wouldst thou be healed of all thine infirmities, whether of body or of mind?" asked the other.

"Nothing do I desire more greatly," was the answer.

Standing within the fountain was a pure white stone, shaped like a mussel shell, and covered by a few inches of water.

"If what thou sayest is true," said the elder, who had first spoken, "step now into this mussel shelf."

Astolpho did as he was bidden, and the water began of its own accord to rise about him. Three times it lifted itself and gushed over his head; and then the aged men bade him step out of the fountain. As he did so, he felt as if the balmiest days of his youth had returned, and that he should never again be oppressed with weariness or pain.

"Go thou," said the elders, "and may no evil thing betide thee!"

Then Astolpho went straight to the palace wherein dwelt the king. The walls which stood around this palace were of the purest white marble. The drawbridge was of ivory, and the chain and bolts were of gold. The gate was a wondrous piece of workmanship, wrought of precious metals and costly stones; and above it was placed the horn of a horned snake, so that nothing unclean could pass through. The inner gates were of ebony, inlaid with gold. At each end of the palace was a high tower; and on each of these a carbuncle and an apple of gold were placed; and by day the golden apple shed a soft radiance over the palace and all the country around, while at night the carbuncle shone as brightly as the sun at noon. The wide courtyard was floored with onyx,—a stone which gives strength and courage to the feeble-hearted. The architraves, the joists, the ceilings of the palace, were of the mystic Sethym wood: the roof was of ebony, and so built that fire could never touch it. Heavy curtains, and carpets of every hue and texture, added comfort to riches. In wall and roof and pavement were countless pearls and purest gems. And in the great assembly-hall was a wondrous mirror, reached by five and twenty steps of porphyry and serpentine, in which the king could see at a glance every thing that was happening in every corner of his kingdom.

No man knew how long this country had been ruled by Prester John; for, in a land so blessed with every comfort and every luxury, the years were all golden, and men noticed not the flight of time. The great Prester John kindly welcomed Astolpho to his court, and ordered that the best guest room in the palace should be made ready for his use. But the knight was surprised to see, that, although the king was surrounded with every thing that could add to one's happiness, there was an air of sadness on his face, as if he were harassed by some fearful evil which he could not escape.

It so happened that the day was a great feast day, when all the earls and noblemen in the kingdom were bidden to court, and a rich banquet was to be served in the hall. And Astolpho was invited to sit at table with the rest.

"I hope, indeed, that they will not come to-day," the king was overheard saying to one of his courtiers. And the knight wondered who it could be whose company was so undesirable.

At the appointed hour the guests were led into the banquet chamber. There the ceilings were very high and vaulted, the windows were large, and the doors were broad. The floor was waxed and polished until it shone like a mirror. The tables were of ebony, inlaid with amethyst and gold, and supported upon legs of ivory. Astolpho was seated on a raised platform at the right hand of the king; and the noblest men of the realm—dukes, earls, archbishops, and bishops—sat near him. While the attendants were placing the food before them, the king, pale and trembling, as if fearing some great danger, told Astolpho the story of his sad misery.

"You would think," said he, "that a man living in the midst of all these delights would be supremely happy. And yet I am the most miserable of earth's creatures. I will tell you why. Far to the south there is a beautiful mountain, the like of which is found in no other land. On that mountain, it is said, there is everlasting spring; and there old age is unknown, and death never comes. Long was it my wish to discover that earthly paradise, and long did I aspire to add it to the kingdoms of my realm. At last, in an evil hour, I marshalled my hosts, and with a noble array of knights and lords I marched across the southern desert, determined to carry my banners to the very summit of that famous mountain. But when we reached it, sad was our disappointment. The white cliffs rose up before us, like the walls of a great city; and, when we tried to scale them, the rocks rolled down upon our heads; the dark gorges opened and swallowed up my warriors; fire and smoke belched forth from the peaks; and rivers of melted rock poured down upon us. And then I heard a voice saying, 'Think not, vain man, to pry into the secret things of the Most High. Go back into thine own country, and be thankful that thy life is spared.' Then I turned, and fled with all speed from that forbidden ground. And, of all the mighty host that had gone with me thither, not more than a tenth returned with me to this land. And the Harpies, who since the days of Jason and the Argonauts had been penned up in the cave of the Winds, were freed from their prison, and sent to harass me every day of my life. And now, like Phineus of old, I am miserable in the midst of delights, I am tormented with hunger while all around me is plenty; for no sooner is my table ready, than those loathsome creatures swoop down, and snatch the food from my plate, and leave me naught to satisfy my hunger. It is thus that Heaven punishes him who would lay hands upon forbidden things."

The king had scarcely finished speaking, when Astolpho heard a strange noise above them, like the whirring of many wings in the upper air. The old king covered his face with his hands, and cried out, "They come! there is no ridding ourselves of them." And many of the guests arose and fled from the hall.

Then, through doors and windows, the Harpies came flying in. Seven in number were they,—pale-faced, blear-eyed, with long crooked talons, and snake-like tails knotted in many a fold. Down upon the feast table they swooped, and they stopped not their greedy onslaught until every morsel of food was snatched from the board. Astolpho drew his sword and struck manfully about him; but as well might he have smitten the wind, for the sharpest blade could not cut through the feathery armor of those loathsome fowls.

"Ah, me!" cried the king, "is there no escape? Must I endure this torment forever?"

Then Astolpho bethought him of a horn which he carried at his girdle. The weird woman Melissa had given it to him long before, and had said to him, "Whenever your sword fails you, blow this horn." So, after the king and all who were in the hall had filled their ears with wax, he lifted it to his lips and blew such a bugle-blast as had never before been heard in the land of Prester John. The palace itself shook from turret to foundation stone; the leaves of the trees quivered as in a storm; the rocks rolled down the mountain-side. The Harpies, more affrighted than when, in the olden time, they had been chased by the sons of old Boreas, flew in wild dismay from the hall. Astolpho quickly mounted his winged charger, and followed them, blowing peal after peal upon his wondrous horn. Southward the creatures flew, across the great sandy desert; nor did they slacken their flight until they reached the mountain whereon the earthly paradise was said to be. Into a dark and narrow cavern in the mountain's side they flew,—the prison-house into which the sons of Boreas had driven them long before. And Astolpho, with trees and stones, and whatsoever else would serve as a wall or hedge, wedged up the cavern door; so that never again shall those loathsome creatures visit the air to torment mankind with their horrid presence.

And the poets tell of many other wondrous deeds that Astolpho did in the land of Prester John,—how he visited the earthly paradise, and talked there with the patriarchs of old; how he flew to the moon's orb, and was shown the place where all things are stored that have been lost on earth; how he found there the lost senses of the unhappy Roland, and brought them in a phial back to the earth; how he visited the place where the

Fates spin the thread of life, and weave the woof of doom for every creature; and how he healed the sick, and restored sight to the blind. But, whether these stories be true or false, I will not stop to repeat them to you. Let us hasten to find the now long-lost Roland.

When Astolpho had learned from the Fates the whereabouts of Roland, and the manner in which that knight should be made himself again, he went into the presence of Prester John, and asked a boon of that king.

"You shall have whatsoever you wish," said the grateful monarch.

And Astolpho asked that a band of warriors should be allowed to go with him across the desert, to invade Algeria and the land of the Moors, and thus lend aid to his liege-lord Charlemagne. The king was well pleased to grant this request. He sent forth his heralds to bid all the bravest warriors of his realm to come and join the standard of Astolpho. And there came from every mountain stronghold and from every countryside, troops of knights and armed men, equipped and ready for the long march. Some came on the backs of elephants, some on camels; but the greater number were on foot, for there were no trained horses in that country. But, when they learned that they were expected to march across the Great Desert, they shook their heads, and hesitated.

"We shall never live to cross those terrible sands," said some: "for the South Wind will come upon us like the breath of a furnace, and will scorch the skin of our bodies, and parch our tongues with thirst; and then the whirlwind will take up the burning sand in its arms, and hurl it down upon us, and bury us alive."

But others said, "Cannot he who has done such wonders in our midst control even the South Wind? We will trust him."

On the evening previous to the day which had been set for the march, Astolpho secretly mounted his winged courser, and flew away toward the south. On and on he flew, until he came to the land where dwell the summer's heat and the fierce fire-forces. There, in a cave, the South Wind has her home. Every day, at early morn, she comes out of her dwelling, and roams over the earth, kissing the buds and blossoms, and causing them to open to the sun; rippling the waters of the lake, and rustling among the canebrakes and the corn; melting the snow and the ice on the mountain tops, and laughing with the rivulet which pours its waters over the rocky ledge; unlocking the frozen rivers, and sending great icebergs floating out to sea; speeding the heavily laden ships on their homeward voyage; stirring the waves into fury; and feeding the death-dealing whirlwinds which sweep over the desert and the sea. Oh, a kind blessing, as well as a fearful curse, is the South Wind! When Astolpho came to her dwelling, she had retired to rest. Not a leaf was stirring on the trees, not a ripple could be seen on the lake. All nature seemed asleep. Even in the cavern of the South Wind no sound was heard, save that of her heavy breathings as she lay reposing in her golden chamber. Astolpho hearkened a moment, and then carefully spread a magic net across the cavern's mouth; so that when the South Wind should awaken from her slumber, and should step forth from her dwelling, ready dight for her wondrous journey over the world, she should be caught and held fast in the meshes. Then he turned the head of his winged courser, and was soon safely back in the palace of Prester John.

A FLIGHT TO THE LAND OF PRESTER JOHN

At sunrise the dreaded march across the desert was commenced. And the warriors who followed Astolpho wondered what had become of the South Wind, and why no sand storms overtook them; for the only breeze that met them was the gentle, cooling West Wind, which cheered and strengthened them during their long journey. And at last the gray peaks of the Atlas Mountains, and the tall palm trees of Algeria, came in sight, and their perilous march was at an end. Then the South Wind, who had at last rid herself of the troublesome net, came tripping across the desert after them. She climbed the mountains behind them, and played among the treetops in the valleys, and whistled gleefully in the glens; but she had no power to do them any harm.

In the old poems, you may read wonderful stories of the manner in which Astolpho supplied his foot-soldiers with steeds by turning stones into horses; of how he routed Agramant and the other Saracen chiefs in battle; of how Charlemagne, hearing of his exploits, crossed the sea, and laid siege to Africa; and of many wondrous feats of arms performed by the Christian knights. Let us return to the pitiable fortunes of our hero.

Wandering aimlessly from place to place, as if drawn by some unseen hand, Roland advanced each day farther and farther south. At length he came to a little seaport town. The Straits lay before him, and beyond them was Africa. He was possessed with a mad wish to go onward, forever southward; and he felt that neither mountains nor seas should hinder him. A ship had just left the shore, with a party of Moorish soldiers on board. He rushed to the water's edge, calling to the sailors to come back, and take him into the vessel. But they, seeing his ragged clothing, and his wild, furious gestures, guessed rightly that he was some poor maniac, and paid not any attention to his cries. When Roland found that the vessel would neither turn back nor wait for him, he leaped madly into the sea, as if determined to swim across. Long and manfully did he buffet the waves, now rising high on the top of a swell, and now sinking deep into the trough of the sea. Both the land and the ship were out of sight; but still he struggled onward, knowing only that his life depended upon his keeping his head above the water. Yet he certainly would have been drowned, had not another vessel hove that way. The valiant swimmer was taken on board and carried across the Straits: for the Moorish knights who were in the ship pitied his forlorn case; and, when they reached their own shores, they allowed him to wander whithersoever he would.

It happened at this time, that the Christian hosts, with Charlemagne and Astolpho, were encamped not far from the sea, waiting for ships and a fair wind to bear them back to France. One day a strange man, ragged and tanned, came suddenly into the camp. He turned not aside for any thing that stood in his way. He hurled the warriors right and left from his path; he overturned the tents; he frightened the horses; he threw every thing into a panic. Astolpho and the knights who were with him seized their weapons, and ran hastily out to see what was going on. You may judge of their wonder and delight when they found that this strange madman was their old friend and comrade, Roland. By Astolpho's orders, they closed around him, and seized him from behind. Fiercely he struggled; and ill would his assailants have fared, had not their armor protected them from his mad blows. At length he was thrown to the ground and bound hand and foot. Then the good Astolpho took the precious phial of sense which he had carried so long and so carefully, and held it beneath the madman's nose.

A great change came over Roland. His unsettled mind at once regained its firmness, and his understanding became as strong and as clear as it had been of yore. He gazed about him, like one who wakes from a dream and finds himself in a strange place. He saw Astolpho and Oliver and Ogier standing over him, and he wondered why it was that he lay bound and unarmed upon the beach. Then the wild, vacant look passed from his face, and he seemed as calm and as composed as he had been in his happiest days. His friends knew that his madness had left him. They quickly unbound him and raised him to his feet. They led him to Astolpho's tent, and clothed him in raiment becoming the noblest of knights, and told him the strange story of his madness. And the next day a feast and a tournament were held in his honor, and the good Archbishop Turpin offered a public thanksgiving for the happy return of the wanderer. And many stories are told of Roland's prowess while yet the French army was delayed in Africa,—how, single-handed, he defeated three kings in a deadly passage at arms, and by so doing saved the life of his brother Oliver; how he regained by force the matchless helmet which Ferrau had carried away; how he won also for himself the sword Durandal, which Mandricardo the Tartar had stolen; and how, in every case, he dealt wisely and uprightly, and never sought undue advantage over his foes.

ADVENTURE XXX

HOW THE PEERS RETURNED TO FRANCE

When Charlemagne and his host embarked for France, the sky was fair and the sea was calm. But soon a storm arose. The waves ran mountain-high, the ships were at the mercy of the winds. The king and his peers sat together in the same vessel; and the heroes who had faced unflinching the dangers of a hundred fierce battles, now felt their hearts sinking with fear.

"I know well the art of the tourney and the battle," cried Roland, the peerless chief; "but what avails that art here in this wilderness of waves?"

And Ogier the Dane, said, "I know how to wield the sword, and how to touch the harp and bring forth sweet melody; but such knowledge is of little use to quell the fury of these winds."

Then Oliver, the look of gladness all faded from his eyes, drew his sword from its scabbard, and, gazing tenderly at its flashing edge, said, "No fear have I for myself, but I grieve that Haultclear shall find so inglorious a grave."

"If I only knew a way to save myself," said Ganelon,—but he said it very low,—"little would I reck what evil fortune befell the rest of you."

The good Archbishop Turpin sighed deeply, and said, "We are the warriors of Heaven's kingdom. Come thou on the waves, sweet Saviour, and deign to deliver us from peril."

Said Sir Richard of Normandy, "Wait for me, ye demons! Long and well have I served you, and soon will I be with you."

"I have given wise counsel to many," gravely remarked

Duke Namon; "but in the salt sea good words of advice are as rare and as little needed, as sweet water or pleasant fruit."

Then good father Riol said, "An old warrior am I, and not much longer can I live in any case. And yet I would fain finish my course by leaving my old body upon dry land, rather than by losing it in this watery waste."

And Sir Guy, the courteous chevalier, sought to conceal his terror by singing,—

"I would I were a little bird!
Quickly to my nest I'd fly."

Then Garin, the lover of good cheer, said, "May Heaven save us from pain! Pleasanter by far would it be to drink a single cup of red wine than to treat one's self to all the water in the sea."

And Sir Lambert, the witty, responded, "Be sure we shall not be forgotten! Yet happier would I be to eat one good fish, however small, than to be devoured by that same fish."

"For me," said Duke Godfrey, the noble, "I accept my lot. Happy am I in knowing that I shall fare no worse than those who are better than I."

All this time King Charlemagne stood at the helm. He spoke not a word; but he guided the vessel with a strong hand, until at length the fury of the waves was exhausted. And, behold! the shores of their own loved France lay before the sea-tossed warriors, fragrant with the odor of blossoms and of the ripe summer fruit.

As the king and his knights rode homeward between the vineyards and the rich fields with which the peaceful country was now everywhere covered, the people greeted them with glad shouts and heartfelt blessings. And as they drew near the city of Paris, the fair home from which they had been absent so long, a noble company of knights and ladies came out to welcome them; and together they entered the city gates. The streets were strewn with garlands and green leaves and fragrant roses; from every tower and every housetop, gay banners floated in the breeze; young maidens walked before them, singing triumphal songs; and all the people shouted for joy. At every turn of the street gorgeous arches had been built, where were displayed the trophies taken in war, and many an inscription relating to the deeds of the returning heroes. And the whole city was given up to merry-making. And many a tourney was held, and many a mask and ball. And, for a long time thereafter, nothing was heard or talked about in Paris, save music and mirth, and brave feats of arms, and the happy restoration and return of Roland.

ADVENTURE XXXI

HOW CHARLEMAGNE FOUGHT AGAINST OGIER

SHALL I tell you of the sad war which Charlemagne waged for so long a time against one of the noblest of his vassals? Sorrowful, indeed, were those days, and much shame did the peers suffer on account of the proud-faced king.

Ogier the Dane had married Belicene, the daughter of the Lord of St. Omer; and he had one son named Baldwinet. Tall and comely grew the lad, and proud of look; and Ogier loved him more than all things else. One day the king's son Charlot played at chess with Baldwinet; and, much to the surprise of the prince, the young lad checkmated him. Very furious frew Charlot. He seized the golden chessboard, and struck Baldwinet so fiercely that he stretched him dead on the marble floor. When Ogier heard of the bloody deed, he hastened to the hall where his son still lay, he lifted the cold and bloody body in his arms, and kissed the fair white face. The knights who stood around, sorrowful and horror-stricken, wept at the sight. Then Ogier sprang angrily to his feet again: he seized a huge club, and sought Charlot from chamber to chamber to kill him. But Charlemagne, too blind to the faults of his wicked and foolish son, had hidden him in a secret closet. Ogier sought the king, and asked that due punishment should be meted out to the black-hearted prince. But the king mocked him and banished him from the court.

"Take thyself hence," said he angrily; "and, if to-morrow's

sun sees thee in France, thou shalt find thyself in the darkest dungeon in our kingdom."

Ogier, despairing of justice, and filled with sorrow and rage, mounted his good steed Broiefort, and rode away from the king's court. He went straight to his castle of Garlandon, —a fief which he held of the king in Southern France. But, when Charlemagne heard that the bereaved and sorrow-stricken knight was still within his domains, he called his host together and laid siege to Garlandon. Then Ogier, not wishing to fight against the king, secretly quitted the castle, taking with him neither palfrey nor sumter horse, but only his brave steed Broiefort. He crossed the snowy Alps, and came at length to the city of Pavia, and presented himself before Didier, the King of the Lombards.

"Fair king," said he, "I am a man who has been exiled, hunted, from sweet France. Charlemagne has driven me out of his kingdom; and he has left me neither town nor castle, not even so much land as I could lie upon. It was all because I demanded justice for the death of the young lad Baldwinet, whom I loved so well. And now I come to you, and beg your aid; for I may have need of it. And I will serve you with sword and lance so well that you shall love me."

"What is thy name?" asked Didier.

"My name is Ogier, and men call me 'the Dane.' "

At this word Didier leaped to his feet, and right warmly he welcomed the Dane. And he gave to Ogier as fiefs two famous strongholds,—Castle-Fort on the Rhone, which had never been entered by a foe, and Mount Quevrel on the Rock.

The next spring, King Charlemagne held an Easter feast at Paris. Never since the days of Alexander the Greek, of

Lucian of Acre, or of Clovis, who was next after Cæsar, had a king held a feast so grand. There sat at his table seventeen kings, thirty bishops, and full a thousand knights. And, while they feasted, some one with slight discretion spoke the name of Ogier.

"The traitor!" cried the king, striking his knife upon the table. "He is the guest of Didier of Lombardy, but he shall not long be so. Who now is there among you, brave knights, who will go beyond the mountains, and bid Didier send me this rebel as a captive?"

Not one of the knights made answer, for those who did not love Ogier feared him. Yet at last Namon the Wise arose. Very old and frail was he, and his hair and beard were white as snow.

"Sir king," said he, "since no younger man offers to go, I will bear your message; for it is the first duty of every knight to serve his lord."

But the king would not let him go. Then Namon turned to his son Bertram, who sat by his side, and bade him undertake the errand.

"It is well," said the king. "Bertram shall go."

And Bertram, although very loath to do so, departed at once. Had it not been for his father's wishes, he would not have gone.

When the young knight reached Pavia, he went at once to the king's palace. Didier was sitting at his table in his feast hall, and Ogier sat beside him. When Bertram was shown into the hall, the Dane knew him at once as the son of his old friend, Duke Namon. He knew him by the checkered helmet which he wore, and the silver eagle on either side, and the sword-hilt of purest gold; and he would have given all the treasure in the world to have been elsewhere. He whispered to Didier, and begged him to treat the messenger kindly, and not let his ill-mannered Lombards insult the young man.

Bertram then delivered his message: "If Didier does not send the Dane back in chains, like a greyhound, then Charlemagne will come and destroy Pavia, and overrun and ruin his kingdom of Lombardy and place a better knight on the throne."

When he had spoken, Ogier arose, and answered: "Didier owes no vassalry to Charlemagne, save the succor of ten thousand men for sixty days, in case the French king makes war in Italy. As to myself, Ogier the Dane, I do not believe that Didier will fail me. If Charlemagne would overrun and ruin Lombardy, let him come. He shall find us not asleep."

Then Bertram answered by accusing Ogier of treason to the king, and of not yet having paid the tribute which his father Godfrey had owed for the fief of Denmark. Very angry grew Ogier; and in a great passion he seized a knife and flung it at the young knight. Happily, the weapon missed its mark, only cutting the fringe of Bertram's hauberk. Then better thoughts came to the Dane, and he remembered the kind counsels and the generous help he had so often received from Namon the gentle duke. And so he answered the rash messenger mildly, as a worthy knight, as a wise and well-taught man.

"For the sake of thy father, Namon the flowery-bearded," said he, "the spear of Ogier shall never be levelled against thee. Charlemagne has driven me from sweet France: he has disherited me, and made me an outlaw. And all this has been for no wickedness of my own, but only because I dared open my mouth when Charlot slew Baldwinet, the son whom I loved so well."

The next morning Didier called his barons together, and they talked over the message which Charlemagne had sent. And they bade Bertram carry this word back to the French king: "We have pledged our friendship and aid to Ogier the Dane, and we will not deliver him over to his enemies. If Charlemagne would decide this matter by a trial of arms, let him meet us in May, in a pitched battle under Ajossa."

When Bertram returned to France, and delivered his message, Charlemagne began at once to make ready for war. He called together an army of fifty thousand warriors. But the peers Roland and Oliver and Reinold joined not the standard of the king: they would take no part in this unrighteous war. The king's host crossed the mountains, and camped in the meadows before St. Ajossa. There, as Charlemagne sat before his tent, he saw a great company of folk coming down the hills on his right. It was Gerard of Viana, with ten thousand crossbow-men. He looked to the left, and saw another ten thousand warriors coming up through the meadows, their hauberks and shields flaming in the sunlight, and their banners fluttering toward the sky.

"What host of strangers is this?" asked Charlemagne.

"It is Baldwin of Flanders, and his far-famed Flemish spearmen," answered Duke Namon.

The two armies were drawn up in battle-array before St. Ajossa. Terrible was the shock with which they met in combat; fierce and long was the fight. At length, however, the Lombards were beaten, and King Didier sought safety in flight. Everywhere the French were victorious; for they were the braver knights, and better trained. Ogier, on the back of his faithful Broiefort, fled from the lost field with fifteen thousand foes close following behind him. But the good horse distanced his pursuers, and carried his master safely out of danger. The hunted Dane hastened now to reach the shelter of his own stronghold, Castle-Fort on the Rhone, which Didier the Lombard had given him.

One day, overcome by fatigue and long wakefulness, he stopped in a mountain glen, and lay down behind a huge rock to rest. He lifted the helmet from his head, and placed it on the grass beside him; and such was his weariness, that, ere he was aware, he had fallen asleep. While he slept, a company of Frenchmen came up with him, and, had it not been for Broiefort, he would have fared but ill at their hands. The good horse, seeing that danger was near, neighed loudly and struck the ground with his hoofs; but Ogier still slept. Then the noble beast seized his master by the collar of his hauberk, and shook him until he awoke. The Dane had barely time to mount the faithful steed and gallop out of the glen. That afternoon, as he hurried onward, closely followed by his foes, he came to a little castle, standing in the edge of the wood by the side of a wide morass. There was no town nor any farmlands near; and the place, even if not deserted, seemed very poorly guarded. The gate was wide open; and, as no sentinel or warder was there to challenge or prevent him, Ogier rode boldly in. The courtyard was empty; and neither lord nor servitor could be seen, although the Dane thought he heard loud voices, and sounds of life, in the low-built halls. He had no time, however, for ceremony; for his pursuers were already in sight. He quickly dismounted, and drew up the bridge, and shut and barred the gates behind him. Then, without hesitation, he went into the dining hall, where he found the owner of the castle and all his family sitting at the table.

"Kind sir," said he to the man, "I am a knight, who, for no fault of my own, am banished from my own country, and hunted from place to place like a felon. If thou wilt give me shelter, I will richly repay thee."

But the man rose up in a furious passion, and tried to drive Ogier from the hall.

"If thou art so lacking in courtesy as to thrust a stranger thus rudely from thy house," said the Dane, "thou must not complain if I take forcible possession of all that thou hast." And he drew his sword, and drove the man and his family out through the postern gate, which he closed and bolted behind them. Then he searched every part of the castle, from the deep cellars to the highest tower, to see whether the place were well victualled. And he found great plenty of salt meat, and bread and wine, and dainties of every sort. The table was loaded with rich food, cakes, and red wine, and cranes, and geese, and every kind of wild game. There were provisions enough for a small garrison.

Not long was it until Charlemagne, with ten thousand warriors, came up, and laid siege to the castle. He pitched his tent right before the gate, and placed armed men on every side,—a thousand squires, a thousand spearmen, a thousand crossbow-men. The walls were not very high; but the ditch was wide and deep, and there seemed no way of crossing. At length, by the king's orders, the besiegers cut down the willows of the marsh and the brushwood in the forest, and threw them into the moat to fill it up. And ten great ladders were placed against the walls. But Ogier defended himself right manfully, and kept his enemies at bay until nightfall, when they returned to their tents, vowing that he should not escape them on the morrow. It was a fearful night. The rain fell in torrents, the lightnings flashed, the thunder rolled, and there was such a tempest as has seldom been known. But Charlemagne set two thousand men on guard, and watchfires were built for seven leagues around.

Ogier's heart sank within him. "Never in my life," said he to himself, "have I done good to any one who did not in the end seek my destruction." He did not think of the great-hearted Roland, who all this time held himself aloof from the king.

When the earliest dawn of that long night began to appear, the Dane went to the stables to find Broiefort. The noble creature knew his master; he neighed softly, and scratched his foot for joy.

"Horse," said Ogier lovingly, "there was never a steed so good, so proud, in every way so worthy, as thou. Thou hast done me good service in many a quest: canst thou help me once more? In all the world there is not one man who holds me dear; and, if thou shouldst fail me, I would be undone."

The good horse raised his head as if he understood his master: he neighed again, and struck uneasily with his foot. The knight put on the saddle, and threw the golden reins upon the proud charger's neck; and, just as the cocks were crowing, he opened the castle-gate and looked out. All was quiet in Charlemagne's camp, and the watchers seemed to be asleep. Softly did Ogier let down the bridge; he vaulted into the saddle; he breathed a short prayer to Heaven, and dashed boldly away. The camp was aroused: the men rushed to arms. Many of them saw Ogier galloping away; but they pitied his plight, and would not harm him. Others, who were his kinsmen, or who had fought by his side in many a hard-won fray, secretly blessed him as he passed. And, ere Charlemagne could rally his squires and crossbow-men, the gallant Dane was well on his way to Castle-Fort.

Right hearty was the welcome which Ogier received when he rode into his own castle. And the three hundred warriors who were there at once made every thing ready for a siege. On one side of Castle-Fort there was a marsh so soft and deep that no man could ride across it; and on the other was the swift-running Rhone, washing the foot of the tower. Within the walls there was a spring and a little brook so wide and so deep that dames and damsels, burgesses and knights, might bathe in it; and ere it poured its waters into the river, it turned three mills, which stopped not the whole year round.

Soon Charlemagne's army arrived, and laid close siege to Castle-Fort. And the king summoned Malrin, the engineer, and promised him a thousand marks of gold, and twenty war steeds, if he would batter down the stronghold. And forthwith Malrin called together three hundred and eighteen skilled carpenters, and more than four thousand workmen; and they built before the gate an engine seven stories high, whereon a thousand one hundred and seventy bowmen could stand. And day and night they shot great bolts of steel, and iron-shod arrows, into the fort; while Malrin, from the uppermost story, threw Greek fire upon the roofs of the houses, and kindled flames such that neither water nor wine, but only cold earth and soft clay, could quench.

Ogier and his men were at length driven into the tower, and they stabled their horses in the deep dungeons underneath. But still the bolts and arrows and stones, and the dreadful Greek fire, poured down upon them. The tower was of stone, cemented with mortar mixed with dragon's blood; and no missile nor storm of fire could harm it. Yet one by one the valiant defenders were picked off by Malrin's sharp-sighted bowmen, until at length Ogier was left all alone. He was now without squire or page or serving-man. He must needs grind his own corn, draw water from his own well, heat it on the fire which he himself had kindled, sift his own flour, knead the dough, heat the oven, bake his own bread. He was his own cook, his own butler, his own groom. Yet he knew full well, that one man never held a castle long against his foes.

What Ogier next did, says the poet who told this tale, no other man ever did. He cut down the small oaks and the branchy trees which grew in the courtyard, and shaped them into wooden men; he dressed them with hauberks and helmets, and girded swords upon them, and hung shields on their necks, and put battle-axes in their hands; and then he fixed them on the battlements, so that the French would think that the fort was still well garrisoned. Charlemagne was amazed. He wondered how so many men could subsist in the tower, and how they could live amid the storm of iron and fire which was hurled down upon them. He began to think that some unseen power was fighting for Ogier.

But ere long the gallant Dane became sorely pressed with famine. His face grew pale with fasting: he wasted away until he looked like a giant skeleton. In his extremity he again mounted his good Broiefort, and early one moring dashed recklessly out of the gate. A thousand base-minded squires pursued him; but Broiefort swam the rapid River Cercle, and left them far behind. When Charlemagne learned that Ogier had again escaped him, he was very angry. He warned the knights who were with him, that they should on no account favor the rebellious Dane, on pain of being punished as traitors. And then he returned with his host to Paris.

Meanwhile, Ogier hastened on his way toward Denmark, for there he felt that he would find friends. One day he stopped by the roadside to rest; and, feeling weary and worn out, he ungirt his sword Short, and lay down beneath a tree to sleep. While he slept, it so happened that Archbishop Turpin, with a following of knights and squires, passed that way. They saw the warrior lying in peaceful slumber upon the grass, and they remarked the nobleness of his horse and the beauty of his armor. And, when they drew nearer, all knew that it was Ogier. The good archbishop was sorely troubled. He would fain not harm his brother-in-arms; yet, if he did not take him prisoner, Charlemagne would drive him from the kingdom. So, after much ado, they took Ogier's horse and sword, and overpowered and bound the Dane himself.

"My once kind friend," said Ogier to the archbishop, "thou doest me too great an injury. If thou wouldst befriend me, kill me at once, rather than give me up to the king."

But Turpin bade him be of good cheer. He assured him that he would take him to Reims, and put him in his own dungeon, and see that no harm came to him.

When Charlemagne heard that the Dane had been taken at last, and that he was in prison at Reims, he was very glad, and he began making ready to have him hanged like a common thief. But Archbishop Turpin came before him with a retinue of knights, bishops, and abbots, and begged that he would spare the life of the unhappy Dane. And Gerard of Rousillon and full sixty dukes and barons joined them in this petition, and threatened, that, if Charlemagne slew Ogier, they would declare war against him. And Turpin promised, that, in case the knight's life were spared, he would keep him in his own dungeon, where he should never see his hands or his feet, and where he should have for his daily allowance not more than a quartern of bread and one cup of water and wine mixed.

"Only give him his life," said the archbishop, "and he shall never cause you trouble again."

At last the king relented, and good Turpin returned in great joy to Rheims. He had a silver cup made, which held a whole gallon of wine; and a bushel of flour he made into two loaves, so that seven knights could not eat a quartern. And Ogier fared most royally in the archbishop's dungeon, for he wanted neither comfort nor amusement. Yet he was often sad and downhearted, and he grieved greatly for his friends. And in his loneliness, shut out from the sunlight and the companionship of those whom he loved, his long hair and beard became white as the snow.

But by and by there came a change in Ogier's fortunes. France was being threatened with invasion by Brehus, a Saracen chief of great valor and distinction; and Charlemagne had marshalled his host, and was making ready to repel the invaders. The French were waiting the king's orders to march; and all the peers, save Ogier, were in their places. Then Turpin went into the presence of the king, and said,—

"My lord, we can scarcely expect Heaven's blessing to rest

Charlemagne pardons Ogier.

on this enterprise while one of the peers is absent. There are twelve of us, but here are only eleven."

At the same time three hundred squires, all sons of the noblest men in the kingdom, began to cry out, "Ogier! Ogier!" And Duke Namon boldly advised the king to pardon the good Dane, and set him free.

"But he is dead," said the king.

"Not so," answered Namon. "He is alive and well, in the archbishop's dungeon."

"If that is true," said the king, "thou shalt take him out, and we will make him all due amends."

When word was brought to Ogier that the king was willing to pardon him in order that he might lead his fighting-men against the Saracens, he seemed but little gladdened by the news.

"Never," said he, "will I don breastplate or shield, or lift the lance, until Charlot, who slew my gentle son, shall be given over into my hands."

Charlemagne was in distress. He knew that, unless Ogier were with them, the peers would not advance against the Saracen but would rather defy his authority. And yet his love for the foolish Charlot was as great as ever. At last, however, by Duke Namon's advice, he yielded, and sent word to Ogier that he should do with Charlot as he wished. The Dane was brought out of his prison, and dressed in his own armor, which the good archbishop had carefully kept for him. He was tall and straight, and his look was proud as that of a lion. When he had donned his arms, he looked anxiously around him.

"Where, now, is my horse Broiefort," asked he,—"the good friend who stood by me when all others failed?"

The archbishop could not tell; but a monk who stood near remembered having seen the steed drawing a heavy cartload of stones at Meaux. "When Ogier was thrown into prison," said he, "the abbot of Meaux took charge of his horse. The old man was very proud of his steed, and very impatient to try him; and so, when he was ready to leave Reims, he mounted him, intending to ride home on his back. But the horse, who had been used to the giant weight of Ogier and his armor, hardly knew that any one was on his back, so small and light is the good abbot. He started off at a great speed, running up hill and down at a rate which frightened the abbot almost out of his senses; and, as he passed the convent of Jouaire, he threw the good man off, right before the eyes of the abbess and her nuns. This accident so angered and mortified the abbot, that he has kept the horse hard at work ever since, hauling stones for the new chapel which he is building."

Messengers were at once sent to Meaux, who returned soon after with the horse. But he was not the noble-looking steed that he had once been. He was thin and poor; and his sides had been galled by the shafts; and his eyes had no longer any look of human intelligence about them. Yet he remembered his old master: he whinnied softly, and struck the ground with his hoofs, and then lay down before him for very humbleness. Ogier rubbed the horse's bare flanks with his rich embroidered cloak, and wept as if his heart would burst. And the squires covered the steed with rich trappings of cloth-of-gold and of ermine; and they put a golden bit in his mouth, and reins of silk upon his neck. And the whole company departed for Laon, where the king awaited them.

When Ogier came into the presence of Charlemagne, he

asked that the king should fulfil his promise by giving up Charlot for punishment. But the father's heart of Charlemagne made him hesitate. Then Turpin and Duke Namon, and all the peers, besought the king to yield, not only for his own honor's sake, but for the sake of the people and of Christendom. And so he sent for Charlot to come and deliver himself up to Ogier. Trembling with fear, the wicked young prince obeyed. He cast himself with crossed hands upon the ground, and with bitter tears he besought Ogier's pardon. Duke Namon, too, and the other peers, begged Ogier to be merciful. But the Dane bade them hold their peace. He drew from its scabbard, the rich-lettered brand Short, and flourished it angrily about Charlot's head. The king, in great horror and distress, fled to the chapel, and knelt with covered head before the altar. Then Ogier gently lifted Charlot from the ground, and pardoned him for the great wrong which he had done him, and bade him go in peace. And after this, he went into the chapel, where the king still knelt; and the two embraced each other in the presence of the host, and mutually forgave each other, and pledged anew their faith, and a lifelong friendship.

ADVENTURE XXXII

THE VALE OF THORNS

SEVEN years passed. In all the world there was not such another king as Charlemagne. Wherever his arms were carried, there victory followed; and neither Pagan nor haughty Christian foe dared lift up hands any more against him. His kingdom stretched from the Baltic Sea to the Italian shores, and from beyond the Rhine to the great Western Ocean. Princes were his servants; kings were his vassals; and even the Pope of Rome did him homage. And now he had crossed the Pyrenees, and was carrying fire and sword into the fair fields and rich towns of the Spanish Moors; for he had vowed to punish Marsilius, king of Spain, for the injuries he had done the French in former years. And he had overrun the whole of that haughty land, and had left neither castle, nor city, nor wall, unbroken, save only the town of Saragossa.

One day Charlemagne sat beneath the blossoming trees of an orchard near Cordova. White was his beard, and flowered was his head; yet still handsome was his body, and proud his form. Around him were the noblest of his knights, Roland and Oliver and old Duke Namon, and fifteen thousand of the choicest men of France. It was a gala-day for the French, and the warriors amused themselves with field-sports, and many pleasant games. Then a party of Moorish messengers were brought before the king. They came from Marsilius at Saragossa, who had sent to beg peace of Charlemagne.

"What will Marsilius give for peace?" asked the king.

"If you will go back to your own country, and cease this

unhappy war," answered they, "then Marsilius binds himself to do this: he will go to Aix at Michaelmus, and be baptized; he will do homage then for Spain, and will faithfully hold it in fief from you; he will give you great store of treasures,—four hundred mules loaded with gold, and fifty cartloads of silver, besides numbers of bears and lions and tame greyhounds, and seven hundred camels, and a thousand moulted falcons. Too long has this cruel war been waging. Marsilius would fain have peace."

Charlemagne listened to the words of the messengers, but he was not quick to answer. He called together his peers, and laid the matter before them.

"What think you of the Moor's offers of peace?" asked he.

"Put no trust in Marsilius!" cried Roland. "He is the most faithless of Pagans, and speaks only lies. Carry on the war as you have begun, and talk not of peace until Saragossa is ours."

Charlemagne's face grew dark, yet he said not a word. It was plain that he coveted the treasures which Marsilius had promised. Then Ganelon arose, and with curling lip, thus answered,—

"If Marsilius offers to do fealty for Spain, and to hold it as a gift from you, wherefore should we refuse his plea? He who would advise you otherwise cares not what manner of death we die."

And Namon of Bavaria added, "If the Moor is beaten, and cries for mercy, it would be an unknightly act to continue warring against him. My voice is for peace."

And all the peers, save Roland and Oliver, cried out, "The duke hath spoken wisely. Let us have peace!"

"It is well," answered Charlemagne; "and so it shall be.

But whom shall we send to Saragossa to treat with Marsilius, and to receive the pledges of good faith which he shall give?"

Then arose a great dispute among the peers as to which should undertake this dangerous errand. Duke Namon, who was never known to shirk a duty, offered to go; but the king would not consent. He liked not to part with his wise old friend, even for a single day.

"I will carry the message," said Roland.

"Not so, my brother," interrupted Oliver. "Thy pride will get the better of thy judgment, and thou wilt act rashly. Let me undertake the errand."

But Charlemagne refused them both. "Neither of you shall go," said he. "But you may choose one from among these other barons to be the messenger."

"Then send Ganelon of Mayence," said Roland. "He is in favor of this peace, and he is most fit to carry the message."

"Yes, send Ganelon of Mayence!" cried all the peers.

Ganelon rose from his seat in rage. Fire flashed from his hazel eyes; his lips quivered; he tore the sable border from his crimson tunic, and stood proudly before Roland. "Fool!" cried he. "Who art thou who wouldst send me to Marsilius? If I but live to come again from Saragossa, I will deal thee such a blow as thou shalt never forget."

"Speak softly, Sir Ganelon," said Roland. "Men know that I care not for threats. If thou art afraid of the danger, mayhap the king will allow me to go in thy place."

Hotter than before was Ganelon's wrath; but he held his tongue, and turned humbly toward the king.

"My lord," said he, "since you will that I bear this message to Marsilius, I go. But I know too well the false-hearted

Moor to hope that I shall ever return. I pray you, care for my fair son Baldwin, to whom I leave my lands and all my fiefs. Keep him well, for these eyes of mine shall never see him again."

"Thou art too fearful, and too tender of heart," said the king, as he offered to Ganelon the staff and the glove which messengers were wont to carry as signs of their office. "Go now, and doubt not the issue of thine errand."

Ganelon took the staff; but his hand trembled, and the glove fell to the ground.

"An evil omen is that," whispered the peers who saw it. "It is a sign of no good fortune, either to him or to us."

Then Ganelon bade the king good-by, and went on his way. But he said to himself, "This is Roland's doings, and I shall hate him all my life long: neither shall I love Oliver his brother, nor any other of the twelve peers."

When he reached Saragossa, Ganelon was led into the presence of Marsilius. The Moorish king sat under a pine-tree, and twenty thousand warriors stood around him.

"What answer bring you from your liege-lord Charlemagne?" asked he.

Ganelon had studied well what he should say; and he answered, like one long used to cunning guile, "If thou wilt be baptized and become a Christian, Charlemagne will give thee the half of Spain to hold in fief. If thou wilt not accept this offer, then he will besiege thee in Saragossa, and take thee prisoner; and he will send thee bound upon the back of a sumter horse to Aix, and there he will have thee put to death. This is the message while Charlemagne sends thee."

Great was the anger of the Moorish king, and he raised his

javelin to strike the messenger dead. But Ganelon, no whit daunted, set his back against the trunk of a tree, and drew his sword part way from its scabbard.

"Good sword," said he, "thou art fair and bright, and thou hast done me many a service. Never shall it be said that Ganelon died alone in a strange land."

But the courtiers of King Marsilius stepped in between them. "It were better," said they, "to treat with this man than to slay him. If his face slander him not, he is a man who may be persuaded to help us. Try him."

Then Marsilius called Ganelon to his side, and offered him five hundred pounds of gold for his friendship. And the two sat long together, and plotted bloodshed and treason.

"Indeed, what think you of this Charlemagne?" asked the Moor. "Through how many lands has he carried that old body of his? How many scars are there on his shield? How many kingdoms has he stolen, and how many kings impoverished? Methinks that his days are well-nigh spent. He must be more than two hundred years old."

But Ganelon, although a traitor, would say naught against the king. "None can see him," said he, "but will say that he is a man. None can so praise or honor him, but that there shall yet be in him more worth and goodness."

"Yet, methinks," said the Moor, "that he is very old. His beard is white; his hair is flowered. It is strange that he grows not tired of fighting."

"That he will never do so long as Roland, his nephew, lives," answered Ganelon. "There, too, is Oliver; and there are the other peers of the realm, all of whom the king holds most dear. They alone are worth twenty thousand men."

"I have heard much of Roland," said the Moor; "and I would fain put him out of the way. Tell me how it can be done, and thou shalt have three baggage horse-loads of gold, three of silver, and three of fine silk and red wine and jewels."

Now Ganelon desired, above all things, the death of Roland; and he eagerly made known his plans to Marsilius.

"Send to Charlemagne," said he, "great store of rich gifts, so that every Frenchman shall wonder at your wealth. Send also hostages, and promise him that on next Michaelmas you will be baptized at Aix and do him homage for Spain. Pleased with your promises, he will return to sweet France. But this rearguard, with Roland and Oliver, and twenty thousand Frenchmen, will be long among the passes of the Pyrenees. A hundred thousand Moors could well cope with them there."

Then the two traitors exchanged promises and pledges; and Ganelon, taking with him the keys of Saragossa, and rich presents for Charlemagne, went back to Cordova.

Right glad was Charlemagne to hear the message which the lying traitor brought. He was tired of warring, and he longed to return in peace to his own sweet France. The next day the trumpets sounded throughout the camp. The tents were struck; the baggage was packed on the sumter horses; the knights mounted their steeds; banners and pennons waved thick in the air; the great army began its glad march homeward. Joyful was the beginning of that march; but, ah, how sad the ending! The French did not see the crafty Moors following them through the upper valleys, their banners furled, their helmets closed, their lances in rest.

That first night the king was troubled with sad dreams. He thought that Ganelon seized his lance and shook it, and that it fell in pieces. He thought that he hunted in the forest of Ardennes, and that both a boar and a leopard attacked him. A thousand fearful fancies vexed him. Mountains fell upon him and crushed him; the earth yawned and swallowed him; perils beset him on every side: but amid them all, the face of Ganelon was ever to be seen.

By and by the army came to the Pyrenees, and the great land of France lay just beyond the mountains.

"To whom now," said the king to his peers, "shall we intrust our rearguards while we pass safely through the mountain gates?"

"Give it to Roland, your nephew," said Ganelon. "There is none more worthy than he."

"And who shall lead the vanguard?"

"Ogier, the Dane. Next to Roland, he is the bravest of your barons."

Right willingly did Roland accept the dangerous trust.

"I will see to it," said he, "that no harm come to the French while passing through the gates. Neither pack-horse, nor mule, nor palfrey, nor charger, nor man shall we lose, that shall not be paid for by the blood of our foes."

Then he mounted his steed, and rode back to the rear. And with him went Oliver and Gerin and Gerer and Josse and Berenger and Jastor and Anseis, and Duke Gaifer, and proud Gerard of Rousillon, and Turpin the archbishop, and twenty thousand valiant fighting-men.

High were the mountains, and gloomy the valleys; dark were the rocks, and fearful were the glens. But the day was fair, and the sky was clear; and the bright shields of the warriors glittered in the sunlight like flashes of fire. All at once a sound, as of a thousand trumpets blowing, was heard in the valley below them. The French knights harkened.

"Comrades," said Oliver, "methinks that we are followed by the Moors."

"And may God grant us battle and victory!" said Roland earnestly. "Well is it that we are here to defend the king. For one should never murmur that he suffers distress for his friends: for them, he should lose, if need be, both blood and flesh and even life itself."

Then Oliver climbed a high pine tree, and looked down into the grassy valley behind them. There he beheld such troops of Pagan folk as he had never seen before.

"Comrades," cried he, "we shall have such a battle as no man has known. The passes are full of armed Moors: their hauberks and glittering helmets fill the lower valleys. Great mischief is in store for us, but may we stand to the field like men!"

"Shame be to him that flees!" said the warriors who heard him.

Bewildered and amazed at sight of so terrible an array of Pagans, Oliver descended from the tree.

"Brother Roland," said he, "I pray thee blow thy horn. The king will hear it, and he will turn him about and come to our succor."

"To do so would be to act as a craven," answered Roland. "Never shall it be said that I feared a foe. I will strike strong strokes with Durandal. Ill shall it fare with the Pagan traitors."

"Comrade Roland," again said Oliver, "now blow thy horn. Charlemagne will hear it, and he will make his host return."

"Never," answered Roland, "shall my kinsmen upbraid me, or be blamed by me. But I will strike with Durandal. The brand which the king gave me when he knighted me, that shall be our succor."

Then Oliver prayed him the third time, "Comrade Roland, sound now thine ivory horn. Charlemagne, who is passing the gates, will hear us and come to our aid."

"No man shall ever say," answered Roland, "that I have blown my horn for Pagans. My kinsmen shall not bear that reproach. But when the great battle is joined, then you shall see the lightning flashes of Durandal in the thickest of the fight. A thousand and seven hundred times shall the blade be dyed in the blood of the Moors. Better would it be to perish than suffer shame."

But Oliver was not yet satisfied. "I have seen the Moorish host," said he. "The mountains and the plains, the valleys and the groves, are full of them. Never have we fought against such great odds."

"Friend and brother," answered Roland, "say not another word. The king has left us here, with a rearguard of twenty thousand men, and he esteems every one of us a hero. Do thou strike with thy lance and thy good blade Haultclear. As for me, Durandal shall serve me well. And, if I die, men shall say, 'This sword belonged to a noble knight.' "

Then the good Archbishop Turpin rode down the ranks, holding a sword in one hand and a crucifix in the other. "Comrades," cried he, "the king has left us here. He trusts in us, and for him we shall die. Cry now your sins to Heaven. Pray God's mercy, and ask his blessing."

In a moment every knight among those twenty thousand

horsemen had dismounted. Humbly and reverently every knee was bent, and every head was bowed. And the good archbishop blessed the company in God's name.

"If ye die," said he, "ye shall have places in paradise."

Then the warriors arose, light-hearted and hopeful. They rode into the place which is called Roncevaux, the Vale of Thorns, and there they put themselves in battle-array, and waited the onset of their foes. Roland sat astride of his good war steed, and proudly faced the Moorish host. In his hand he held the bared blade Durandal, pointing toward heaven. Never was seen a more comely knight. Courteously he spoke to the warriors about him. Then, putting spurs to his steed, he cried,—

"Comrades, ride onward! The day shall be ours!"

"Forget not the war-cry of Charlemagne," said Oliver.

At these words the rocks and valleys rang with the cry, "Monjoie! Monjoie!" And every warrior dashed forward to meet the foe.

Long and fierce was the fight, and terrible was the slaughter. With heart and strength the French knights struck. The Moors were slain by hundreds and by thousands. For a time victory seemed to be with the French. Many and valiant were the deeds achieved by Roland and Oliver and the archbishop and the peers that were with them. But at length Marsilius came down upon them with a fresh troop of seven thousand Moors. They hemmed the French heroes in on every side. Roland saw his knights falling one by one around him. All were slain save sixty men.

"Oliver, my fair dear comrade," said he, "behold how many brave vassals have fallen! The battle goes hard with us. If, now, we only knew how to send news to Charlemagne, he would return and succor us."

"It is too late," answered Oliver. "Better would we die than suffer shame."

Then said Roland, "I will sound my ivory horn. Mayhap Charlemagne, who is passing the gates of Spain, will hear it and return."

"Do no such thing," answered Oliver. "Great shame would would be upon you and your kinsmen forever. You would not blow your horn when I advised it, and now you shall not do so because the day is lost."

Then the archbishop rode up, and said, "The day is indeed lost, and to blow the horn would now no more avail us. But, should the king hear it, he will come back through the passes. He will find us dead: his men will lift us in biers and carry us home to be buried in minsters, and we shall not be left as food for wolves and dogs."

"Thou sayest well," said Roland. And he placed the horn to his lips. High were the hills, deep and dark were the gorges, narrow were the ways among the mountains. Yet the sound of that horn was heard for thirty leagues. Charlemagne and Duke Namon heard it while yet they were between the gates.

"Hark!" said the king. "I hear Roland's horn. The felon Moors have attacked him: he is hard pressed in battle."

"You are foolishly mistaken," said Ganelon. "There is no battle. You are old, your beard is white, your head is flowery, you are growing childish. You love your silly nephew, Roland, too well. He is only hunting among the mountains. He would blow his horn all day for a single hare, and then he would boast before you of his valor. Ride on. Your own France is not far ahead."

But the king was not to be deceived. He ordered Ganelon to be seized and bound and given in charge of his cooks, who were to hold him a close prisoner. They bound him with a great chain, and laid him across the back of a sumter horse; they pulled his beard; they struck him with their fists; they beat him with sticks. Sorry indeed was the traitor's plight, but his punishment was just. As for Charlemagne, he turned and, with all his host, hastened back to the succor of Roland and the valiant rearguard. High were the mountain walls, and darkly did they overhang the way; deep were the mountain gorges; swift and strong were the torrents; narrow and steep was the road. The trumpets sounded: anxiously and with haste the king and his horsemen retraced their steps.

Fiercely still the battle raged in the fated Vale of Thorns. One by one the French knights fell; but for every one that was slain ten Pagans bit the dust. At length Oliver was wounded unto death; but still he sat on his horse and struck valiantly about him with his good Haultclear. His eyes lost their strength: he could not see. He met Roland, and struck him a blow which split his helmet down to the nose-piece, but luckily wounded him not.

"Brother," said Roland softly and gently, "thou has not done this willingly. I am Roland, he who has loved thee so long and so well."

"Ah, comrade!" said Oliver, "I hear thee; but I cannot see thee. Pray forgive me if I have harmed thee."

"I am none the worse," answered Roland; "and there is naught to forgive."

Then the two brothers bent over from their steeds, and embraced each other; and amid much love and many hasty words of farewell, they parted.

And now all the French were slain, save only Roland and the archbishop. The hero was wounded in a dozen places: he felt his life-blood oozing away. Again he drew his ivory horn, and feebly sounded it. He would fain know whether Charlemagne were coming. The king was in the pass, not far away, and he heard the failing blast.

"Ah, Roland!" said he, "the battle goes ill with thee." Then he turned to his host, and said, "Blow loud your trumpets, that the hero may know that succor comes."

At once sixty thousand bugles were blown so loudly that the valleys and the caves resounded, and the rocks themselves trembled. Roland heard it and thanked God. The Pagans heard it and knew that it boded no good to them. They rushed in a body upon Roland and the archbishop. Roland's horse was slain beneath him; his shield was split in twain; his hauberk was broken. The archbishop was mortally wounded, and stretched upon the ground. Again the trumpets of Charlemagne's host were heard, and the Pagans fled in great haste toward Spain.

Then Roland knelt by the side of the dying archbishop. "Kind friend, so good and true," said he, "now the end has come. Our comrades whom we held so dear are all dead. Give me leave to bring them and lay them in order by thee, that we may all have thy blessing."

"It is well," answered the good Turpin. "Do as thou wilt. The field is thine and mine."

So Roland, weak and faint, went all alone through that field of blood, seeking his friends. He found Berenger and Otho and Anseis and Samson, and proud Gerard of Rousillon; and one by one he brought them and laid them on the grass before the archbishop. And lastly he brought back Oliver, pressed gently against his bosom, and placed him on a shield by the others. The archbishop wept; and he lifted up his feeble hands and blessed them: "Sad has it been with you, comrades. May God, the glorious King, receive your souls in his paradise!"

Then Roland, faint with loss of blood, and overcome with grief, swooned and fell to the ground. The good archbishop felt such distress as he had never known before. He staggered to his feet; he took the ivory horn in his hands, and went to fetch water from the brook which flows through the Vale of Thorns. Slowly and feebly he tottered onward, but not far: his strength failed and he fell to the ground. Soon Roland recovered from his swoon and looked about him. On the green grass this side of the rivulet, he saw the archbishop lying. The good Turpin was dead.

And now Roland felt that he, too, was nigh death's door. He took the ivory horn in one hand, and Durandal in the other, and went up a little hill that lies toward Spain. He sat down beneath a pine-tree where were four great blocks of marble. He looked at the blade Durandal. "Ha, Durandal," he said, "how bright and white thou art! Thou shinest and flamest against the sun! Many countries have I conquered with thee, and now for thee I have great grief. Better would it be to destroy thee than to have thee fall into the hands of the Pagan folk."

With great effort he raised himself on his feet again. Ten times he smote with Durandal the great rock before him. But the sword was bright and whole as ever, while the rock was split in pieces. Then the hero lay down upon the grass, with his face toward the foe. He put the sword and the horn under him. He stretched his right glove toward heaven, and an unseen hand came and took it away. Dead was the matchless hero.

Not long after this King Charlemagne with his host came to the death-strewn Vale of Thorns. Great was the grief of the king and of all the French, when they found that they had come too late to save even a single life. Roland was found lying on the grass, his face turned toward Spain. Charlemagne took him up tenderly in his arms, and wept.

"Friend Roland," said he, "worthiest of men, bravest of warriors, noblest of all my knights, what shall I say when they in France shall ask news of thee? I shall tell them that thou art dead in Spain. With great sorrow shall I hold my realm from this time on. Every day I shall weep and bewail thee, and wish that my life, too, were ended."

Then the French buried their dead on the field where they had fallen. But the king brought Roland and Oliver and the archbishop to Blaye in France, and laid them in white marble tombs; and there they lie until this day, in the beautiful little chapel of St. Roman's. And he took the ivory horn to Bordeaux, and filled it with fine gold, and laid it on the altar of the church in that city; and there it is still seen by the pious pilgrims who visit that place.

The death of Roland.

THE AFTER WORD

Such is the story of Roland as gathered from the songs and poems of the middle ages.

When Charlemagne returned, sad, and worn with many cares, to his own chosen home at Aix, a fair damsel met him on the threshold of his palace. It was Alda, Oliver's sister, the betrothed wife of Roland.

"Where now is Roland the hero, the worthiest of the barons of France?" asked she.

Scarcely could the king make answer, so great was the sorrow which lay at his heart. "Sister, fair friend," said he gently, "that noble knight whom we both loved so well can nevermore come to thee, nor will his strong arm ever again defend us."

Faded then the color from the faithful maiden's cheeks. She cried not, nor uttered a sound. She tottered, and fell to the stone pavement at Charlemagne's feet. God is kind: he takes the broken-hearted home. The maidens in the palace raised her up tenderly, and bore her into the quiet little chapel, where they watched over her body, and prayed for her soul, until the break of day; and then, with many sad tears and bitter lamentations, they buried her close by the altar, and full great honor did the king pay to her.

As for Ganelon the traitor, he was brought before the council of peers, loaded with irons and chained like a felon. "Lord barons," said the king, "here is Ganelon, whom I pray you will judge as beseemeth you just. He has traitorously taken from me twenty thousand of my host, and my nehpew, whom he shall never see, and Oliver the brave and the courteous; and he has betrayed the twelve peers for gold."

And the song goes on to tell how, through the advice of Thierry of Anju, Ganelon was sentenced to be torn in pieces by horses,—a just punishment for one so base and vile. But Charlemagne's heart was overburdened with sorrow and care; and naught could bring again the hopeful days of the past. "O God!" said he in despair, "so painful is my life!" And he wept with his eyes, and pulled his snow-white beard.

Here ends the song which Turold sang. But another poem tells us that, not long after this, the great king died, and that at the moment of his death all the bells in the kingdom tolled, of their own accord, a solemn dirge. He was buried in Aix-la-Chapelle, in a tomb, which, according to one account, was very rich and well made. And on his tomb were painted all the battles which he had fought and won. But on that side which faced toward the Pyrenees Mountains, where he had been outwitted and defeated by the Moors, there was not any thing painted; for he had not yet avenged himself for the latest injuries which he had there received.

As for Ogier the Dane, it is related by one of the older song-writers, from whom I have already borrowed much, that he lived a long time in Hainault and Brabant, doing good, and hating evil, and protecting the poor and friendless. Wherever he went, the people called down Heaven's choicest blessings upon him; and when he died, full of years and honors, he was buried in the abbey at Meaux. But another and later poem tells us a very different story. It relates, that, before the death of Charlemagne, Ogier, with a thousand French knights, and assisted by his brother Guyon of Denmark, led a crusade into the Holy Land. On every hand the Saracens were subdued, and at length Ogier was crowned King of Judæa. But not long did he enjoy his kingdom. He was ill at ease and unhappy, so far from the court of Charlemagne, and he determined to return to France. One night he embarked secretly, and sailed across the sea. The sky was clear, the wind was fair, and the vessel sped swiftly onward, but not in the way which its master desired. A mountain of magnetic iron drew it toward an unknown shore, where it was dashed to pieces upon the rocks. With difficulty Ogier escaped from the wreck. The country in which he found himself was a strange land, not like any he had ever before seen. While he stood, uncertain which way to go, a beautiful horse, stronger and fairer even than Broiefort, came across the sands, and knelt before him, as if asking him to mount. Nothing fearing, Ogier leaped upon his back. With a neigh of delight, the horse, who was none other than Papillon, the fairy-steed of Morgan the Fay, bounded forward. Over rocks and hills, through forests, and among steep precipices, he ran with lightning speed, and paused not until he arrived at a wondrous palace built in the midst of a most beautiful landscape. There were gardens and orchards and lakes and waterfalls and fountains, and every thing that could charm the senses of the hero. It was the island Vale of Avalon—

> "Where falls not hail, or rain, or any snow,
> Nor ever wind blows loudly; but it lies
> Deep-meadowed, happy, fair with orchard lawns,
> And bowery hollows crowned with summer sea."

There he was kindly welcomed by Morgan the Fay, the queen of that land. A crown of roses was placed upon his head, and he lost all remembrance of his former life. There, through long years of happiness, he had the companionship of King Arthur and his knights, and of all the great heroes that have ever lived on earth; and he was freed from death and every mortal care. But once on a time he bethought him that he would return to France and visit his friend Charlemagne again. The fairy queen consented, and the sea-goblins carried him back. But everything was changed. Paris was no longer the city he had once known. He made his way to the palace, and inquired for Charlemagne. Men laughed at him, and told him that Charlemagne had been dead two hundred years, and that Hugues Capet was king of France. The good Dane felt now that the world had no joys for him; and not long afterward he was carried back again to the sweet Vale of Avalon, where he still lives with the blissful company of heroes.

And in various countries of Europe men tell marvellous tales of the re-appearance of Charlemagne. It was said by some that the great king returned to life at the time of the Crusades, and, with the same martial vigor as of old, led his hosts to mortal combat with the Saracens. Some say that he has been seen in the mountains of Untersberg, in company with Frederick Barbarossa, waiting for the time when he shall return to his kingdom. Others believe, that in Desenberg he bides the coming of the millennial day. A German poet* says, "Charlemagne the great king lives still with his heroes. It is in Desenberg that he rests from his conquests. The mountain dwarfs guard his dwelling. There, in the broad halls, the heroes repose, overpowered with sleep, bound by an unseen hand. Around them are their glittering arms, ready to be donned for

*Oebecke, in Karl Simrock's Kerlingisches Heldenbuch.

the battle. They breathe softly; they dream of war and victory. And at a marble table in the middle of the hall Charlemagne sits: his head reclines upon his breast; his countenance beams with the fire of youth; his hair and beard fall in long white waves to the ground. Long time has he waited there with his comrades. Oftentimes the dawning of their new life seems at hand, and a hum of joy runs through the halls. Then all the warriors rise to their feet: they seize their lances and their swords; but suddenly their joy is quenched, and again their eyes are closed in slumber. Only the king remains awake for a while; and he cries out, until the sound is echoed through the mountains, 'Ye dwarfs who guard my dwelling, what year is this?' The dwarfs answer; and the shadows settle again upon his features. 'Sleep on, comrades,' he says, 'the hour has not yet come.' With a dull sound, each warrior falls prone upon the earth: they sleep, and await the hour when the spell shall be broken. The king, with his long white beard, and his flowing hair, and his countenance glowing with youth, sits again at the marble table."

THE WINGED STEED